SERIES

Macmillan Texts for Industrial Vocational and Technical Ed

Technical Drawing with Design

A. Yarwood

MACMILLAN

Macmillan Education
Between Towns Road, Oxford OX4 3PP
A division of Macmillan Publishers Limited
Companies and representatives throughout the world

www.macmillan-africa.com

ISBN 0 333 60161 0

Text © A. Yarwood 1994
Design and illustration © Macmillan Publishers Limited 1994

First published 1994

Illustrations and photographs by A. Yarwood

Cover illustration courtesy of Telegraph Colour Library

Printed and bound in Malaysia

2005 2004 2003
13 12 11 10 9

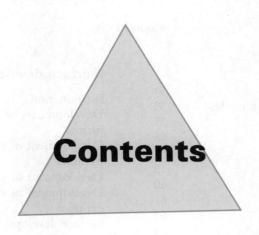

Contents

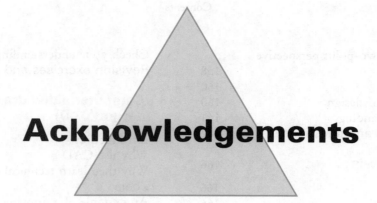

Acknowledgements

Registered trademarks

The following trademarks are registered in the US Patent and Trademark Office by Autodesk Inc:
   Autodesk,
   AutoCAD®,
   AutoSketch®,
   AutoCAD for Windows,
   AutoSketch for Windows,
   AutoCAD AEC.

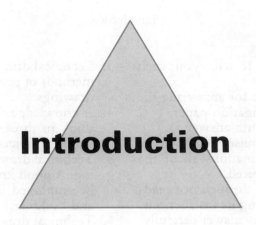

Introduction

About this book

This book has been written to help pupils and students to prepare for examinations in Technical Drawing and Geometrical and Mechanical Drawing. The book covers a wide range of syllabuses and courses at secondary level. All aspects of the syllabuses for these examinations have been covered. The book contains numerous technical drawings describing methods of working, which readers are advised to work. A large number of graded technical drawing exercises are included for the reader to answer in order to test whether the contents of each chapter have been fully understood, as well as a number of technical drawing design exercises which the reader is advised to attempt. Technical drawing is the basis for communicating design ideas in industries such as engineering and building. If one wishes to become successful in such industries, a good knowledge of technical drawing is an essential. Technical drawing is a medium necessary for the smooth functioning of a modern industrial, technological society.

The author has had a number of successful books published in this subject area and has been an examiner in technical drawing for some 30 years. He has also been a Chief Examiner in subjects such as Engineering Drawing, Technical Drawing and Graphic Communication with two Examination Boards, a moderator in Design for a third and a marking examiner for a fourth. He has also been a Head of Technical Department in each of three schools.

The discipline of technical drawing

The discipline of technical drawing involves:

1. Gaining good draughting skills for the production of clear and precise drawings.
2. Technical drawing is based in geometry. Thus the following are necessary:
   a) A good knowledge of **plane geometry** – geometry in 2 dimensions.
   b) A good knowledge of **solid geometry** – geometry in 3 dimensions.
   c) A good knowledge of **orthographic projection**.
3. Applications of plane and solid geometry and orthographic projection to the production of good quality technical drawing which will fully describe objects, articles, components and assemblies.

Answering questions in examinations

1. Before the day of the examination spend time on revision.
2. Go into the examination room with clean hands, clean equipment and well sharpened pencils.
3. Do not panic. If you have revised properly, you will have enough time to answer the examination questions and gain good marks.
4. In the examination room, when told to start answering the examination paper, first read the **rubric** of the examination paper carefully. The rubric is the set of instructions at the beginning

of the examination paper. It tells you such details as:
   a) How much time you have for answering the questions set in the examination paper.
   b) Which questions you should answer.
   c) Which questions are compulsory – should be answered. In some examinations all of the questions should be answered.
   Marks are sometimes lost through not reading the rubric and following its instructions.
5. Read each question you are to answer carefully. Make sure you fully understand what you should do before starting its answer.
6. Always attempt compulsory questions.
7. When answering a question, if you become stuck and cannot complete the answer, do not worry, just go on to the next question. It is surprising how many marks part of an answer can gain.
8. When answering geometry questions do not rub out your construction lines. The examiner who marks your answers will be giving marks for those constructions which are correct. But do line-in the lines of the answer. An answer to a geometry question should show a lined-in answer in black, but crisp lines, with the construction lines in thin light lines.

Why learn technical drawing?

1. Technical drawing is a universal language. Many people can understand drawings and other forms of graphics more easily and quickly than they can understand words.
2. Technical drawings are the means by which those working in industries such as mechanical engineering, building, architecture or electrical engineering communicate their ideas of the shape, form and dimensions of the articles being made.

3. Technical drawing encourages tidy and accurate methods of presenting those ideas in the form of drawings.
4. A knowledge of technical drawing allows you to think in three-dimensions – height, width and depth of objects being drawn.
5. Technical drawing is a basis for vocational training. A good knowledge will help if you wish to be employed in industries such as engineering and building.
6. Technical drawing is important as a design tool for communicating ideas between people working on any project:
   a) in industries;
   b) between organisations;
   c) between countries;
   d) in the media – newspapers, magazines, and television.

■ CHECK YOUR UNDERSTANDING

● Technical drawing is an essential part of the processes in the designing and making of manufactured goods.
● A good knowledge of technical drawing will help you obtain employment in any of the manufacturing or building industries.

REVISION QUESTIONS

Questions

1 State three reasons why you believe learning technical drawing could be an advantage for you.
2 Where are technical drawings used? Have you seen any in use?
3 Read pages vii and viii dealing with answering questions in an examination again. Can you think of anything to add to the list given there?

Technical drawing equipment

Introduction

Specific materials and drawing instruments are required in order to undertake technical drawing. As technical drawing is now a universal language it is governed by rules regarding methods of drawing and the symbols used. Those rules and symbols are laid down in **ISO** (International Standards Organisation) standards. British Standards (**BS**) follow the ISO standards.

Examples of symbols from BS:308

BS:308 *Engineering drawing practice* and BS:1192 are both based on ISO:128 *Technical drawings – general principles*. Figure 1.1 shows some examples of symbols from BS:308 *Engineering drawing practice*. The same symbols would be found in ISO:128 *Technical drawings – general principles*.

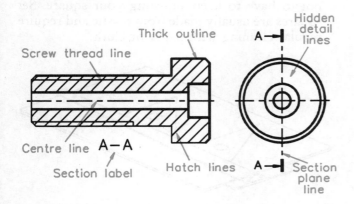

Figure 1.1 A BS:308 technical drawing

'A' size drawing sheets

The ISO also specifies an 'A' size series of drawing sheets for technical drawings. Figure 1.2 shows the basic A0 sheet, the area of which is 1 square metre.

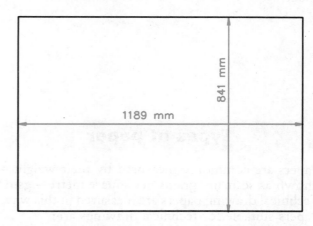

Figure 1.2 The sizes of an A0 size drawing sheet

Other A size sheets are A1, A2, A3, A4 and A5. All A size sheets have their edge lengths in the same proportion. This proportion is in the ratio of short side : long side = $1 : \sqrt{2}$.

Each lower size sheet in the A series is obtained by exactly dividing the A sheet along its middle as shown in Figure 1.3 (page 2). This results in the following range of sizes.

A0 = 841 mm × 1189 mm = 1 square metre
A1 = 841 mm × 594 mm
A2 = 594 mm × 420 mm
A3 = 420 mm × 297 mm
A4 = 297 mm × 210 mm
A5 = 210 mm × 148 mm

1

There are larger size A sheets (e.g. 2A0, 4A0) and smaller (e.g. A6) than these. In school, college and examination technical drawing the sizes most commonly used are A2, A3 and A4 sheets.

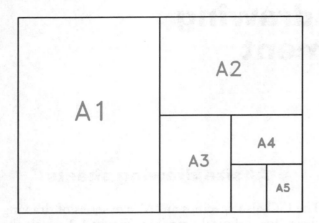

Figure 1.3 Some of the A size series of drawing sheet

Types of paper

Papers are commonly measured by their weight – known as so many grams per square metre – **gsm**. Technical drawing papers are measured in this way. Papers suitable for technical drawings are:

- **Cartridge paper** – a good quality paper for pencil drawings. A weight often used is 90 gsm, but thinner or thicker cartridge paper may be used. Made from esparto grass.
- **Detail paper** – a lighter paper for pencil and colour work. A common weight is 50 gsm.
- **Grid papers** – often of A4 size. Very suitable for the freehand sketching out of a layout for a technical drawing. Square, isometric and perspective grids.
- **Tracing paper** – 38 gsm to 63 gsm. For making tracings of technical drawings.
- **Papers** and **boards** for **ink work**. If wishing to draw with inks – black and/or coloured inks – a large variety of different papers and boards is available.

Technical drawing instruments

The following minimum set of instruments is required in order to construct good quality technical drawings:

- **Drawing board** – most often made from wood, often from 12 mm thick plywood. Sizes vary, but for school and college work one measuring 650 mm by 470 mm is suitable for working with A2 size (or smaller) papers. The surfaces of all drawing boards should be cleaned at regular intervals, by wiping with paper or cloth and occasionally by re-sandpapering to ensure the surfaces are flat, smooth and clean.
- Fixing sheets of paper to the board – **drawing paper** can be fixed with pieces of sticky tape – masking tape is the best as well as being the cheapest, although 'Sellotape' type of tape can also be used. Clips are often used in schools. It is best to avoid using drawing pins for this purpose because they tend to damage the corners of the board after long use.
- **Tee square** – usually made from hardwoods, the best are from mahoganies, but good quality beech squares are suitable. Make sure the blade length is long enough for your board. Tee squares must be kept clean. Wipe regularly with paper or cloth and occasionally plane the drawing edge to keep it straight. Screws holding the blade to the handle may need to be tightened.
- **Set squares** – two are necessary, unless you have an adjustable square. See Figure 1.4. A 60,30 and a 45,45 are needed. If you have an adjustable square (Figure 1.5), it can be adjusted to the angle required, but even then it is also probably best to have a 60,30 and a 45,45 as well in order not to have to keep adjusting your square. Set squares are usually made from plastic and require regular cleaning with paper or cloth.

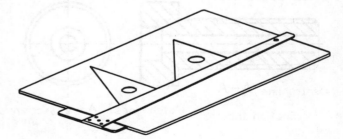

Figure 1.4 Drawing board, tee square and two set squares

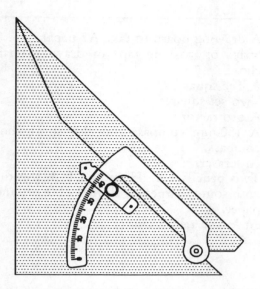

Figure 1.5 An adjustable set square – can be set to any angle between 45 degrees and 90 degrees

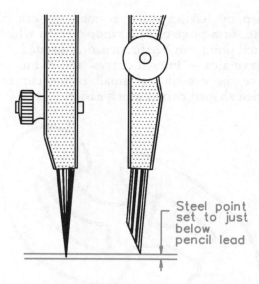

Steel point set to just below pencil lead

Figure 1.7 Positioning the lead of a pencil compass

- **Protractor** – for constructing angles which are not set square angles. A plastic protractor, measuring up to 180 degrees is suitable.
- **Compasses and dividers** – a good quality pair of compasses which can draw circles up to 150 mm radius is an essential item of equipment. A pair of smaller 'spring bow' compasses is a valuable asset when drawing circles of 25 mm and less radius. Although not absolutely essential a pair of dividers can prove to be of use at times, e.g. when measuring from another drawing to determine an unknown dimension. See Figure 1.6. Set the steel point of the compass just a little lower than the tip of the compass pencil. See Figure 1.7.

- **Erasers** – essential for correcting mistakes. Vinyl erasers are preferable to rubber erasers – they make a cleaner job of 'rubbing out'. Be careful of rubber dust formed when erasing from a pencil drawing. It can be a source of annoyance causing smudges on your drawings if it is allowed to accumulate unnecessarily.
- **Pencils** – can be purchased in nine grades of 'hardness' – from H to 9H – and six grades of 'blackness' – from B to 6B. There are also two other grades – F and HB. Two pencils are advisable – a 2H or 3H for drawing with instruments and an HB for freehand drawing such as lettering. Many draughtsmen like to sharpen their 2H pencils to a 'chisel' point and their HB pencils to a round point – Figure 1.8. Keep your pencils

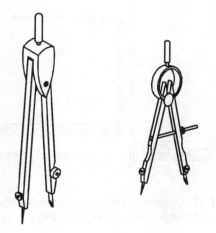

Figure 1.6 A 150 mm compass and a spring bow compass

Figure 1.8 Sharpening of 2H (or 3H) and HB pencil points

sharp by having either a small smooth file at hand, or a piece of fine sandpaper on which the pencil point can be sharpened as needed.
- **Curve aids** – 'French curves' and radius curves make the drawing of small radius curves and varied shaped curves much easier.

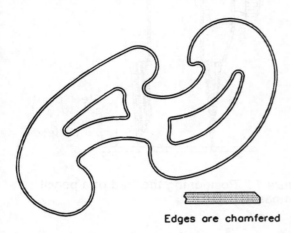

Edges are chamfered

Figure 1.9 A 'French curve'. There are many different shapes of these curves. They are chamfered along their upper edges to allow them to be used when drawing with ink pens

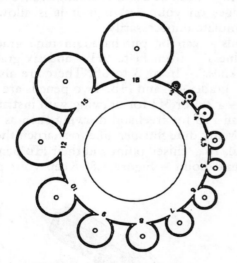

Figure 1.10 A metric radius curve

A minimum set of technical drawing equipment

A minimum set of equipment for the production of good quality drawings would be:

- A drawing board to take A2 paper.
- Strips of masking tape or drawing board clips.
- A Tee square.
- Two set squares.
- A protractor.
- A 150 mm compass and also spring bow compass.
- An eraser.
- Two pencils – a 2H and an HB, together with some sharpening device – file or sandpaper.
- At least a radius curve.

Drawing sheet layouts

Figure 1.11 shows two typical drawing sheet layouts for school or college use when working on A2, A3 or A4 sheets of drawing paper. The sheets can be in either an upright position, which is known as 'portrait' or in a horizontal position, known as 'landscape'. Note the following:

- **Border** or **margin lines**: these surround the drawing. For an A4 size sheet these should be set in 10 mm; for an A3 sheet, 15 mm and for A2, 20 mm. The idea of a margin is so that the outer edges of the drawing area are protected if the sheet edges become damaged – at least the drawing area may not be affected.

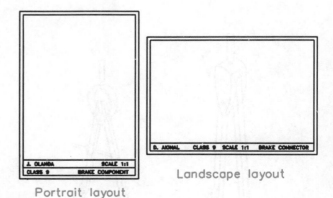

Portrait layout   Landscape layout

Figure 1.11 Drawing sheet layouts suitable for school or college technical drawings

- **Title block area**: the examples in Figure 1.11 show the portrait layout with a double rectangle title block and the landscape layout with a single rectangular title block. In the title block details are shown such as:

- Your name.
- Your class, form or group number.
- The title of the article being drawn.
- The scale of the drawing.

- **Height of lettering**: in title blocks, features such as names, article titles, etc. are usually printed in capital letters. Their height will vary according to the size of the drawing sheet in use. Suggested heights are 6 mm for A4 sheets, 8 mm for A3 sheets and 10 mm for A2 sheets.

Figure 1.12 shows a type of sheet layout which may be found in use by engineering companies. The sheets will be pre-printed so that draughtsmen can start working on the sheet without having to add details such as those shown in the title block. Note also the set of reference numbers around the margins of this sheet – anyone using the drawing can indicate any part by reference to the marginal letters and figures.

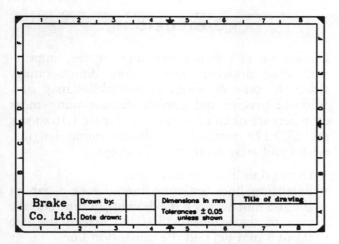

Figure 1.12 An example of a drawing sheet layout such as would be used in an engineering company

Types of lettering

Figure 1.13 shows the type of lettering which should be used in technical drawings. Lettering should be simple, so that it can be easily read. As

ABCDEFGHIJKLMNOP
QRSTUVWXYZ
1234567890
abcdefghijklmnop
qrstuvwxyz

ABCDEFGHIJKLMNOP
QRSTUVWXYZ
1234567890
abcdefghijklmnop
qrstuvwxyz

Figure 1.13 Types of lettering for technical drawings

mentioned above, the height of letters should vary according to the size of drawing sheet in use. Notes and dimension lettering and figures should be drawn at a lower height than title block lettering. For example, on A4 sheets 3 mm high notes and dimension figures would be suitable; on an A2 sheet a height of 5 or 6 mm would be better.

Lines

Figure 1.14 shows some of the types of lines for

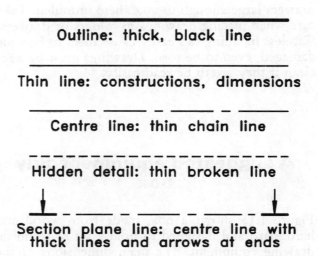

Outline: thick, black line

Thin line: constructions, dimensions

Centre line: thin chain line

Hidden detail: thin broken line

Section plane line: centre line with thick lines and arrows at ends

Figure 1.14 Types of line for technical drawings

technical drawings. Note that the lines for the **outline** of drawings should be thicker than other lines. This makes the outline stand out clearly against the other details in your drawings. BS:308 recommends that outlines should be about twice as thick as other lines.

- Overall length: 330 mm.
- Overall depth: 270 mm.
- Height: 25 mm.
- Thickness of sides: 10 mm.

Storing equipment and drawings

When a session of drawing is finished, it is important that the equipment which has been in use is stored neatly in clean and dry conditions. Dirty and damaged equipment does not help in the production of good, neat and clean drawings. Drawing boards can be either placed in purpose-made racks or stacked one on top of the other. Tee squares should be placed in properly made racks, which make sure that the drawing edges are not damaged and that their two parts do not become separate. Set squares must be kept in a clean condition. They may pick up dust and erasing particles and if they are stored in such a condition other equipment becomes dirty. Pencils can be placed in racks made from blocks of wood with appropriately sized holes. Compasses are easily damaged if not stored properly.

The best method of storing drawings is for each pupil or student to have a **folder** in which his or her drawings can be placed without their being folded. Other drawings, such as those used to demonstrate the principles of working should be stored flat in drawers large enough to take them unfolded. Take care when placing drawings in folders or drawers. Careless handling can easily cause them to become damaged, even to be torn. Drawings must be kept clean if they are to be read easily.

A suggested equipment tidy box

Figure 1.15 shows a box, made from wood and hardboard and designed to hold a set of technical drawing equipment. The main dimensions of the box are:

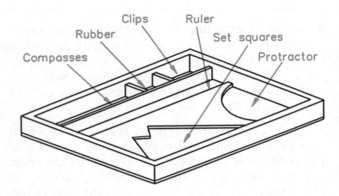

Figure 1.15 A suggested technical drawing equipment tidy box

Dimensions

Dimensions in technical drawings are very important. Most drawings will require dimensioning, although some drawings of assemblies may not. Without precise and correct dimensioning most drawings are often of little value. Figure 1.16 shows the ISO:128 methods of dimensioning lengths, circles and arcs. Note the following:

- Dimension lines are thin lines.
- Extension lines are thin lines. Leave a gap of about 3 mm between the drawing outline and the start of the extension line and extend the line about 3 mm beyond the dimension line.
- Arrows should usually be about 3 mm long. Other types of 'arrow' will be shown later in this book.
- Figures of dimensions should be about 3 mm high for A4 sheets; 5 mm high for A3 sheets and 6 mm high for A2 sheets.
- Use the abbreviations for circle diameter and circle radius as shown before the figure of the dimension.
- The bottom left drawing shows dimensioning from a datum. All dimensions are taken from the bottom left hand corner of the outline.

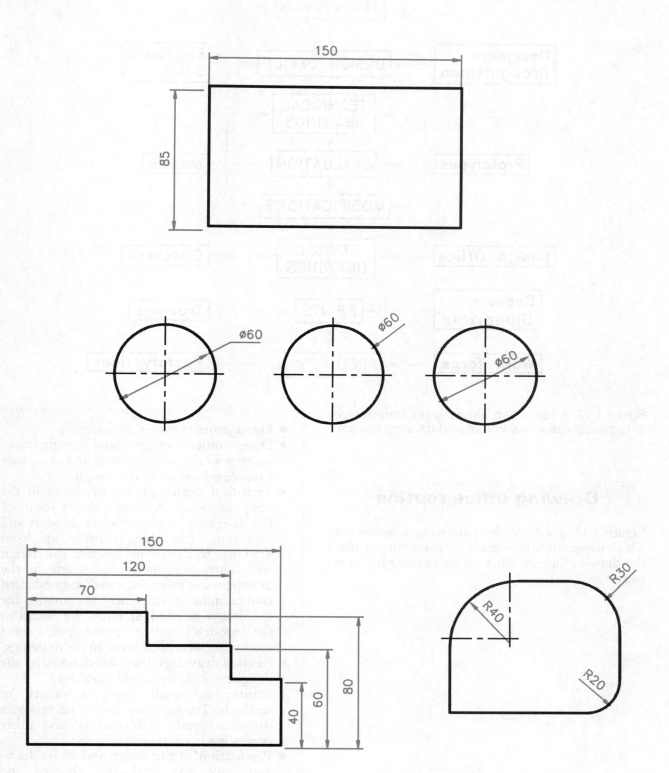

Figure 1.16 Methods of dimensioning technical drawing

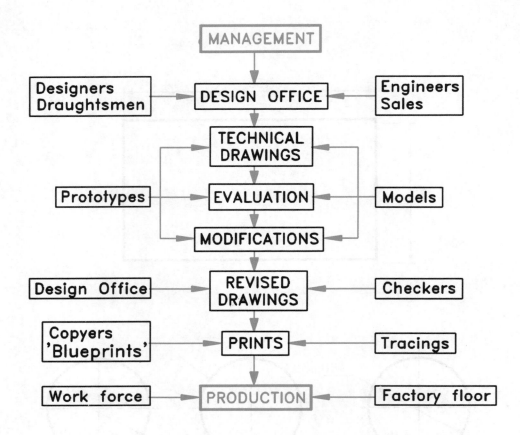

Figure 1.17 A flow chart showing the importance of technical drawings in a manufacturing system

Drawing office routine

Figure 1.17 is a flow chart showing a method by which design decisions made by management affect the drawing/design office of an engineering company.

- **Management**: makes decisions.
- **Design office**: designers and draughtsmen/women work, with research and assistance from engineers and sales people.
- **Technical drawings**: are produced in the design/drawing office as a direct result of the designing so far achieved. Models and prototypes (the designs made up from drawings to determine whether the design will function properly) are made to the drawings and these are tested and evaluated to determine whether they are suitable for the design in hand. If faults are found in the models and/or prototypes, some modifications will be made to the drawings.
- **Revised drawings**: these are checked by the designers with the aid of checkers.
- **Prints**: are made using a variety of methods. Tracings may also be necessary in order to produce 'blueprints' and other copies made via tracings.
- **Production**: if the design and all its drawings have been evaluated, checked and found to be correct, the design can go into production and be manufactured.

■ CHECK YOUR UNDERSTANDING

● Technical drawing is based on a recognised set of international rules and symbols, laid down in International Standards (ISO) and in the British Standards (BS).

● The 'A' series of metric size drawing sheets are those in most common use for technical drawings.

● Several types of paper are used in making drawings – cartridge papers, grid papers, detail papers, tracing papers and boards and papers for ink work.

● A minimum set of technical drawing equipment is – a drawing board (suggested size A2); a Tee square; two set squares; a protractor; a pair of compasses (but preferably two pairs); an eraser; well sharpened pencils. In addition a file or sandpaper for sharpening pencils. Curve aids such as a radius curve are useful additions.

● Drawings can be laid out in 'portrait' or 'landscape' format. A margin and a title block should be included in a drawing.

● Lettering should be simple in form so that it can be easily read.

● ISO:128 recommends several types of lines. Look back to Figure 1.14 on page 5.

● Dimensions are important to most technical drawings.

REVISION EXERCISES AND QUESTIONS

Exercises

1 What do the abbreviations ISO and BS stand for?
2 What is the total area of an A0 sheet of drawing paper?

3 You should attempt memorising the sizes in millimetres of some A size drawing sheets. The two most frequently used are A3 and A4. Look up page 2 to find out the sizes of these two A sheets and then repeat them until you are able to remember their dimensions.
4 Make a list of equipment suitable for technical drawing.
5 It is important to keep your equipment clean. How can you achieve this?
6 How many grades of pencil are there? Which grades do you think are most suitable for use in technical drawing?
7 What is meant by a 'radius curve'?
8 What is the difference between a 'portrait' and a 'landscape' layout?
9 Why are dimensions so important in technical drawings?

Questions

1 Have you seen sizes of drawing paper other than the A size series?
2 Why is technical drawing based on recognised standards of symbols? Name some standards which are important in technical drawing.
3 Go back to page 8 and look at the flow chart in Figure 1.17 again. Try to memorise it. Can you draw another flow chart in a different form?
4 Are there any other items of technical drawing equipment you think you might need to use?
5 What is the advantage of using an adjustable set square over using one which cannot be adjusted?
6 What are the reasons for the suggestion that an equipment box would be a good idea for use in technical drawing?

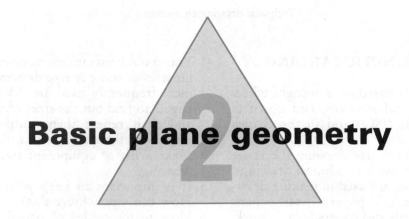

Basic plane geometry

Introduction

In order to become an expert in technical drawing you must have a good knowledge of basic geometry. There are two forms of geometry you need to understand:

- **Plane geometry** – This deals with the geometry of flat surfaces (planes). Plane geometry is two-dimensional (2-D) because it only deals in height and width.
- **Solid geometry** – We will look at this later in the book (page 85). This deals with the geometry of three-dimensions (3-D) – solids in three planes – height, width and depth.

Drawing lines

1. Clip, or tape a piece of A4 drawing paper on to your drawing board. Check that the top edge of the paper lines up with the edge of your Tee square. Draw a border line 10 mm in from the paper edges with the Tee square and a set square. Where the words A4 paper appear in Figure 2.1, draw in your name as carefully and accurately as possible in 6 mm high letters, working freehand with your HB pencil. It is best if your name is in capital letters. Add the title – Drawing lines – also in capital letters. To assist accuracy in lettering draw two faint guide lines with the Tee square, 6 mm apart between which the lettering can be drawn. The guide lines allow the lettering to be the required 6 mm high.

2. With your Tee square and set squares draw lines as shown in Figure 2.1. The lines can be any length.
3. Drawing 7 shows how lines at angles other than those at Tee square and set square angles can be drawn by placing the two set squares edge to edge. Try drawing lines at the following angles to the top edge of the Tee square using two set squares in a variety of edge to edge positions:
   115 degrees; 75 degrees; 120 degrees;
   105 degrees; 135 degrees.
4. Make sure you know the meaning of the two words **horizontal** and **vertical**.

Bisecting lines

A line is **bisected** when it is divided exactly into two equal parts. To bisect a line follow the example shown in Drawing 1 of Figure 2.2.

1. Draw a horizontal line 105 mm long. Its length can be measured with your ruler.
2. Set a compass to about two-thirds of the length of the line.
3. With the compass centred at A draw two pairs of arcs, above the line, and below the line.
4. Without altering the compass draw another pair of arcs crossing the first pair with the compass centred at B.
5. C and D are the intersections of the arcs.
6. Draw a line from C to D with either the edge of a set square or with a ruler.

When you have completed the bisection note:

E is the centre of AB. E is the bisection point of the line. AE = EB.

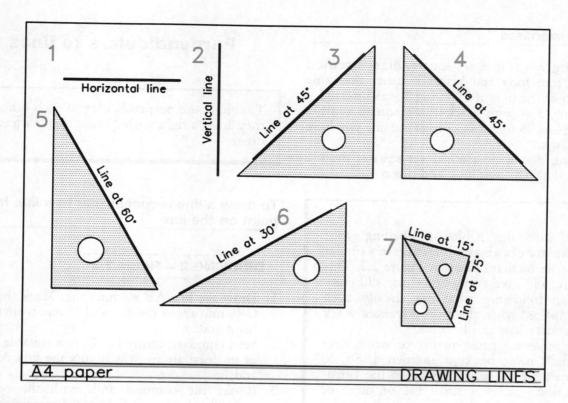

Figure 2.1 Drawing lines

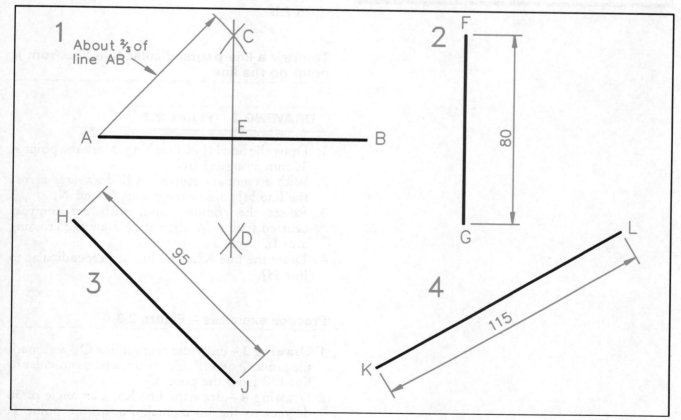

Figure 2.2 Bisecting lines

Practice exercises

1 **Drawing 2** – with a set square, draw a vertical line 80 mm long and bisect it using the same method as the line of Drawing 1 was bisected.
2 **Drawing 3** – with a 45,45 set square draw a sloping line 95 mm long. Bisect the line you have just drawn.
3 **Drawing 4** – with a 60,30 set square, draw a sloping line 115 mm long and bisect it.

Notes
1. Get into the habit of labelling your geometry drawings with letters in a similar manner to that shown in Figure 2.2. This habit will save you getting into difficulty when following what has already been completed when the more advanced work is undertaken at a later stage.
2. To achieve a good quality of work your pencils must be kept sharpened. So do remember the advice given in the Introduction – have a small file or piece of sandpaper at hand for this purpose.

Perpendiculars to lines

Two lines are **perpendicular** to each other if they are at a right angle (90 degrees) with each other.

To draw a line perpendicular to a line from a point on the line

DRAWING 2 – Figure 2.3

1. Draw the line AB 80 mm long. Mark the point C 40 mm above the line and 25 mm from the left hand end.
2. Set a compass, centred at C, to a suitable size so as to draw an arc which cuts the line AB at E and F.
3. Re-set the compass and, with the compass centred at E, then at F draw the crossing arcs G.
4. Draw a line CG. The line CD is perpendicular to AB.

To draw a line perpendicular to a line from a point on the line

DRAWING 2 – Figure 2.3

1. Draw the line HJ 70 mm long. Mark the point K 30 mm along HJ from J.
2. With a compass centred at K draw arcs across the line HJ to give the points M and N.
3. Re-set the compass and, with the compass centred first at M, then at N draw the crossing arcs L.
4. Draw the line KL. The line is perpendicular to line HJ.

Practice exercises – Figure 2.3

1 **Drawing 3** – draw the vertical line OP and mark the point Q on OP. Construct a perpendicular to line OP from the point Q.
2 **Drawing 4** – draw the line RS at an angle of 30 degrees to the horizontal. Locate the point T. Construct a perpendicular to RS from T.

3 Drawing 5 – Draw the line UV at 45 degrees to the horizontal. Mark the point W on UV. At W construct a line perpendicular to the line UV.

Complete your drawing by adding border lines and a title block. The border line is set in 10 mm from the paper edges. The lettering in the title block should be 6 mm high. Use capital letters.

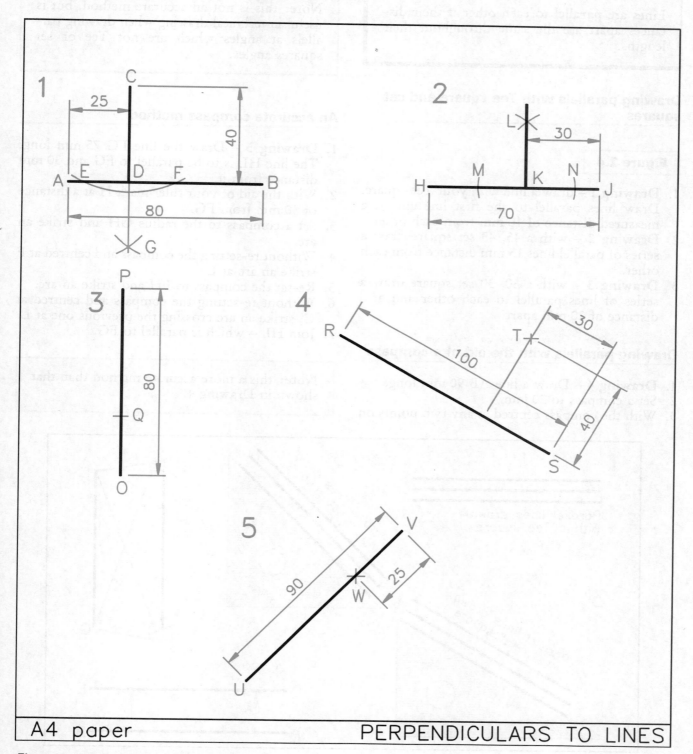

A4 paper

PERPENDICULARS TO LINES

Figure 2.3 Perpendiculars to lines

Parallel lines

Lines are **parallel** to each other if their distances apart are the same throughout their lengths.

Drawing parallels with Tee square and set squares

Figure 2.4

1. **Drawing 1** – draw a line with your Tee square. Draw lines parallel to the first line and at a measured distance of 10 mm from each other.
2. **Drawing 2** – with a 45, 45 set square draw a series of parallel lines 15 mm distance from each other.
3. **Drawing 3** – with a 60, 30 set square draw a series of lines parallel to each other and at a distance of 20 mm apart.

Drawing parallels with the aid of a compass

1. **Drawing 4** – Draw a line AB 90 mm long.
2. Set a compass to 20 mm.
3. With the compass centred at any two points on the line, draw the arcs C.
4. Draw a line DE touching the two arcs.

Note: this is not an accurate method, but is useful in technical drawing when drawing parallels at angles which are not Tee or set squares angles.

An accurate compass method

1. **Drawing 5** – Draw the line FG 75 mm long. The line HL is to be parallel to FG and 30 mm distance from it.
2. With the aid of your ruler mark H at a distance of 30 mm from FG.
3. Set a compass to the radius GH and strike an arc.
4. Without re-setting the compass and centred at F strike an arc at L.
5. Re-set the compass to FH and strike an arc.
6. Without re-setting the compass and centred at G, strike an arc crossing the previous one at L.
7. Join HL – which is parallel to FG.

Note: this a more accurate method than that shown in Drawing 4.

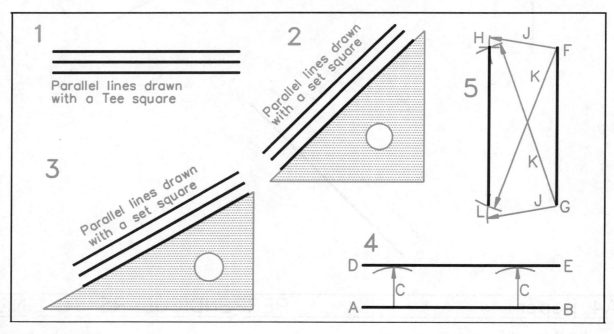

Figure 2.4 Parallel lines

Dividing a line into parts

The method shown can be used either for dividing a line into parts of equal lengths or into lines which are proportional in length to each other.

Dividing a line into parts of equal length

1. **Drawing 1** (Figure 2.5) – Draw line AB 93 mm long with a Tee square.
2. Draw line AC from A at any angle to AB. The angle should be similar to that shown in Figure 2.5.
3. Set a compass to about 20 mm and with it, step off five equal spaces along line AC – giving the points 1 to 5.
4. Set up a ruler with a set square along its edge, so that one edge of the set square is along the line B5.
5. Hold the ruler firmly on to the paper, slide the set square along the ruler until its edge is at point 4 on line AC. Draw a line to touch the line AB. This line is parallel to line B5.
6. Draw other parallels in the same way through points 1, 2 and 3 on AC.
7. AB is divided into 5 equal parts at the points where the parallel lines touch AB.

Dividing a line into proportional parts

1. **Drawing 2** (Figure 2.5) – Draw line DE 147 mm long.
2. Draw line DF at any suitable angle.
3. Set a compass to about 20 mm and with it mark off the 7 equal spaces along DF.
4. Draw line E7 as indicated in previous exercise.
5. Using the same method of drawing parallel lines as was used in Drawing 1, draw a parallel to E7 through point 4 on line DF.
6. DG is now 4/7ths of DE.

> **Note:** A **proportion** (or **ratio**) such as the length DG in relation to DE is shown in the following manner:
>
> **DG:DE = 4:7**

Practice exercises

1. Draw a line 103 mm long and divide it accurately into 7 equal parts.
2. Draw a line 115 mm long and divide it into 2 parts so that the parts are in the ratio 4:9.

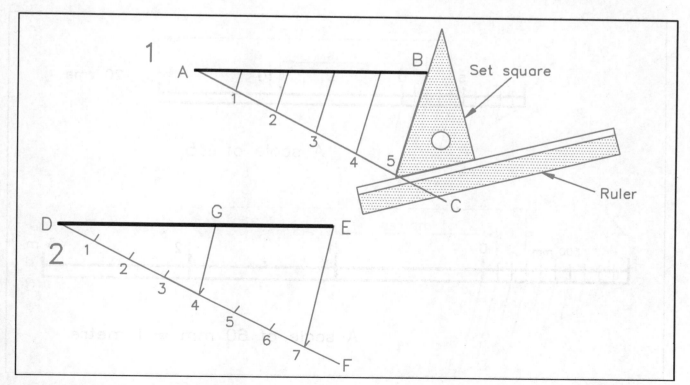

Figure 2.5 Dividing a line into parts

Drawing scales

Many technical drawings will be drawn to scales in which the drawing is either smaller or larger than its correct full-size. When drawing to a scale all parts of the drawing are reduced or enlarged by the scale factor. Common scales in use with the metric system of measurement are:

> • In engineering drawings – 1:2; 1:5; 1:10; 2:1; 5:1.
> • In building drawings – 1:20; 1:50; 1:100; 1:200.

Drawing 1 (Figure 2.6) – Constructing a scale of 1:5. Each 1 mm on the drawing represents 5 mm on the item being drawn.

1. Draw line AB 150 mm long. Draw CD at 5 mm parallel to AB.
2. Divide AB into 3 equal parts – measuring with a ruler. Draw verticals 10 mm high at the division points.
3. Divide the first 50 mm AE of AB into 10 equal parts.
4. Complete the scale as shown in Figure 2.6.

> **Note:** two examples of taking scaled measurements from the scale are shown in Figure 2.6. Examine the scale and you will understand why the scale is numbered with 0 being at the first division point along AB.

Drawing 2 (Figure 2.6) – Constructing a scale of 60 mm represents 1 metre.

1. Draw FG 240 mm long. Then draw HJ at 5 mm parallel to EF.
2. Divide FG into 4 equal parts and draw verticals at the divisions 10 mm high.
3. Divide the first 60 mm of FG into 10 equal parts.
4. Complete the scale as shown in Figure 2.6.

Practice exercises

1. Draw a scale of 1:5 to measure up to 1.25 metres in millimetres.
2. Draw a scale of 50 mm represents 1 kilometre to measure up to 8 km in 0.1 km.
3. Draw a scale of 1:2 to measure in millimetres up to 300 mm.
4. Construct a scale of 5:1 to measure up to 20 mm.

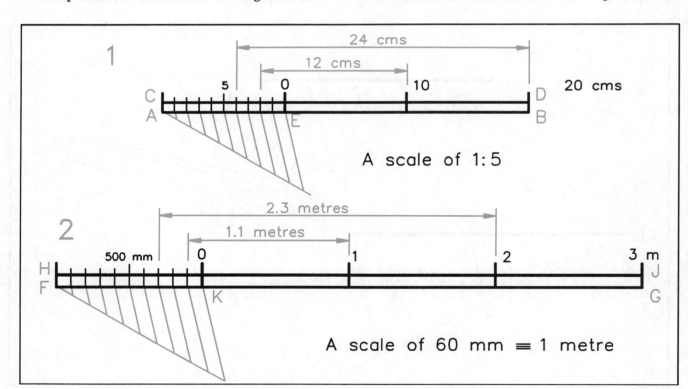

Figure 2.6 Drawing scales

Drawing diagonal scales

Diagonal scales are used where great accuracy is required. If accurately drawn, measurement down to millimetres in scales such as 1:2 or 1:5, can be made with the aid of these scales. The scale to be constructed in this example is one of 1:2.5 to read in millimetres up to 300 mm.

Figure 2.7

Stage 1 – To a scale of 1:2.5, 100 mm is represented by 40 mm.
1. Draw AB 120 mm long.
2. Step off three 40 mm divisions along AB.
3. Draw verticals at the division points.
4. Draw 10 lines above and parallel to AB at distances of 3 mm apart.

Stage 2
5. Divide the first 40 mm division DE into 10 equal parts.

Stage 3
6. Draw a line from the first 1/10 division from E to the first division point F on AB.

7. Draw parallels to the line just drawn as shown in Figure 2.7.
8. Number the scale as shown in Figure 2.7.

Note: the bottom drawing of Figure 2.7 shows how measurements greater than 100 mm are taken from a diagonal scale. The sequence is:

1. Centre a compass or a pair of dividers on the vertical line for the hundreds part of the measurement, where the horizontal line for the last figure of the measurement meets the vertical 100s line.
2. Read off the 10s figure of the measurement figure from the 10s figures along the bottom of the first 40 mm division of the scale.
3. Set the compass or dividers to the resulting position on the scale.
4. Mark off the length with the compass or the dividers on to the scaled drawing.

Practice exercise

1. Construct a diagonal scale of 30 mm = 1 km to read in divisions of 10 metres up to 4 km.

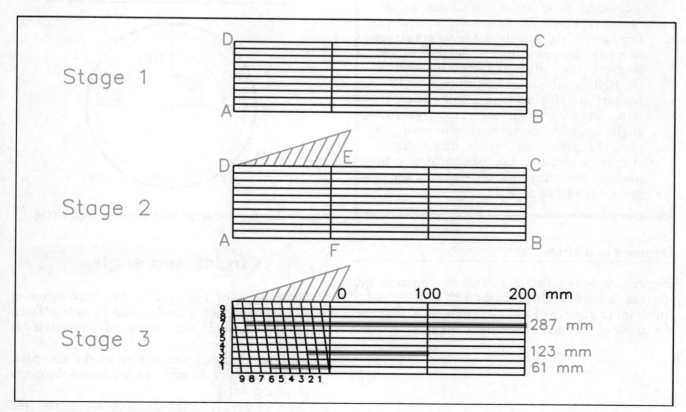

Figure 2.7 Drawing diagonal scales

Circles and parts of circles

Figure 2.8 gives the names of parts of a circle:

- **Circumference**: the actual line of the circle.
- **Arc**: part of the circumference of a circle.
- **Chord**: a straight line, with each end touching the circumference.
- **Diameter**: the longest possible chord of a circle. A line passing through the centre of the circle, with both ends touching the circumference.
- **Radius**: any of the straight lines from the centre of a circle to its circumference. The radius of a circle is half the diameter of the circle.
- **Sector**: part of a circle enclosed by two radii and the arc joining the ends of the two radii.
- **Segment**: part of a circle enclosed by a chord and the arc touching both ends of the chord.
- **Protractor**: a protractor is illustrated in Figure 2.9. Protractors are for drawing or measuring those angles that cannot be easily drawn with a Tee square and set squares. Protractors are usually made to construct or measure angles from 0 degrees to 180 degrees, from either the left hand end or the right hand end of the protractor. Protractors are also made in a full circle pattern. These will measure or construct angles up to 360 degrees, without having to turn the protractor upside down. Semi-circular protractors can, of course, also be used for constructing and measuring angles greater than 180 degrees.

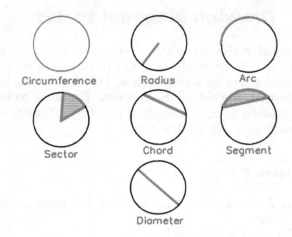

Figure 2.8 Parts of a circle

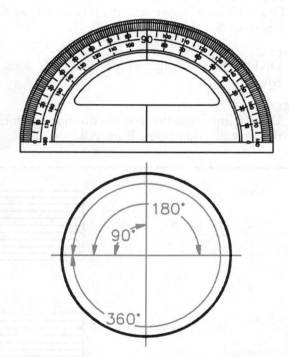

Figure 2.9 A protractor and degrees in a circle

Degrees in a circle

Figure 2.9 shows that a full circle contains 360 degrees; a semi-circle contains 180 degrees and a quadrant (a quarter of a circle) contains 90 degrees. An angle of 90 degrees is a right angle.

Circles and angles

1. **Drawing 1** of Figure 2.10. Set a compass to 40 mm and draw a circle. Add its centre lines, passing through the centre of the circle as shown.
2. Without changing the setting of the compass, and with centre A, strike an arc across the circle to give point 1.
3. With centre 1, strike another arc across the circle to obtain point 2.

4. Continue in the same way until it is found that with the compass centred at point 5, the arc 6 is crossing the circle at the start point A.

> **Note:** no matter what the size of the circle, its radius can always be stepped off 6 times around the circumference. The actual length of the circumference is 2π times the radius.
>
> Circumference = 2πR.

Constructing angles of 60 and 120 degrees

1. **Drawing 2** – Figure 2.10. Draw a line BC 50 mm long.
2. Set a compass to about 30 mm and with centre B draw an arc crossing BC at D.
3. Without altering the compass and centred at D draw an arc crossing the first arc at E.
4. Draw BF through the intersection of the two arcs.
5. The angle CBF is 60 degrees.

> **Note:** by stepping of the radius of a circle exactly 6 times around its circumference.

6. HGL of 120 degrees (**Drawing 3**) step off the radius twice along the arc from J.

To bisect an angle

1. **Drawing 4** – Figure 2.10. Draw any angle. Draw any arc PQ. Set compasses to a sensible size and with the compass centred first at P, then at Q draw crossing arcs at R.
2. Draw MS passing through R. The angles NMS and SMO are equal.

Angle in a semi-circle

> The angle contained in a semi-circle is a right angle.

All the angles in **Drawing 5** – SUT, SVT and SWT are right angles.

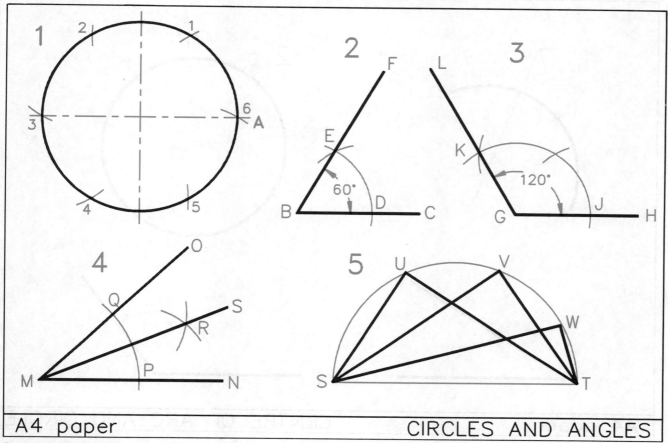

Figure 2.10 Circles and angles

Finding the centre of arcs and circles

> The **bisector** of any arc passes through its centre. It follows that if any two arcs of an arc or a circle are bisected, they must intersect at the centre of the arc or circle.

1. Draw any arc – **Drawing 1** Figure 2.11.
2. Mark off any three points C, D and E on the arc.
3. Bisect the two arcs CD and DE. The bisection lines cross at O, which is the centre of the arc.
4. Check that you have found the correct centre by centring a compass at O and attempting to complete the circle of which the arc is a part.
5. Draw any circle – **Drawing 2** Figure 2.11.
6. Mark off any three points F, G and H on the circle's circumference.
7. Bisect the arcs FG and GH. The bisection lines cross at O – the circle centre.

Acute and obtuse angles

1. **Drawing 3** of Figure 2.11 is an **acute angle** – it is less than 90 degrees.
2. **Drawing 4** of Figure 2.11 is an **obtuse angle** – it is between 90 degrees and 180 degrees.

Practice exercises

1 Draw an arc of radius 50 mm. Then find its centre using the method described above.
2 Draw a circle of 60 mm radius. Find its centre using the method described above.
3 Draw any acute angle. Then measure its size in degrees with the aid of a protractor.
4 Draw any obtuse angle. Measure its size in degrees with the aid of a protractor.
5 Draw a line AB 55 mm long. On AB construct an angle of 60 degrees.
6 Draw a line CD 75 mm long. On CD construct an angle of 120 degrees.
7 With a set square draw a right angle. Bisect the angle to obtain an angle of 45 degrees.

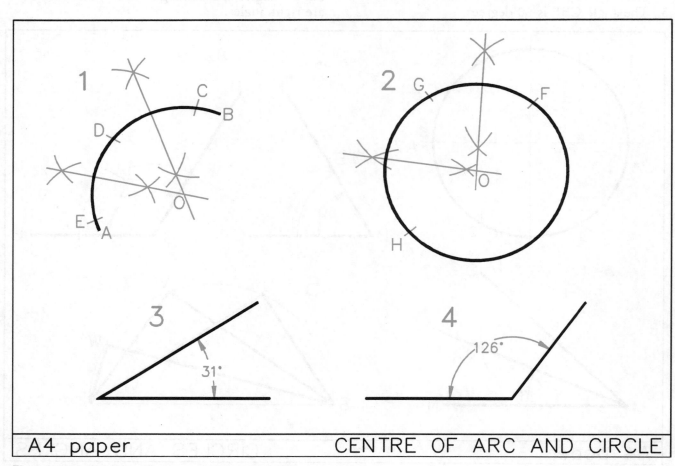

Figure 2.11 Finding the centre of an arc and a circle

Constructing angles

1. **Drawing 1**, Figure 2.12 – Construct an angle of 60 degrees. Bisect to obtain 30 degrees.
2. **Drawing 2** – Construct an angle of 60 degrees. Bisect to obtain 30 degrees. Bisect to 15 degrees.
3. **Drawing 3** – Construct an angle of 120 degrees. Bisect the angle between 60 degrees and 120 degrees to obtain an angle of 90 degrees.
4. **Drawing 4** – Construct an angle of 90 degrees. Bisect it to obtain an angle of 45 degrees.
5. **Drawing 5** – Construct an angle of 90 degrees. Bisect between 90 and 180 degrees to obtain an angle of 135 degrees.
6. **Drawing 6** – Bisect the angle between 90 and 120 degrees to obtain an angle of 105 degrees.

Constructing an angle with the aid of a protractor

Figure 2.13 shows the method of constructing an angle of 74 degrees with the aid of a protractor.

1. Draw the base line of the angle.
2. Place the protractor in position on the line with the protractor cross lines on the end of the line.
3. Make a light pencil mark against the figures of the angle to be drawn.
4. Draw a line from the end of the base line through the pencil mark.

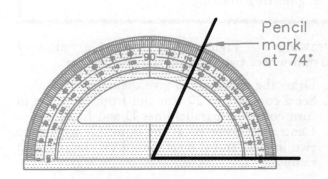

Figure 2.13 Constructing an angle with the aid of a protractor

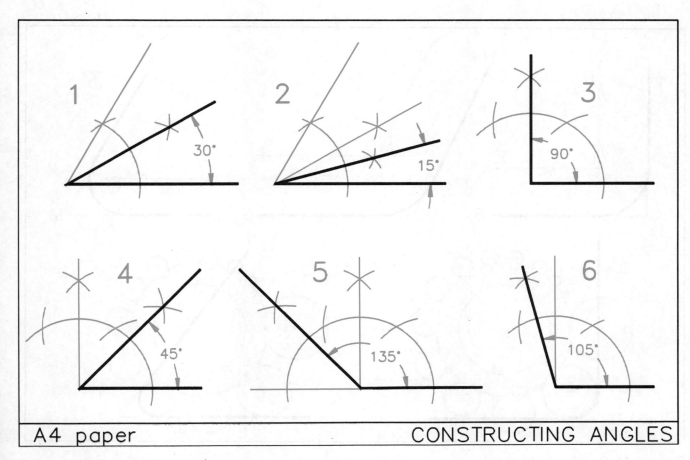

Figure 2.12 Constructing angles

Drawing radii at corners of angles

The drawing of a radius at a corner where lines meet to form an angle is known as drawing a **fillet**, particularly when working with engineering drawings.

Drawing 1 – Figure 2.14. Drawing a radius of 20 mm where two lines meet at 90 degrees.

1. Draw the two lines to give the angle BAC.
2. Set a compass to 20 mm and from each line in turn construct parallel lines D and E.
3. Centre the compass at the point O, where the two lines D and E meet, and draw the required radius.

Drawing 2 – Figure 2.14. Drawing a radius of 25 mm where two lines meet at 120 degrees.

1. Draw the two lines to give the angle GFH.

2. Follow the same procedure as for the first radiused corner, except that the compass is set to 25 mm.

Drawing 3 – Figure 2.14. Drawing a fillet of 15 mm to two lines meeting at 60 degrees.

1. Draw the two lines to give the angle LMN.
2. Follow the same procedure as for the first radiused corner, except that the compass is set to 15 mm.

Drawing fillets with the aid of a radius curve

Drawing 4 – Figure 2.14, shows a **radius curve** used to draw a fillet of radius 15 mm at the corner of a 90 degree angle. The radius curve is carefully placed in position so that the 15 mm arc is touching both lines of the angle. The fillet line is then drawn in with a pencil.

Drawing 5 – Figure 2.14, shows a radius curve being used to draw a fillet of radius 10 at the corner of a 60 degree angle.

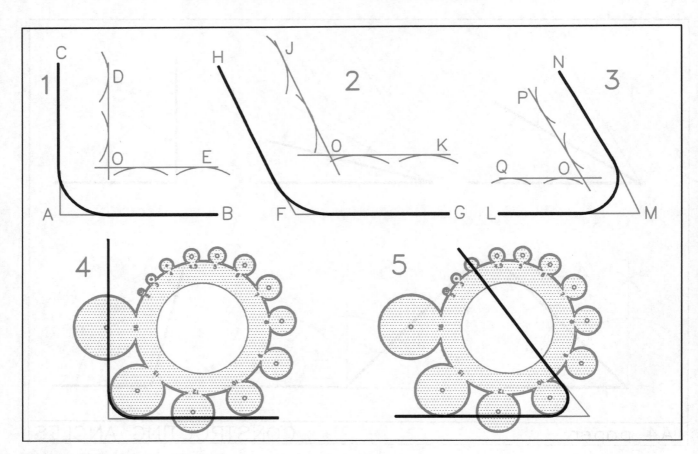

Figure 2.14 Drawing radii at corners

Note: when constructing technical drawings, it is usual practice to use a radius curve for drawing fillets. However the reader is advised to work through these examples in order to learn how to draw radiused corners at angles. When drawing large radiused corners, it is doubtful if the radius curve will have a large enough arc.

■ CHECK YOUR UNDERSTANDING

● **Horizontal** lines parallel to each other can be drawn with the aid of a Tee square.

● **Vertical** lines parallel to each other can be drawn with the aid of set squares.

● A line is **bisected** when it is divided into two equal parts.

● A line is **perpendicular** to another line if the two lines are at right angles to each other.

● Lengths in **proportion** to each other are said to be in the ratio e.g. 3:5.

● Common **scales** in engineering drawings are:
    1:1 (full size); 1:2 (half-size); 1:5; 1:10; 2:1; 5:1.
    Common scales in building drawings are:
    1:1, 1:2 and 1:5 for detail drawings; 1:20; 1:50; 1:100; 1:200 for building plans of various types.

● **Diagonal scales** are constructed to measure lengths to great accuracy.

● The various **parts of a circle** are:
    Circumference; Arc; Diameter, Radius; Chord; Sector; Segment.

● There are 360 degrees in a **circle**.

● There are 180 degrees in a **semi-circle**. An angle of 180 degrees forms a straight line.

● There are 90 degrees in a **quadrant** – a quarter of a circle. A **right angle** is also 90 degrees.

● The angle in a semi-circle is a right angle (90 degrees).

● A circle can be drawn through 3 points by bisecting the spaces between each pair of points.

● The centre of an arc can be found by bisecting two arcs of the arc.

● An angle less than 90 degrees is known as an **acute angle**.

● An angle of size between 90 and 180 degrees is known as an **obtuse angle**.

● **Fillets** can easily be drawn with the aid of a radius curve.

REVISION EXERCISES AND QUESTIONS

Exercises

1 Draw a line AB 85 mm long and bisect it at C.
2 Draw line DE 105 mm long and bisect it at F.
3 Construct a scale of 1:2 to read in centimetres up to 200 mm.
4 Construct the following angles:
    60 degrees; 30 degrees; 135 degrees.
5 Bisect the angles you have just drawn.
6 With a protractor construct angles of:
    53 degrees; 79 degrees; 108 degrees; 207 degrees; 310 degrees.
7 Figure 2.15. Draw AB. Construct the perpendicular to AB at C.

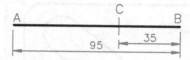

Figure 2.15 Exercise 7

8 Figure 2.16. Draw DE. Construct the perpendicular to DE from F.

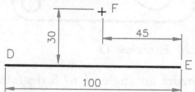

Figure 2.16 Exercise 8

9 Figure 2.17. Draw GH. Divide GH in the ratio of 3:7.

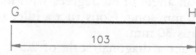

Figure 2.17 Exercise 9

10 Figure 2.18. Construct the three points J, K and L. Draw a circle which passes through J, K and L.

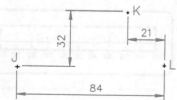

Figure 2.18 Exercise 10

11 Figure 2.19. Construct the given drawing.

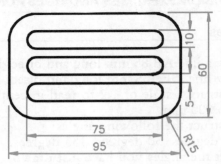

Figure 2.19 Exercise 11

12 Figure 2.20. Construct the given drawing.

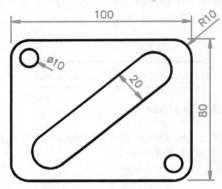

Figure 2.20 Exercise 12

13 Construct an angle of 67.5 degrees, following the sequence:
 a) Construct an angle of 90 degrees.
 b) Bisect to obtain 45 degrees.
 c) Bisect between 45 and 90 degrees.
14 Draw a line 213 mm long and divide it into 13 equal parts.
15 Draw an angle of 60 degrees with its two arms each 80 mm long. Construct a fillet at the angle of radius 30 mm.
16 Construct a diagonal scale of 2.5:1 to read in 0.1 mm divisions up to 60 mm.
17 Figure 2.21. The given drawing shows a kilometre speedometer scale fitted to a car.

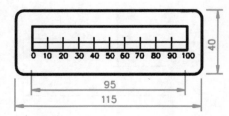

Figure 2.21 Exercise 17

Construct an accurate copy of the given drawing.
18 Figure 2.22. You will remember that the radius of a circle steps off exactly 6 times around its circumference. Using this geometrical fact, draw a regular six-sided figure inside the circle of radius 100 mm. This figure is called a **regular hexagon** – regular because all its sides are of equal length and all its angles are of equal size. Can you state the number of degrees in each angle of a regular hexagon?

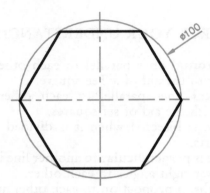

Figure 2.22 Exercise 18

Questions

1 You will see triangles all around you if you look carefully. Why do you think triangles are such an important feature of constructions such as pylons?
2 The sides of most roads and railway lines can be said to be parallel to each other. Have you seen any other parallel lines such as these?
3 Circles are another geometric feature which can be seen in many places. The sun, the centre of many flowers. Can you name any others?
4 Buildings are made with their sides as vertical as it is possible to construct them. Why is this?
5 For what purposes do you think diagonal scales are used?
6 Can you name the various parts of a circle?
7 How many degrees in:
 a) a circle?
 b) a semi-circle?
 c) a quadrant?
 d) a right angle?
8 What is the size in degrees of the angle in a right angle?

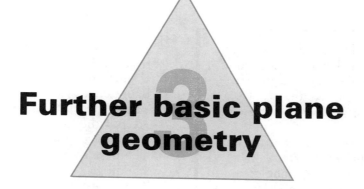

Further basic plane geometry

Introduction

In Chapter 2 the more elementary parts of plane geometry were described – lines, the division of lines, angles and scales, arcs and circles. In this chapter the more advanced geometry, involving the use of these features, is given to complete the basic geometry necessary for those wishing to become expert in the construction of accurate technical drawings. Thus the construction of triangles, polygons of various types, circles in relation to triangles and polygons, tangents and ellipses are included in this chapter. These are the basic construction tools of technical drawings.

Triangles

- Triangles have three sides.
- Triangles have three angles. The sum (adding together) of the three angles always gives 180 degrees.

Types of triangle

There are four types of triangle – shown in Figure 3.1:

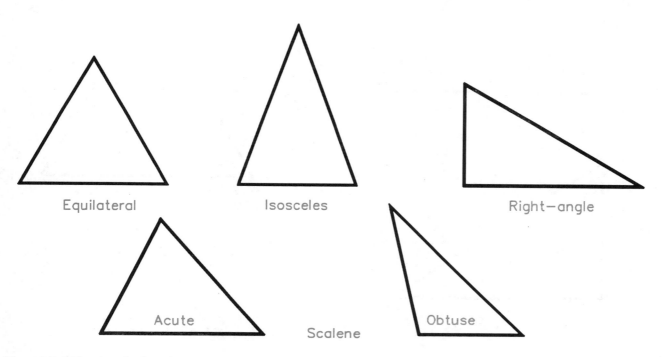

Figure 3.1 Types of triangles

1. **Equilateral** – All sides are of equal length. All angles are of equal size = 60 degrees.
2. **Isosceles** – Two angles are of equal size. Two sides are of equal length.
3. **Right-angle** – One angle is a right-angle = 90 degrees.
4. **Scalene** – all sides are of different lengths. All angles are of different sizes.
   Two main types of scalene triangle:
      Acute – all angles are acute = less than 90 degrees.
      Obtuse – one of the three angles is obtuse = between 90 and 180 degrees.

1. Triangle **vertices** are often lettered, using capitals, when the triangle may be, for example triangle ABC.
2. If **sides** are lettered, lower case is used, e.g. a and b and c.
3. The **angles** of triangle ABC are BAC, ABC and ACB – the middle letter being the angle where the letter is positioned.
4. The **base** of a triangle is the side on which it is standing.
5. The **altitude** is the vertical height above the base.
6. The term **hypotenuse** is only used with reference to right-angle triangles.
7. The **vertical angle** is the angle opposite the base.
8. Note the term **vertex**. Its plural is **vertices**.

Parts of triangles

Figure 3.2 shows the names of the parts of triangles.

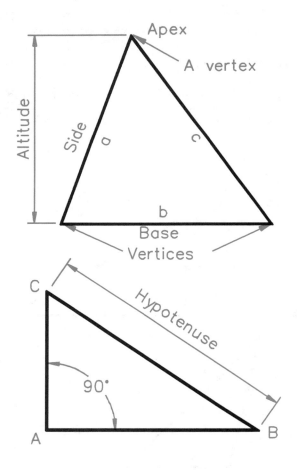

Figure 3.2 Parts of triangles

Constructing an equilateral triangle

Figure 3.3 shows two methods of constructing an equilateral triangle:

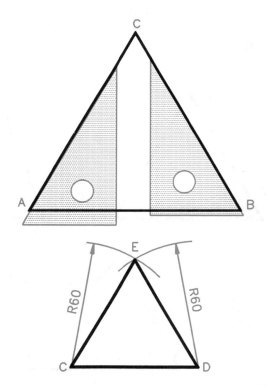

Figure 3.3 Constructing equilateral triangles

1. With the aid of a 30,60 set square, using the 60 degree angle. Start by drawing the base, AB, then draw lines, meeting at C, at 60 degrees from each end of the base with the aid of the set square.
2. Strike off compass arcs with the compass set to the length of the side. Thus in the lower of the two drawings of Figure 3.3, the side length of the equilateral triangle is 60 mm. Start by drawing the base – a line 60 mm long; then set a compass to 60 mm and strike arcs from each end of the base; draw lines from the ends of the base to the intersection of the two arcs.

The 3: 4: 5 right-angle triangle

The upper of the two drawings of Figure 3.4 shows a triangle with sides in the proportion 3: 4: 5. Such a triangle is always a right-angle triangle. This is because:

> The square on the hypotenuse is equal to the sum of the squares on the other two sides.

Taking the 3: 4: 5 triangle:

a) The square on the hypotenuse = 5 × 5 = 25.
b) The square on the shortest side = 3 × 3 = 9.
c) The square on the other side = 4 × 4 = 16; and 9 + 16 = 25.

Thus: if the sides of a triangle are 30 mm, 40 mm and 50 mm long, the triangle is a right-angled one.

If the sides are 27 mm, 36 mm and 45 mm in length the triangle is a right-angled one.

Other 3: 4: 5 triangles are found for example in a triangle ABC, in which AB = 28 mm, BC = 21 mm and AC = 35 mm. And also in triangle XYZ in which: XY = 57 mm, YZ = 76 mm and XZ = 95 mm.

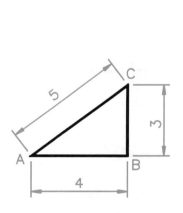
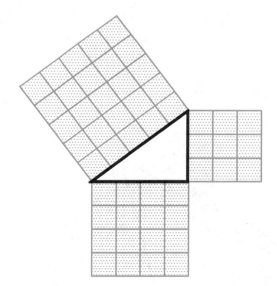

Figure 3.4 In a right-angle triangle, the square on the hypotenuse is equal to the sum of the squares on the other two sides

More triangles

Note: DEF is another isosceles triangle.

Figure 3.5.

To construct triangle ABC

1. Draw the base AB, 50 mm long. Set a compass to 70 mm.
2. With the compass centred first at A, then at B strike intersecting arcs to give C.
3. Join AC and BC to complete the triangle.

Note: triangle ABC is isosceles.

To construct triangle DEF

1. Draw DE. Set a compass to 60 mm.
2. With the compass centred first at D, then at E strike intersecting arcs to obtain F.
3. Join DF and EF to complete the triangle.

To construct triangle GHJ

1. Draw GH 85 mm long.
2. Set a compass to 90 mm and from G strike an arc J.
3. Set a compass to 60 mm and from H strike an arc crossing J.
4. Join GJ and HJ to complete the triangle.

To construct triangle KLM

1. Draw KL 70 mm long.
2. With the aid of a protractor construct a 105 degree angle at L, and draw a line from L at that angle.
3. Set a compass to 100 mm. With the compass centred at K strike an arc across the arm of the line at 105 degrees from L, to give M.
4. Join LM to complete the triangle.

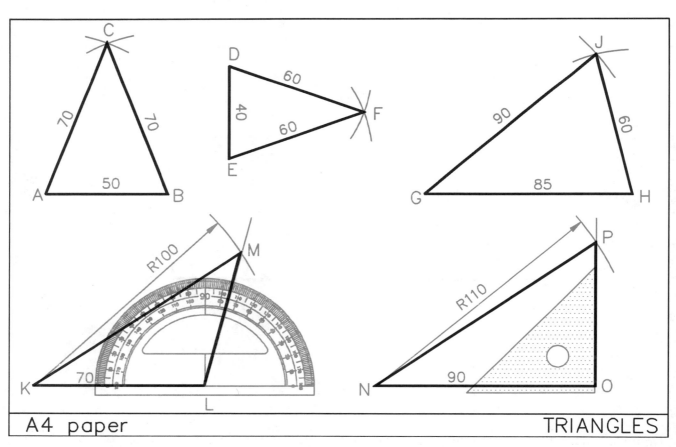

Figure 3.5 Triangles

Note: KLM is a scalene triangle, which is obtuse.

To construct triangle NOP

1. Draw NO 90 mm long.
2. Draw the angle NOP with a set square.
3. Set a compass to 110 mm. With the compass centred at N strike an arc across the 90 degree line from O to give P.
4. Join NP to complete the triangle.

Note: NOP is a right-angle triangle.

Revision hint: do not erase constructions. They will remind you when you are revising for examinations.

Right-angle triangles

Note: the right-angle triangle is an important geometrical figure.

DRAWING 1 – Figure 3.6.

Constructing the triangle

DRAWING 2 – Figure 3.6.

1. Draw the base FG 100 mm long.
2. Bisect the base FG.
3. At the bisection point of FG, draw a semi-circle of radius equal to half FG.
4. With a compass set to 50 mm, and centred at G strike an arc across the semi-circle to give H.
5. Join GH and FH to complete the triangle.

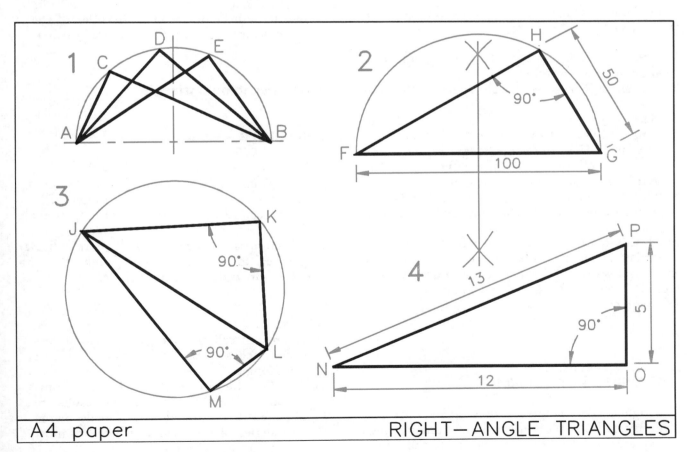

A4 paper   RIGHT—ANGLE TRIANGLES

Figure 3.6 Right-angle triangles

Note: FHG is a right-angled triangle because the angle at H is an angle within a semi-circle.

A cyclic quadrilateral

DRAWING 3 – Figure 3.6.

If two triangles are drawn within a circle with a common diameter of the circle as a base and with the vertical angles touching the circumference of the circle, they are said to form a **cyclic quadrilateral. Quadrilaterals** – plane figures with four sides – are described later in this chapter.

Note the following details about the cyclic quadrilateral JKLM.

1. The angle LKJ is a right-angle – angle of a triangle in a semi-circle.
2. The angle JML is also a right angle for the same reason.
3. Because there are 180 degrees in a triangle the sum (addition) of the two angles KJL and KLJ of triangle JKL must be 90 degrees.
4. In the same way the sum of the two angles JLM and LJM must also be 90 degrees.
5. Thus the sum of the two angles KJM and KLM of the cyclic quadrilateral must be 180 degrees.

From this it can be seen that a feature of cyclic quadrilaterals is that the sum of their opposite angles is always 180 degrees. In fact a quadrilateral must be cyclic if the sum of its opposite angles is 180 degrees.

DRAWING 4 – Figure 3.6.

The right-angle triangle NOP with its sides in a ratio of 5:12:13 is another example of one in which the square on the hypotenuse is equal to the sum of the squares on the other two sides.

Triangles and circles

A circle circumscribing a triangle

DRAWING 1 – Figure 3.7.

1. Construct the triangle ABD in which: AB = 70 mm; BD = 65 mm: AD = 45 mm.
2. Bisect AB and AD. The bisection lines cross at C.
3. C is the centre of a circle circumscribing ABD.
4. Set a compass to CA (or CB, or CD) and draw the circumscribing circle centred at C.

Notes:
- A circle **circumscribes** a triangle if its circumference touches the vertices of the triangle.
- When finding the centre C of a circle circumscribing a triangle, the most accurate results will be achieved if the sides of the triangle nearest to a right angle are bisected.

A circle inscribing a triangle

DRAWING 2 – Figure 3.7.

1. Construct the triangle EFG in which: EF = 90 mm; FG = 50 mm; EG = 95 mm.
2. Bisect the angles EFG and FGE to give I.
3. I is the centre of the circle inscribing triangle EFG.
4. Set a compass to a radius of the perpendicular distance I to any side of the triangle and with centre I draw the inscribing circle.

Notes:
- A circle **inscribes** a triangle if its circumference touches (is tangential to) each side of the triangle.
- As with the construction of the circumscribing circle, the most accurate results are obtained if the bisections are made of the two angles of the triangle which are most near to being right-angles.

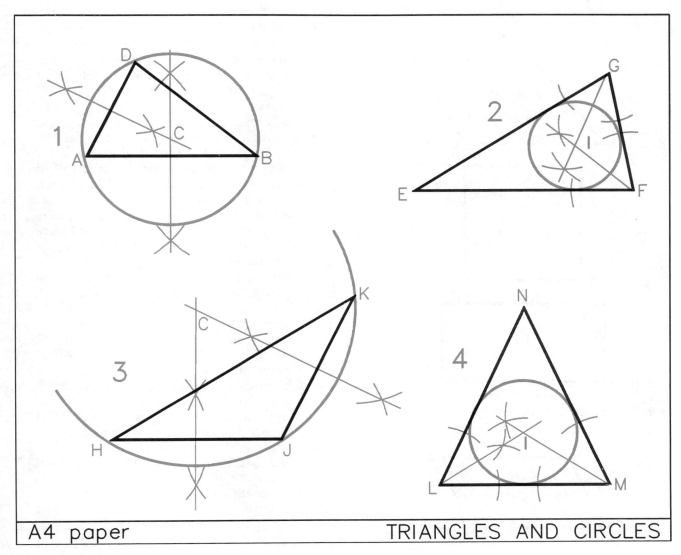

A4 paper   TRIANGLES AND CIRCLES

Figure 3.7 Triangles and circles

DRAWING 3 – Figure 3.7.

1. Construct triangle HJK in which:
   HJ = 70 mm; JK = 65 mm; HK = 115 mm.
2. Bisect the sides HJ and JK and draw the circumscribed circle to HJK.

DRAWING 4 – Figure 3.7.

1. Construct the triangle LMN in which:
   LM = 70 mm; MN = LN = 80 mm.
2. Bisect the angles MLN and LMN and draw the inscribed circle to LMN.

Types of quadrilateral

Quadrilaterals are **polygons** which have four sides and four angles. Quadrilaterals may be **irregular** or **regular**. A polygon is regular if all its sides are of equal length and all its angles are of equal size.

Figure 3.8 and Figure 3.9 both show a number of different types of quadrilateral. In the examples given on page 32, only the square is a regular quadrilateral.

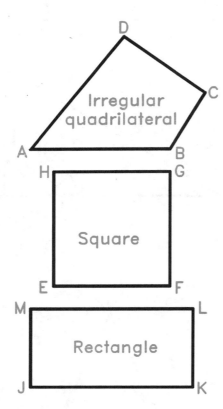

Figure 3.8 Types of quadrilateral

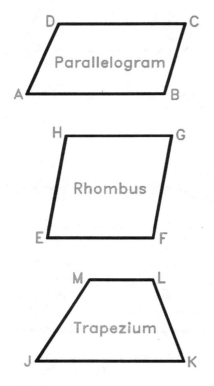

Figure 3.9 Types of quadrilateral

- **Irregular** – sides are of different lengths; angles are of different sizes.
- **Square** – all sides the same length; opposite sides are parallel – in EFGH of Figure 3.8, EF is parallel to GH and FG is parallel to EH; all angles are right angles = 90 degrees.
- **Rectangle** – all angles are right angles; opposite sides are of equal length; opposite sides are parallel – in JKLM of Figure 3.8, JK is parallel to LM and KL is parallel to JM.
- **Parallelogram** – Each pair of opposite sides are parallel – in ABCD of Figure 3.9, AB is parallel to CD and BC is parallel to AD; opposite angles are of equal size – in parallelogram ABCD of Figure 3.9, angle at A = angle at C and angle at D = angle at B; angles on the same side add up to 180 degrees – angle A + angle B = 180 degrees and so on.
- **Rhombus** – a parallelogram in which all sides are the same length; opposite angles are equal – in EFGH of Figure 3.9, angle at E = angle at G and angle at F = angle at H; the diagonals of a rhombus bisect each other at right angles.
- **Trapezium** – One pair of opposite sides is parallel – in the example JKLM of Figure 3.9, JK is parallel to LM.

Polygons with more than four sides

In **irregular polygons** sides are of differing lengths and angles are of differing sizes. In **regular polygons** all sides are of equal length and all angles are of equal size.

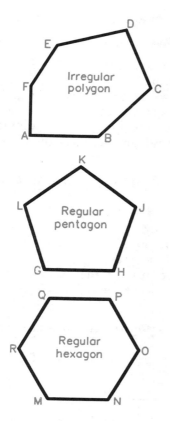

Figure 3.10 Irregular and regular polygons

- **Irregular polygon** – ABCDEF of Figure 3.10 is an irregular polygon of six sides – it is a hexagon.
- **Regular pentagon** – has 5 sides and 5 angles;
  all its sides are of equal length;
  all its angles are of equal size, each being 108 degrees.
- **Regular hexagon** – has 6 sides and 6 angles;
  all its sides are of equal length;
  all its angles are of equal size, each being 120 degrees.
  regular hexagons are frequently used in technical drawings.
- **Regular heptagon** – has 7 sides and 7 angles;
  all its sides are of equal length;
  all its angles are of equal size.
- **Regular octagon** – has 8 sides and 8 angles;
  all its sides are of equal length;
  all its angles are of equal size, each being 135 degrees.
- **Regular nonagon** – has 9 sides and 9 angles;
  all its sides are of equal length;
  all its angles are of equal size.

Note on irregular polygons

Some may have equal side lengths, but with unequal size angles. Some may have several sides the same length. Some may have several angles of the same size. However unless *all* sides are of the same length and *all* angles of the same size, such polygons are **irregular**.

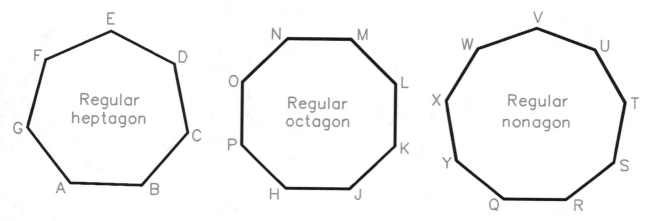

Figure 3.11 Regular polygons

Regular hexagons and octagons

A regular hexagon within a circle

1. **Drawing 1** – Figure 3.12. – Draw a circle of centre O and radius of 30 mm.
2. Starting at B step off the 30 mm radius around the circle.
3. Complete the hexagon by joining the points where the arcs cross the circle.

A regular hexagon drawn with a set square

1. **Drawing 2** – Figure 3.12. Draw the base GH, 35 mm long.
2. With the aid of a 30,60 set square draw lines at 120 degrees to GH at G and at H.
3. Set a compass to 35 mm. From G and H step off 35 mm along the 120 degree lines.
4. Continue with the set square and compass to complete the hexagon.

A regular hexagon drawn with the aid of a set square

1. **Drawing 3** – Figure 3.12. Draw a circle of radius 30 mm.
2. Draw the horizontal diameter and two further diameters at 60 degrees using a set square.
3. Complete the hexagon by joining the points where the diameters meet the circle.

A regular octagon drawn with a set square

1. **Drawing 4** – Figure 3.12. Draw a base line 25 mm long.
2. Draw lines at 135 degrees at both ends of the base.
3. Along these lines step off 25 mm.
4. Continue in the same to complete the octagon with the aid of the set square and the compass.

A regular octagon within a square

1. **Drawing 5** – Figure 3.12. Draw a square of 60 mm sides.

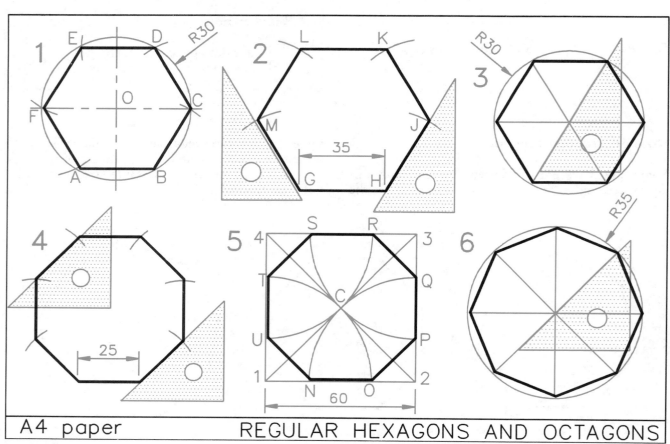

A4 paper   REGULAR HEXAGONS AND OCTAGONS

Figure 3.12 Regular hexagons and octagons

2. Draw the diagonals of the square.
3. Set a compass to the radius – any corner of the square to its centre.
4. From each corner of the square draw arcs.
5. Complete the octagon by joining the ends of the arcs.

A regular octagon within a circle

1. **Drawing 6** – Figure 3.12. Draw a circle of 35 mm diameter.
2. With a 45, 45 set square draw diagonals at 45 degrees to each other as shown.
3. Complete the octagon by drawing lines between the points where the diagonals meet the circle.

Constructing regular polygons

Any regular polygon may be constructed by the methods shown. However, it is common practice in technical drawing to draw regular hexagons and octagons by the methods shown on page 34.

To construct a regular pentagon

1. **Drawing 1** – Figure 3.13. Draw the base 40 mm long.
2. At A and at B, draw lines at 45 degrees and at 60 degrees to intersect at F and G.
3. Bisect FG to obtain O. O is the centre of a circle which will circumscribe the completed pentagon.
4. With a compass set to OA (or OB) and centred at O draw a circle.
5. Set a compass to the side length of 40 mm from A and then from B, strike arcs across the circle to give the points E and C.
6. Without altering the compass setting, strike an arc from E across the circle to give D.
7. Join the points so obtained to complete the regular pentagon.

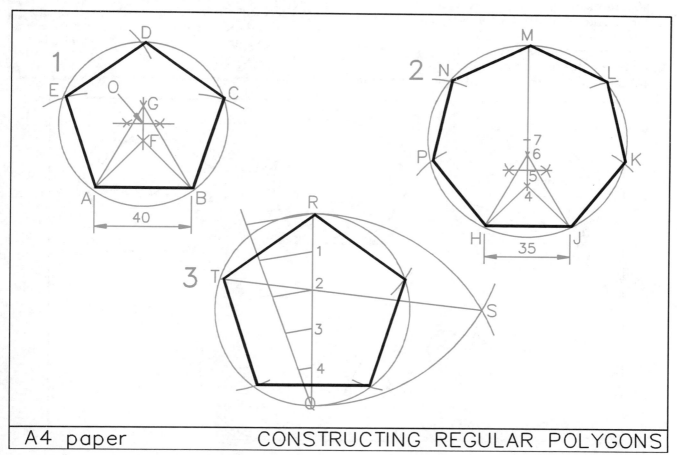

Figure 3.13 Constructing regular polygons

To construct a regular heptagon

1. **Drawing 2** – Figure 3.13. Draw the base line HJ 35 mm long.
2. At H, then at J draw lines at 45 degrees and 60 degrees to intersect at points 4 and 6.
3. Draw a line from 4 to 6 and extend the line upwards.
4. Bisect the line from 4 to 6 to obtain point 5. Note that point 5 would give the centre of a regular pentagon of base length 35 mm.
5. Step off the length from 5 to 6 from 6 along the vertical line to give the point 7.
6. The point 7 is the centre of the required regular heptagon. Proceed as in the previous example (the pentagon) to complete the polygon.

To construct a regular polygon within a circle

1. **Drawing 3** – Figure 3.13. Draw a circle of 80 mm diameter.
2. Draw the vertical diameter QR and divide it into 5 equal parts.
3. Draw arcs radius RQ from R and Q to meet at S.
4. Draw ST through point 2 on RQ.
5. RT is the side of the required regular pentagon.

Circles of polygons

The term **polygon** taken in its broadest sense means any plane figure with at least three sides. **Note:** a **plane figure** is one that is flat – it has only height and width – it is two-dimensional (2-D). For the time being we are only dealing with polygons which possess straight sides. This means that triangles and quadrilaterals, as well as plane figures which have more than four sides are included in the general term polygon.

Three circles are associated with a polygon:

- **Circumscribed circle**: One which touches all vertices of the polygon. **Drawing 1** of Figure 3.14, shows a circumscribing circle to a cyclic quadrilateral (see page 30 for the meaning of a cyclic quadrilateral).
- **Inscribed circle**: One which touches all three sides of the polygon. An inscribed circle is internal to the polygon.
- **Escribed circle**: One which touches one side and the extensions of the sides adjacent to that side. An escribed circle is external to the polygon.

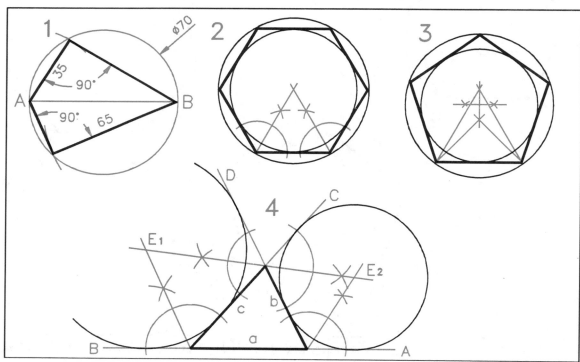

Figure 3.14 Circles of polygons

A circle circumscribing a cyclic quadrilateral

1. **Drawing 1** – Figure 3.14. Draw a circle of radius 70 mm. Draw its horizontal diameter.
2. Set a compass to 35 mm and from one end of the diameter, A, strike an arc to cross the circle, giving the position of the end of the 35 mm side.
3. Set a compass to 65 mm and, centred at B, strike an arc to give the position of the end of the 65 mm arc.
4. Complete the quadrilateral as shown. It is cyclic because the sum of each pair of opposite angles = 180 degrees.

Inscribed and circumscribed circles

Drawing 2 and **Drawing 3** – Figure 3.14 show examples of both inscribed and circumscribed circles to a regular hexagon and a regular pentagon

Escribed circles to a triangle

1. **Drawing 4** – Figure 3.14. Draw any triangle of sides a, b and c.
2. Extend all sides as shown to A, B, C and D.
3. Bisect the external angles on sides b and c as shown to obtain the two escribed circle centres E1 and E2.

4. With centres E1 and E2, draw the two escribed circles touching the sides b and c.

Constructing irregular polygons

DRAWING 1 – Figure 3.15.

1. Draw AB 50 mm long.
2. At B, with the aid of a 30,60 set square draw a line. Set a compass to 70 mm and with the compass centred at B strike an arc along the line to give C.
3. Without altering the compass and centred at C strike an arc in the area D.
4. Set a compass to 50 mm and with it centred at A strike an arc crossing the arc from C to give D.
5. Join CD and DA to complete the quadrilateral ABCD.

DRAWING 2 – Figure 3.15.

1. Draw EF 40 mm long.

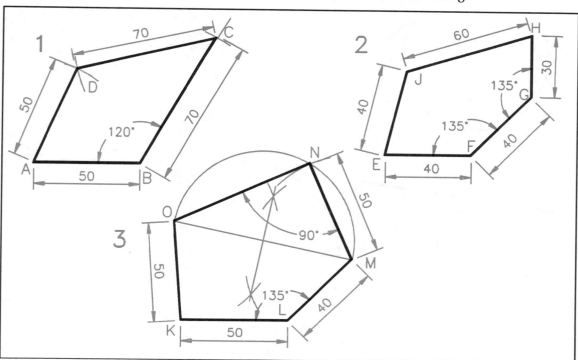

Figure 3.15 Constructing irregular polygons

2. Draw a line from F at 135 degrees with the aid of a 45, 45 set square.
3. From F strike an arc 40 mm long along the 135 degree line to give G.
4. At G draw a line at 135 degrees with the aid of a set square.
5. From G strike an arc 30 mm long along the 135 degree line to give H.
6. To locate point J strike arcs of 60 mm and 40 mm from H and E in turn.
7. Join HJ and JE to complete the pentagon.

DRAWING 3 – Figure 3.15

1. Draw KL 50 mm long.
2. Draw a line from L at 135 degrees with the aid of a 45, 45 set square.
3. From L strike an arc 40 mm long along the 135 degree line to give M.
4. At K draw an angle of 100 degrees with the aid of a protractor.
5. From K strike an arc along the 100 degree line to give O.
6. Draw MO and bisect it and draw a semi-circle.

7. From M strike an arc of 50 mm to cross the semi-circle at N. The angle MNO is 90 degrees (angle in a semi-circle).
8. Draw NO to complete the irregular pentagon.

Line tangents to circles

Line tangential to a circle at a point on its circumference

1. **Drawing 1** – Figure 3.16. Draw circle, centre C, of radius 30 mm. Mark any point P on its circumference.
2. Draw the radius CP.
3. At P construct a right angle to CP.
4. The line AB, at right angles to CP, is tangential to the circle.

Note: if a line touching a circle at a point, forms a right angle with a radius of the circle at the point, then the line is tangential to the circle.

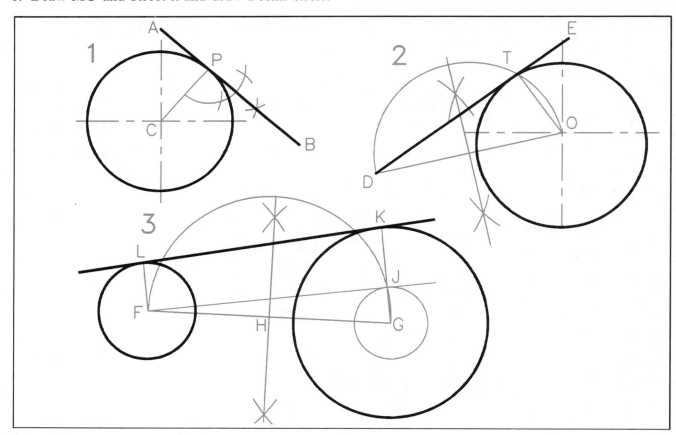

Figure 3.16 Line tangents to circles

Line tangential to a circle from a point outside the circle

1. **Drawing 2** – Figure 3.16. Draw a circle, centre O, of radius 35 mm. Mark the point D at any position outside the circle.
2. Join OD with a straight line.
3. Bisect and draw a semi-circle on OD. The semi-circle crosses the circle O at T.
4. Draw DE passing through T. Then DE is tangential to the circle of centre O.

> **Note:** the angle OTD must be a right angle – it is the angle in a semi-circle. See page 19. Therefore the line DTE must be tangential to the circle O.

External line tangent between two circles of unequal diameter

1. **Drawing 3** – Figure 3.16. Draw two circles with their centres 100 mm apart. Circle centre F of radius 20 mm, circle centre G of radius 40 mm.
2. With centre G draw a circle of radius = radius of circle G – radius of circle F. GJ = GK − FL.
3. Join FG, bisect FG and draw the semi-circle on FG to cross the circle just drawn at J.
4. Draw the tangent FJ (right angle in a semi-circle).

5. Join GJ and extend to K.
6. Draw FL parallel to GK.
7. Join LK. LK is tangential to both circles.

> **Note:** the angle OTD must be a right angle – it is the angle in a semi-circle. See page 19. Therefore the line DTE must be tangential to the circle O.

Internal tangent to two circles

1. **Drawing 1** – Figure 3.17. Draw two circles. Circle centre O of 40 mm diameter, circle centre C of 60 mm diameter. OC is 90 mm.
2. Join OC and bisect to give its mid-point A.
3. Draw a semi-circle with centre A on OC.
4. With centre O draw a circle of radius of the radius of circle O plus the radius of circle C. Thus OE + CD = OB. B is the point where the circle intersects the semi-circle on A.
5. Join CB – the tangent from C to the circle OB (right angle in a semi-circle).
6. Join OB. Draw CD parallel to OB to cut the circle centre C at D.
7. ED is the required internal tangent to the two circles.

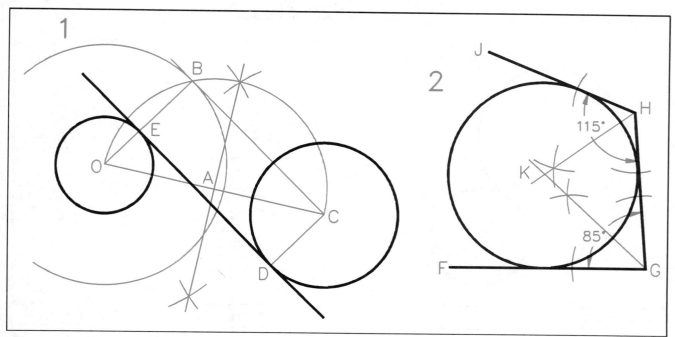

Figure 3.17 Circles and tangents

Circle tangential to three lines

1. **Drawing 2** – Figure 3.17. Draw FG 85 mm long. At G draw GH 65 mm long at an angle of 85 degrees to FG. Draw HJ 65 mm long at an angle of 115 degrees to GH.
2. Bisect the angles FGH and GHJ. The bisectors intersect at K.
3. K is the centre of the circle tangential to the three lines formed by the two angles.

Note:
1. To draw a line tangential externally to two circles subtract their radii – R1 – R2.
2. To draw a line tangentially internally to two circles add their radii – R1 + R2.
3. To draw a circle tangential to the two angles formed by the three arms of two angles, bisect the angles.

Tangential circles – 1

Tangent to an arc at a point

1. **Drawing 1** – Fig 3.18. Draw any arc AB. Mark any point P on the arc.
2. Draw a circle of centre P. Bisect the arc CD. Join EF.
3. Bisect EF. Then GH is the required tangent.

Tangential circle in an angle

1. **Drawing 2** – Figure 3.18. Draw the angle JKL of 40 degrees. JK = KL = 75 mm. The circle is to be 15 mm radius.
2. Bisect the angle JKL. Draw MO parallel to JK 15 mm (radius of circle) apart.
3. O, where MO intersects the bisector, is the centre of the required circle.

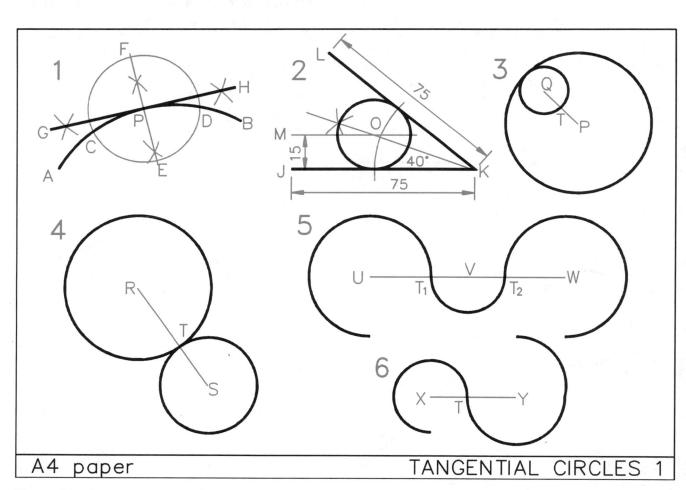

Figure 3.18 Tangential circles – 1

Circles touching internally

1. **Drawing 3** – Figure 3.18. The two circles are of radius 30 mm and 10 mm. Draw circle P of radius 30 mm.
2. Draw a line PQ of length 30 − 10 = 20 mm (radius of circle 1 − radius of circle 2).
3. Q is the centre of the circle tangential internally to the circle P.

Circles touching externally

1. **Drawing 4** – Figure 3.18. The two circles are of radius 30 mm and 20 mm. Draw circle R of radius 30 mm.
2. Draw a line RS of length 30 + 20 = 50 mm (radius 1 + radius 2).
3. S is the centre of the circle touching circle R externally. The two circles are tangential at T.

A curve formed by three tangential arcs

1. **Drawing 5** – Figure 3.18. Circles U and W of radius 25 mm, V radius 15 mm.

2. Draw circle U. Draw the line UW of length radius U + diameter V + radius W = 80 mm.
3. Circle U cuts UW at T1. Mark off 15 mm from T1 to obtain V. Draw arc V. It cuts UW at T2.
4. Mark off 25 mm along UW from T2. Draw circle W.

Drawing 6 – Figure 3.18.

The construction of this example follows that of the previous example. Radius X = 15 mm, radius Y = 20 mm.

Tangential circles – 2

DRAWING 1 – Figure 3.19.

1. Draw the two circles of centres A and B.
2. Set a compass to the addition of the radius of circle A and the 55 mm arc: 20 + 55 = 75. Strike arcs below and above the two circles A and B.

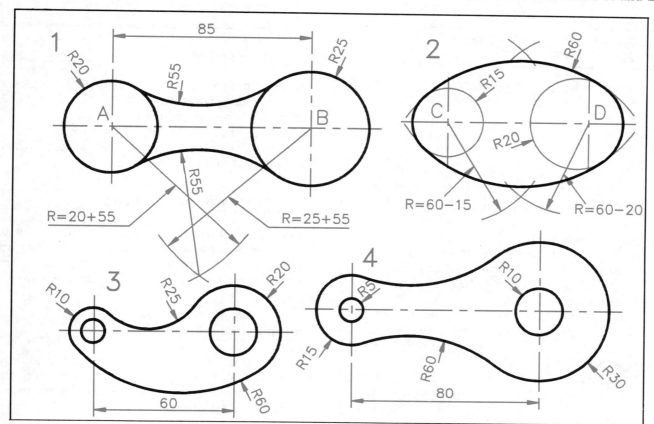

Figure 3.19 Tangential circles – 2

3. Set a compass to the addition of the radius of circle B and the 55 mm arc: 25 + 55 = 80 mm. Strike arcs below and above the two circles A and B.
4. From the points where the two pairs of arcs intersect draw the arcs of radius 55 mm to complete the outline.

DRAWING 2 – Figure 3.19.

1. Draw the two circles of centres C and D.
2. Set a compass to the radius 60 minus the radius of circle C: 60 − 15 = 45 mm. Strike arcs below and above the two circles C and D.
3. Set a compass to the radius 60 minus the radius of circle D: 60 − 20 = 40 mm. Strike arcs below and above the two circles C and D.
4. At the points where the two pairs of arcs intersect draw the arcs of radius 60 mm to complete the outline.

DRAWING 3 and DRAWING 4 – Figure 3.19.

These examples are left as an exercise for the reader to work, following the methods of the first two examples.

Note: when drawing arcs or circles which are tangential to each other the following rules must be observed:
1. If the arcs or circles are to meet externally to each other, the points of tangency are determined by adding the radii of the arcs or circles. R1 + R2.
2. If the arcs or circles are to meet internally to each other, the points of tangency are determined by subtracting the radii of the arcs or circles. R1 − R2.
3. A line drawn between the centres of arcs or circles which are tangential to each other will pass through their common point of tangency.

Ellipses

Ellipses are fairly often found in technical drawings, so you should learn how to draw them in a variety of positions and using a number of different methods. Three methods of drawing ellipses will be described on the next page. Some details about the parts of ellipses are shown in Figure 3.20.
An ellipse can be regarded in two ways:

1. **Drawing 1** – Figure 3.20. If a circle – say a circular coin – is looked at so that the complete circle can be seen and then it is slowly rotated about one of its diameters, eventually the circle edge will be seen as a straight line. Between the full circle and the straight line as the circle is rotated, ellipses will be seen. The diameter about which rotation is taking place will not alter in length, but the ellipses will become smaller and smaller as the rotation takes place.
2. **Drawings 3 and 4** – Figure 3.20. An ellipse can also be regarded as:

> ● the locus of a point which moves so that the sum of its distances to two fixed points is constant.

Parts of an ellipse

An ellipse has two axes, which are at right angles to each other (**Drawing 2** – Figure 3.20):
Major axis: the longer of the two axes.
Minor axis: the shorter of the two axes.
An ellipse has two focal points (**plural foci**), which are commonly named f1 and f2.

To find the two foci of an ellipse

Drawing 3 – Figure 3.20. With a compass set to half of the major axis and centred at one end of the minor axis, strike arcs to cross the major axis. The points at which the arcs cross the major axis are the two focal points.

A property of ellipses

Take any point on the ellipse. The sum (addition) of the lengths of the two lines from the point to the two focal points is always the same and equal to the length of the major axis.
    Thus in **Drawing 4**:
    E + F = G + H = K + J = major axis.

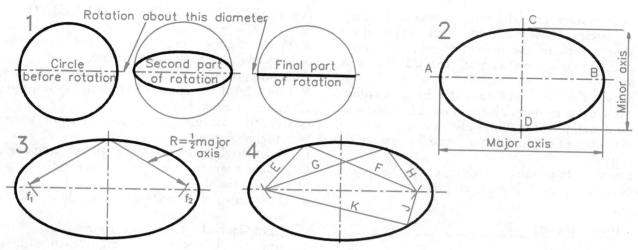

Figure 3.20 Ellipses

Construction of ellipses

Auxiliary circles

1. **Drawing 1** – Figure 3.21. Draw the major axis AB 90 mm long. Draw DE 60 mm long.

2. Draw a circle centred at O of major axis diameter. This circle is the **major auxiliary circle** of the ellipse.

3. Draw a circle centred at O of minor axis diameter. This circle is the **minor auxiliary circle** of the ellipse.

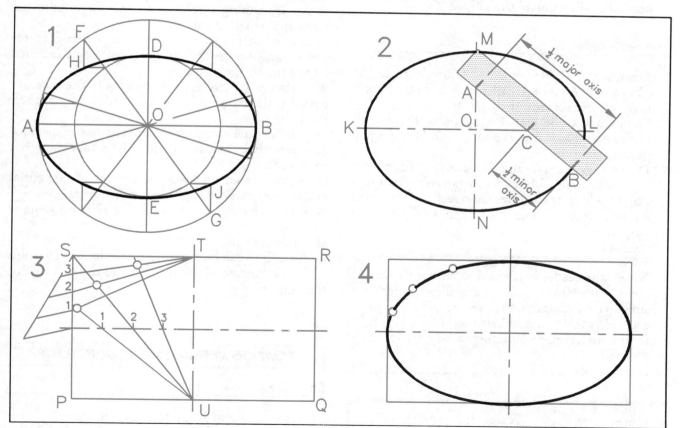

Figure 3.21 Construction of ellipses

4. Draw a number of diameters across both auxiliary circles. These can be drawn at any positions.
5. Where each of the diameters meet the major auxiliary circle draw verticals towards the major axis.
6. Where the diameters meet the minor auxiliary circle draw horizontals towards the minor axis.
7. One example of the lines just drawn is given on diameter FG. The points J and H are on the ellipse.
8. Draw a 'fair curve' through all the points obtained to complete the ellipse.

Trammel method

1. **Drawing 2** – Figure 3.21. On one straight edge of a piece of paper, mark off half the length of the major axis A–B (45 mm) and from one of the marks, mark off the length of the minor axis A–C (30 mm). This is the **trammel**.
2. With the mark C always on the major axis and the mark A always on the minor axis, make pencil marks on your drawing where B occurs.
3. Draw a 'fair curve' through the points so obtained to complete the ellipse.

In a rectangle

1. **Drawing 3** – Figure 3.21. Draw a rectangle 100 mm by 60 mm. Draw major and minor axes through the centres of the sides.
2. Divide half of SP into 4 equal parts, divide half of the major axis into the same number of equal parts.
3. Draw lines from T and U passing through the equal divisions − 1, 2, 3 – as shown. Through points where these lines intersect (at the small circles) draw a 'fair curve' to complete the ellipse.

Note: the reader is advised to accept the first method of construction of an ellipse using its auxiliary circles as that is the one most easy to use. However, the other methods may be found to be more suitable in some circumstances.

Note: a 'fair curve' is one drawn freehand as accurately as possible.

CHECK YOUR UNDERSTANDING

● **Plane figures** are flat – they are two-dimensional and have no thickness.
● A **polygon** is a figure with at least three sides.
● **Equilateral** triangle – all sides of equal length; all angles of equal size.
● **Iscoceles** triangle – two sides of equal length; two angles of equal size.
● **Right-angle** triangle – one angle is a right angle.
● **Scalene** triangles sides of unequal lengths; angles of unequal sizes.
● The sum of the angles in a triangle is 180 degrees.
● **Quadrilateral** – four sides, four angles.
● **Square** – all sides of equal length; each angle is a right-angle.
● **Parallelogram** – both pairs of opposite sides are parallel.
● **Rhombus** – all sides of equal length; angles not right-angles.
● **Trapezium** – one pair of opposite sides are parallel.
● A **circumscribing** circle to a polygon touches all its vertices.
● An **inscribing** circle to a polygon touches (is tangential to) all its sides.
● A line touching a circle at a point where it forms a right-angle with the radius at the point is called a **tangent** to the circle.
● If tangential circles meet externally the distance between their centre is the sum (addition of) their radii.
● If tangential circles meet internally the distance between their centres is the difference between their radii.
● A line drawn between the centres of tangential circles will pass through their point of tangency.
● **Ellipses** have two axes – a major axis and a minor axis.
● An ellipse has two foci.
● An ellipse can be regarded as the locus of a point which is the sum of the distances to the two foci of the ellipse.

REVISION EXERCISES AND QUESTIONS

Exercises

1 Construct and name the two triangles:
ABC: AB = 104 mm; BC = 90 mm; CA = 70 mm.

DEF: DE = 80 mm; EF = 100 mm; FD = 40 mm.

2 Construct the triangle ABC in which AB = 60 mm; BC = CA = 75 mm. What type of triangle is this?

3 Construct a triangle in which all sides are 70 mm long. Name the triangle you have just drawn.

4 Draw the triangle ABC. AB = 90 mm; BC = 120 mm; CA = 150 mm. What type of triangle is ABC?

5 Without using a set square, construct a rectangle of sides 85 mm and 45 mm.

6 Without using a set square construct a square of side length 80 mm.

7 Construct a regular hexagon of side length 60 mm.

8 Construct a regular pentagon of side length 75 mm.

9 Figure 3.22. Construct a regular pentagon of side length 80 mm. Within the polygon just drawn construct the star as shown.

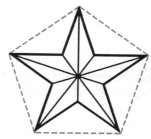

Figure 3.22 Exercise 9

10 Figure 3.23. Construct a regular pentagon of side length 56 mm. Within this regular pentagon construct the outline given. The central circle is 30 mm in diameter and the ends of the 'arms' 10 mm long. The side lines of the 'arms' are drawn to the centre of the pentagon.

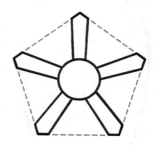

Figure 3.23 Exercise 10

11 Figure 3.24. Construct two interleaved regular pentagons each of side length 60 mm as shown.

Draw the circle circumscribing both pentagons. Then draw another circle 10 mm inside the first. Finally add the other details in the given drawing making each arc approximately 12 mm long.

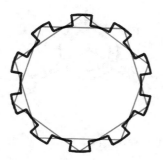

Figure 3.24 Exercise 11

12 Figure 3.25. Construct the pentagon shown. Add the circle of radius 20 mm which is tangential to the two sides of the polygon as shown.

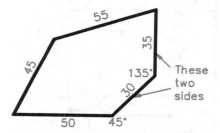

Figure 3.25 Exercise 12

13 Figure 3.26. Construct a regular hexagon of side length 40 mm. Add both the circumscribing and inscribing circles to the hexagon.

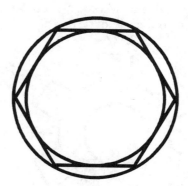

Figure 3.26 Exercise 13

14 Figure 3.27. The given drawing is a view of the arms of a drilling machine. Construct an accurate drawing of the given figure, working to a scale of full size.

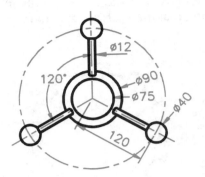

Figure 3.27 Exercise 14

15 Figure 3.28. Construct an accurate copy of the given drawing working to a scale of 1:1.

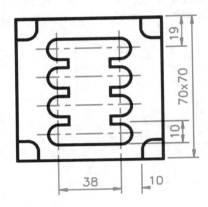

Figure 3.28 Exercise 15

16 Figure 3.29 shows the outline of a locking tab for a hexagonal nut. Make an accurate copy of the drawing to a scale of 1:1.

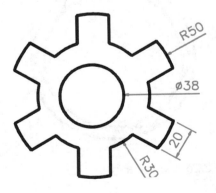

Figure 3.29 Exercise 16

17 Figure 3.30. Make an accurate drawing of the outline given, working full size.

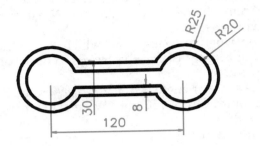

Figure 3.30 Exercise 17

18 Figure 3.31. The given drawing is the outline of a vase. Make an accurate full size drawing of the vase.

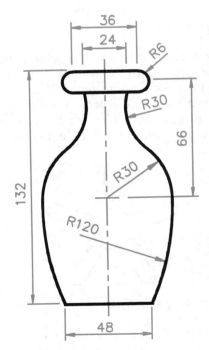

Figure 3.31 Exercise 18

19 Figure 3.32. The drawing shows a locating plate from a machine. Make an accurate full size drawing of the plate.

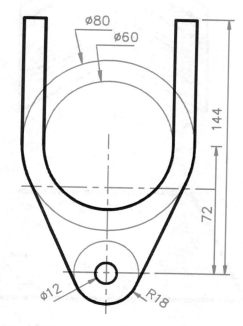

Figure 3.32 Exercise 19

20 Figure 3.33 shows a ratchet catch from a machine. Make an accurate full size drawing of the catch to the dimensions given.

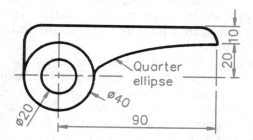

Figure 3.33 Exercise 21

Design exercises

1 a) Working to any convenient sizes make accurate drawings of Figure 3.34 and Figure 3.35. Examine the two drawings you have just constructed. Why is the information 'logo' in a circle and the telephone 'logo' in a rectangle?

b) Working on scrap paper, make freehand sketches of logos you think would be suitable for a sign pointing to an hotel. When satisfied you have achieved a good design make an accurate drawing of your design.

Information

Figure 3.34 Part of Design Exercise 1

Telephone

Figure 3.35 Part of Design Exercise 1

c) In a similar manner design, and make an accurate drawing of, a logo pointing to a farm.

2 Arrows can convey directions by their shape. For example arrow 1 of Figure 3.36 could be said to show the direction of something a short distance away. Arrow 2 could be said to show the direction of something fairly near and round the corner. Drawing 3 shows an arrow pointing to something further away than either of the other two.

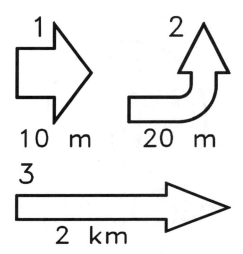

Figure 3.36 Design Exercise 2

Figure 3.37 Design Exercises 3 and 4

a) Make accurate drawings to any suitable scale of the three drawings of Figure 3.36.
b) On scrap paper make sketches for arrows designed to show directions to:
  • A village 5 kilometres down the road.
  • A town 150 km away along the road.
  • An hotel 50 metres around the corner to the left.
  When satisfied with a suitable design for each arrow, make accurate drawings of your chosen designs.

3 Drawing 1 of Figure 3.37 is a suggested design for a 'logo' of a firm named Hexagon Publishing Company.
a) Make an accurate copy of the given design working to any suitable dimensions.
b) On scrap paper make sketches of a suitable design for a logo for a publishing firm known as the Pentagon Publishing Company.
c) When satisfied you have a suitable logo, make an accurate full size copy of your design.

4 Drawing 2 of Figure 3.37 is another suggestion for a logo. This one is for the African Bus Company.
a) Working to any suitable dimensions, make an accurate copy of the given drawing.
b) Working on scrap paper sketch some design suggestions for a logo for your local bus company.
c) When satisfied you have a suitable design, make an accurate drawing of your suggested logo.

5 Drawing 1 of Figure 3.38. The drawing shows a name plate for a classroom in which graphics is taught.

a) Copy the drawing to suitable dimensions. The lettering should be carefully drawn freehand.
b) Using a similar background ellipse and rectangle design draw a similar name plate for the room in which you are taught technical drawing.

6 Drawings 2 and 3 of Figure 3.38 show the construction for a rectangle known as the 'Golden Mean' rectangle. Rectangles drawn to these proportions are thought to give the best possible design proportions for a rectangle. The Golden Mean rectangle has been used by designers for many years.
a) Drawing 2 shows how the rectangle is constructed and Drawing 3 the Golden Mean rectangle. Make an accurate drawing of Drawing 2 working on a base for the rectangle of 120 mm long.
b) Draw another Golden Mean rectangle with its long side vertical and 95 mm long.

7 Drawing 1 of Figure 3.39 shows a layout in Golden Mean proportions for two photographs on a sheet of paper. Each of the photos and the backing sheet are in Golden Mean proportions. With the long side of the paper 125 mm long and the long side of each photo 60 mm long, make an

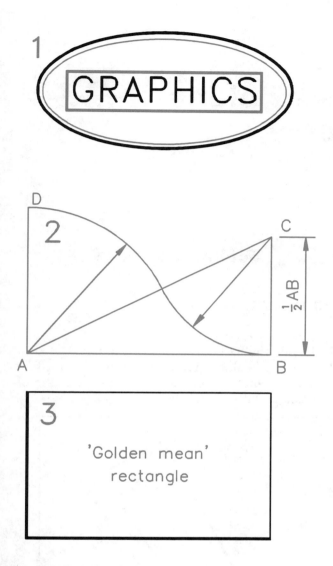

Figure 3.38 Design Exercise 5

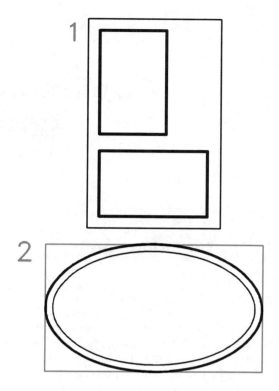

Figure 3.39 Design Exercise 6

accurate drawing of Drawing 1.

8 Drawing 2 of Figure 3.39 shows the outline for an elliptical table top with a bevelled edge with its axes in a Golden Mean proportion.
   a) Make an accurate copy of Drawing 2 with the major axis 115 mm long. The bevel is 5 mm wide.
   b) Make a similar drawing in which the major axis is 90 mm long.

Questions

1 You will see triangles used for all sorts of purposes. Can you identify the types of triangles you see?
2 What is a 3:4:5 triangle?
3 What is equal to the square on the hypotenuse?
4 Try making designs with triangles inscribed in a circle.
5 Doorways are usually some form of quadrilateral. Name that form of quadrilateral.
6 What has a square got in common with a rhombus?
7 What is the name given to the polygon formed by the grub chambers of a beehive?
8 Many flowers have five petals. Try drawing a flower based on a regular polygon of 5 sides. What is the name of the polygon?
9 Regular hexagons are regularly seen in car engines. For what purpose?
10 What is the name of a circle that touches the outside lines of a triangle?
11 Tangents to circles are particularly important. Can you give reasons why this is so?
12 Make freehand sketches of some tools, the shape of which involves tangential arcs. Make an accurate drawing of the tool.
13 Where do ellipses occur in nature?
14 What is the name given to a straight sided figure with 12 sides? The answer will not be found in this book, so you must seek elsewhere for the answer.

Applications of plane geometry

Introduction

In the previous chapter you learned about basic plane geometry. In this chapter we will be dealing with how the plane geometry you learned in that chapter can be applied to solving the type of problem which those, such as draughtsmen in industry, who are engaged in technical drawing, may have to solve. We are, in other words, applying our plane geometry to the solution of drawing problems.

Scaling polygons

DRAWING 1 – Figure 4.1.

1. Draw the triangle ABC.
2. Divide the base AB into 3 equal parts.
3. From E ⅔ along AB, draw EF parallel to BC.
4. Then triangle AEF is drawn to a scale of 2:3 of triangle ABC.

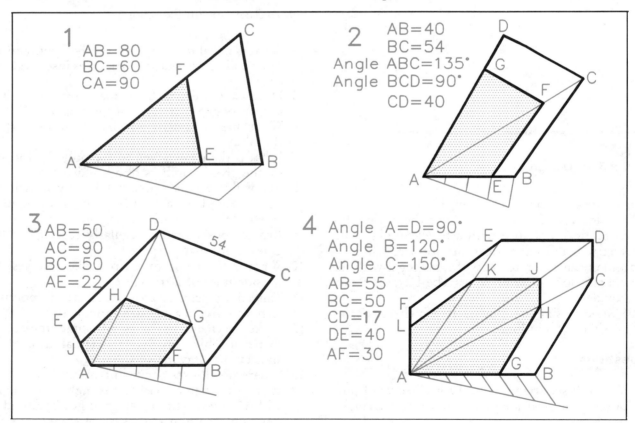

Figure 4.1 Scaling polygons

50

DRAWING 2 – Figure 4.1.

1. Draw the quadrilateral ABCD.
2. Draw the diagonal AC.
3. Divide the base AB into 4 equal parts.
4. From E ¾ along AB draw a line parallel to BC to meet AC at F.
5. From F draw a line parallel to CD to meet the side AD at G.
6. Then quadrilateral AEFG is drawn to a scale of 3:4 of quadrilateral ABCD.

DRAWING 3 – Figure 4.1.

1. Draw the pentagon ABCDE.
2. Draw the two diagonals AD and BD.
3. Divide the base AB into 5 equal parts.
4. From F ⅗ along AB draw a line parallel to BC to meet BD at G.
5. From G draw a line parallel to CD to H.
6. From H draw a parallel to DE to meet AE at J.
7. AFGHJ is scale 3:5 of pentagon ABCDE.

DRAWING 4 – Figure 4.1.

1. Draw the hexagon ABCDEF.
2. Draw the diagonals AC, AD and AE.
3. Divide the base AB into 7 equal parts.
4. Using the same method as for the three previous examples, complete the hexagon AGHJKL to a scale of 5:7 of hexagon ABCDE.

Triangles of same area as polygons

Triangles on the same base and between the same parallel lines are equal in area

Drawing 1 – Figure 4.2. The three triangles ABC, ABD and ABE are equal in area. This follows from the fact that:

$$\text{the area of a triangle} = \frac{\text{base} \times \text{vertical height}}{2}$$

(see page 54).

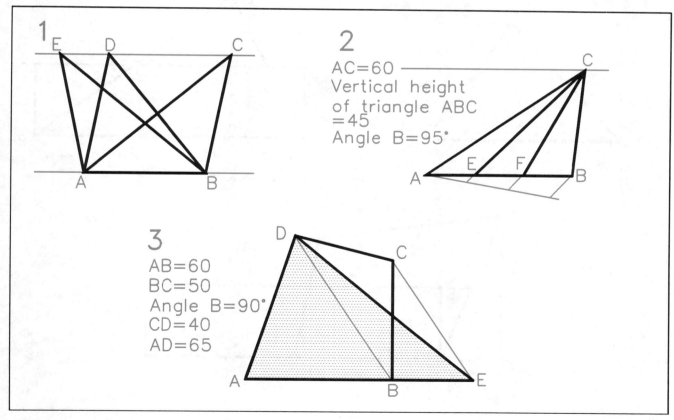

Figure 4.2 Triangles of the same area as polygons

All three triangles in Drawing 1 are on the same base and of the same height. It follows that they must be equal in area.

Dividing a triangle into three triangles of equal area

1. **Drawing 2** – Figure 4.2. Draw the triangle ABC.
2. Divide the base AB into three equal parts.
3. Draw the lines EC and FC.
4. Then the three triangles AEC, EFC and FBC are equal in area – they are on bases of equal length and are all the same vertical height.

To draw a triangle of area equal to a quadrilateral

1. **Drawing 3** – Figure 4.2. Draw the quadrilateral ABCD.
2. Draw the diagonal BD.
3. Draw CE parallel to BD and extend AB to E.
4. Draw DE to complete the triangle AED.

5. Then triangle ADE is equal in area to quadrilateral ABCD.

The two triangles BCD and BDE, are both on the same base BD and are both of equal height being between parallel lines. They must therefore be of equal area. Thus triangle ABD + triangle BDE = triangle ABD + triangle BCD. As triangle ABD + triangle BCD is the quadrilateral ABCD, then triangle ADE = quadrilateral ABCD.

Rectangles of equal area to polygons

A rectangle on the same base as a triangle and of the same height is twice the area of the triangle.

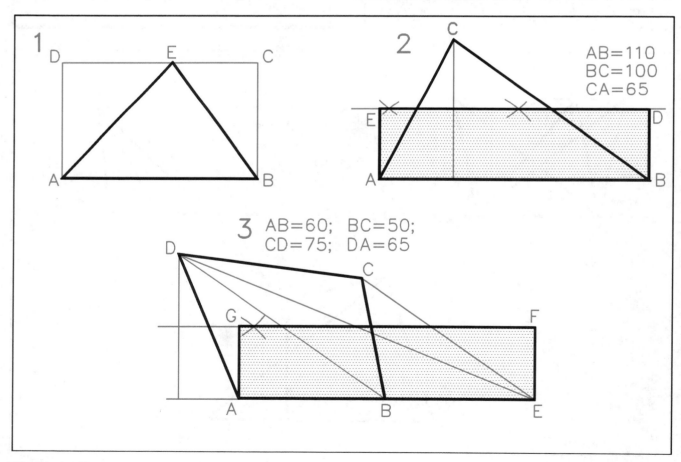

Figure 4.3 Rectangles of equal area to polygons

Drawing 1 – Figure 4.3. The rectangle ABCD is twice the area of triangle ABE. Note that the same principle applies for a parallelogram on the same base and of equal height to a triangle.

To draw a rectangle of area equal to a given triangle

1. **Drawing 2** – Figure 4.3. Draw the triangle ABC.
2. Draw the perpendicular to AB from C with the aid of a set square.
3. Bisect the perpendicular, draw the line ED and complete the rectangle ABDE.
4. Then the rectangle ABDE is the same area as the triangle ABC.

To draw a rectangle of area equal to a quadrilateral

1. **Drawing 3** – Figure 4.3. Draw the quadrilateral ABCD.
2. Draw the diagonal BD. Draw CE parallel to BD.

3. Then a triangle ADE is of area equal to the quadrilateral ABCD.
4. Bisect the perpendicular from D to AE.
5. Complete the rectangle AEFG.
6. Then the rectangle AEFG is equal in area to the quadrilateral ABCD.

> **Note:** the difference between scaling a polygon and drawing triangles and rectangles of equal area to polygons. In the examples given here, the polygons are scaled. Their areas are not in the same ratio as the scaling. These examples are concerned with the areas of the polygons and not their scales.

Squares of the same area as polygons

To draw a square of the same area as a rectangle

1. **Drawing 1** – Figure 4.4. Draw the rectangle ABCD.

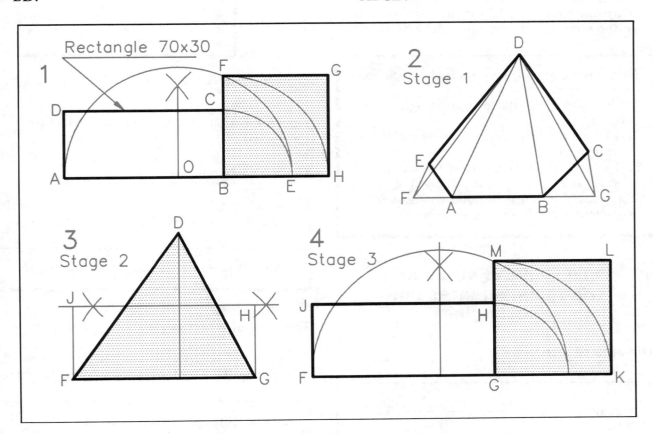

Figure 4.4 Squares of the same area as polygons

2. With compasses set to the side length BC and centred at B, draw an arc to touch the extension of side AB at E.
3. Bisect AE to give O.
4. Draw a semi-circle on AE with centre O.
5. Extend BC to touch the semi-circle at F.
6. BF is the side of the required square, which can now be drawn to give BFGH.

To draw a square of the same area as a pentagon

Stage 1
1. **Drawing 2** – Figure 4.4. Draw the pentagon ABCDE.
2. Construct the triangle FGD of the same area as the pentagon – page 51.

Stage 2
3. **Drawing 3** – Figure 4.4. Construct a rectangle FGHJ of the same area as the triangle FGD – page 53.

Stage 3
4. **Drawing 4** – Figure 4.4. Construct a square GKLM of the same area as the rectangle FGHJ.
5. Then the square GKLM is the required square of the same area as the pentagon ABCDE.

Note: three stages are required in the following order:
1. 'Reduce' the polygon to a triangle of the same area.
2. Reduce the triangle to a rectangle of the same area.
3. Reduce the rectangle to a square of the same area.
This procedure must be followed no matter how many sides the polygon possesses

---

To find the areas of triangles, squares and rectangles

The area of a triangle

$$\text{Area of triangle} = \frac{\text{base} \times \text{vertical height}}{2}$$

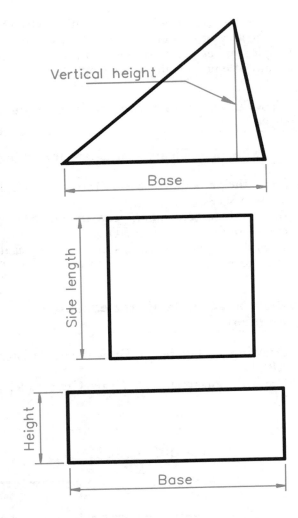

Figure 4.5 Areas of triangles, squares and rectangles

The area of a square

Figure 4.5. The area of a square is found by multiplying a side length by itself:

$$\text{Area of square} = \text{side length} \times \text{side length}$$

The area of a rectangle

Figure 4.5. The area of a rectangle is found by multiplying the length of its base by its height:

$$\text{Area of rectangle} = \text{base} \times \text{height}$$

To find the areas of polygons and circles

The area of a polygon

Figure 4.6. The area of a polygon can be found by dividing the polygon into a number of triangles and adding the areas of the triangles.

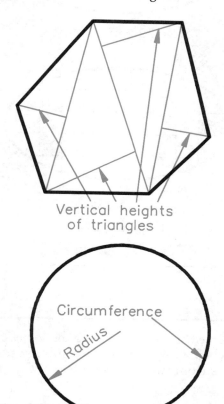

Vertical heights of triangles

Circumference

Radius

Figure 4.6 Area of polygons and circles

The area of a circle

Figure 4.6. The area of a circle is found by multiplying the radius by itself and then multiplying the result by pi. The value of π is approximately 3.14 or $3\frac{1}{7}$:

$$\text{Area of circle} = \pi \times R$$

Note: the figures resulting from the use of these simple formulae will be in square millimetres (mm) when working in millimetres. Square millimetres can be changed to square centimetres (cm) by dividing by 100. Thus if a rectangle with a base of

length 120 mm is 50 mm high, its area is 120 × 50 mm = 6000 mm. Its area in square cm is 6000/100 = 60 cm.

Approximate calculation of areas

These two technical drawing methods of calculating areas are suitable for irregular outlines which are composed of a mixture of curves and straight lines

Method 1 – by ordinates. Example 1

1. **Drawing 1** – Figure 4.7 (see page 56). Draw an outline such as that shown.
2. Divide its base into 10 mm (1 cm) spacings.
3. From the middle point of each 10 mm space draw a line perpendicular to the base – the lines 1 to 10. These lines are called **ordinates**.
4. Measure the length of each of the ordinates and add the results. In the example Drawing 1, these add up to 416 mm – or 41.6 cm.
5. As each section is 1 cm wide, the area of each section is 1 × length of ordinate. The area of each section is added together to give the total area of the shape.
6. From the result of this addition, the area is 41.6 square centimetres (41.6 cm²).

Method 1 – by ordinates. Example 2

1. **Drawing 2** – Figure 4.7. The area of the ellipse was found using the ordinate method.
2. The area of the ellipse is approximately 39.6 square centimetres (39.6 cm²).

Method 2 – by counting squares. Example 1

1. **Drawing 3** – Figure 4.7. Using the same outline as in Drawing 1, divide its shape into squares of 10 mm (1 cm) side lengths.
2. Many of the squares will be whole, complete squares. Count these complete squares.
3. Some of the squares will be incomplete. Add these part squares by approximating the fractions of a complete square each represents.
4. In the example Drawing 3, the whole squares add up to a total of 8 + 21 + 7 = 36.

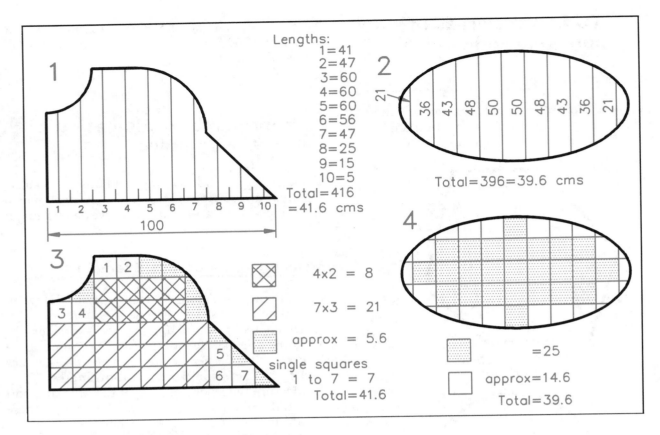

Figure 4.7 Approximate calculation of areas

5. In the example Drawing 3, the part squares are approximately = 5.6 squares.
6. Thus the total approximate area is 36 + 5.6 = 41.6 square centimetres.

Method 2 – by counting squares. Example 2

1. **Drawing 4** – Figure 4.7. Using the same ellipse as in Drawing 2, divide it into squares of 10 mm side lengths.
2. Add the whole squares. Then add the approximate value of the part squares.
3. In the example Drawing 4, the estimated approximate area is 39.6 square centimetres.

Ellipse as a locus and tangents

Construction of an ellipse as the locus of a point

> The ellipse can be regarded as the locus of a point which moves so that the addition of its distances from two fixed points is always the same.

1. **Drawing 1** – Figure 4.8. Draw the major and minor axes of the ellipse.
2. Find the two focal points of the ellipse. Set a compass to half the major axis and from the end of the minor axis strike arcs across the major axis.
3. Strike arcs first from f1, then from f2 so that the addition of radii A + B of the two arcs is always = the major axis. Examples: radius A = 70 mm, radius B = 30 mm; radius A = 60 mm, radius B = 40 mm.
4. In this manner draw arcs to give the points 1 to 8, both above and below the major axis.
5. Draw a 'fair curve' through the points so constructed to complete the ellipse.

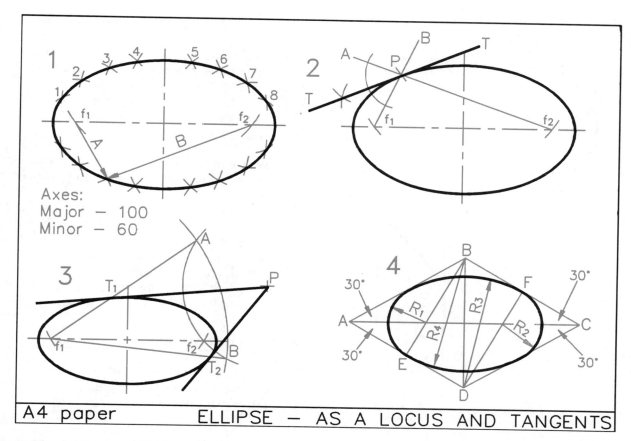

Figure 4.8 Ellipse – as a locus and tangents

Constructing a tangent at a point on an ellipse

1. **Drawing 2** – Figure 4.8. Draw any ellipse. Let P be any point on the ellipse. Draw lines from P to the two focal points.
2. Bisect the angle formed by the two lines. Then TT is the required tangent.

Construction of a tangent from a point outside the ellipse

1. **Drawing 3** – Figure 4.8. Draw any ellipse. Let P be any point outside the ellipse.
2. Set a compass to Pf2 and draw an arc centred at P.
3. Set a compass to the length of the major axis. From f1 draw an arc intersecting the first arc at A and at B.
4. Draw lines from f1 to A and B. The lines intersect the ellipse at T1 and T2.
5. Draw lines PT1 and PT2. These are the required tangents.

Four-arcs method of drawing an ellipse

This method is of value when drawing 'isometric' circles (page 157). It is only an approximate method. Follow Drawing 4 and attempt the method using any sizes.

Parabola and hyperbola

The parabola

A **parabola** can be regarded as the locus of a point which moves so that it is always the same distance from a fixed point (the **focus**) as it is from a fixed line (the **directrix**).

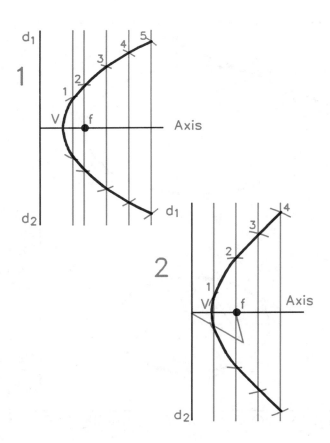

Figure 4.9 Parabola and hyperbola

1. **Drawing 1** – Figure 4.9. Draw the vertical line d1d2. This is the **directrix** of the parabola.
2. Draw the axis at right angles to the directrix. On the axis mark the point f (the **focus**) – in this example at 20 mm from the directrix.
3. Mark V (the **vertex**) half-way between F and d1 d2.
4. Draw a number of lines parallel to the directrix at known distances (8 mm apart).
5. With a compass centred always at the focus and set to the distance each parallel line is from the directrix, strike arcs across each of the parallel lines in turn. This produces the points 1 to 5.
6. Draw a 'fair curve' through the points.

The hyperbola

> The **hyperbola** can be regarded as the locus of a point which moves so as to be at a distance from a fixed point in a ratio that it is from a fixed line. This ratio is known as the **eccentricity** of the hyperbola.

1. **Drawing 2** – Figure 4.9. Draw the vertical line d1d2. This is the directrix of the hyperbola.
2. Draw the axis at right angles to the directrix. On the axis mark the point f (the focus) – in this example at 20 mm from the directrix.
3. Mark V (the vertex) 5/9 of the distance from the focus to the directrix. This makes the ratio

   Vf:d1d2V = 5:4, or an eccentricity of 1.25

4. Draw a number of lines parallel to the directrix at known distances (in the example these are 8 mm apart).
5. With a compass centred always at the focus and set to 1.25 of the distance each parallel line is from the directrix, strike arcs across each of the parallel lines in turn. This produces the points 1 to 4 both above and below the axis.
6. Draw a 'fair curve' through the points to complete the hyperbola.

Note on conic sections

The curves – circle, ellipse, parabola and hyperbola have so far been treated as the loci (plural of locus) of points which move under given rules:

- The **circle** is the locus of a point which moves at a given distance from a fixed point (the centre of the circle).
- The **ellipse** is the locus of a point which moves so that the addition of its distance from two fixed points is always the same. Its **eccentricity** is less than 1.
- The **parabola** is the locus of a point which moves so that it is always the same distance from a fixed point (the **focus**) as it is from a fixed line (the **directrix**). Its **eccentricity** is 1.
- The **hyperbola** is the locus of a point which moves so as to be at a distance from a fixed point in the same ratio that it is from a fixed line. This ratio is known as the eccentricity of the hyperbola. Its **eccentricity** is greater than 1.

Conic sections

These curves are conic sections and will be explained in further detail later – page 100.

Involutes

Wrap a piece of string around a polygon. Without moving the polygon, unwrap the string while holding its end. As the cord is unwrapped the end traces out a locus known as an involute. In the two examples of involutes given here, the first is the involute to a square, the second the involute to a circle. Involutes to circles are important in engineering because efficient gear teeth shapes are usually based on involutes to circles.

Involute to a square

1. **Drawing 1** – Figure 4.10. Draw a square of sides 20 mm.
2. With a compass centred at A and set to the square's side length, draw a quadrant.
3. With a compass centred at B and set to two side lengths of the square, draw a quadrant.
4. With a compass centred at C and set to three side lengths of the square, draw a quadrant.
5. With a compass centred at D and set to four side lengths of the square, draw a quadrant.

6. The curve starting at D through to the end of the last quadrant at 4 is the required involute.

Involute to a circle

1. **Drawing 2** – Figure 4.10. Draw a circle of radius 25 mm.
2. Draw diameters of the circle at 30 degree intervals with the aid of a 30,60 set square. This divides the circumference into 12 equal parts.
3. From the right hand end of the horizontal diameter, draw a vertical line equal in length to the circumference of the circle:

$$2 \times pi \times R = 2 \times 3.14 \times 25 = 157 \text{ mm}.$$

4. Divide the 157 mm line into 12 equal parts.
5. At each end of the diameters through the centre of the circle, draw tangents with the aid of a 30,60 set square.
6. Starting at the first tangential point, mark off a distance of one of the twelve divisions along the length of the circumference.
7. At the next tangential point step off a length of two divisions.
8. At the third tangential point step off a length of three divisions.
9. Continue in this manner at each tangential point until the 12th (the end of the 157 mm circumference length) is reached.
10. Draw a 'fair curve' through the points so obtained to complete the required involute.

Drawing a tangent to the involute to a circle

1. Mark any point T on the involute (Figure 4.11). From T construct a tangent to the circle.
2. The required tangent is at right angles to TA.

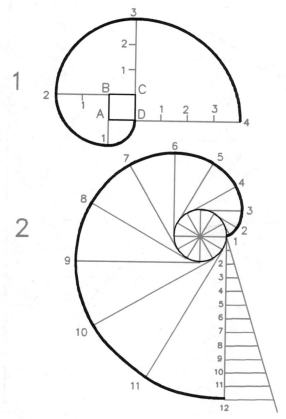

Figure 4.10 Involutes

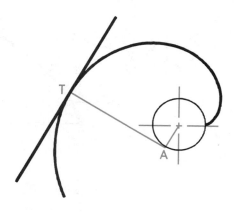

Figure 4.11 Tangent to an involute

Archimedean spiral and cycloid

A **cycloid** is the locus of a point on a circle as it rolls in a straight line along a flat plane.

Drawing an Archimedean spiral

Drawing 1 – Figure 4.12. The **Archimedean spiral** is to commence at a point 20 mm from its centre and finish at a point 50 mm from its centre after one complete revolution.

1. Draw a circle centre C of radius 20 mm and another of radius 50 mm. With a 30,60 set square divide the circles into 12 equal parts.
2. Divide AB into 12 equal parts.
3. With the compass always centred at C, draw arcs from each of the 12 divisions along AB to meet the diagonals 1 to 12 in turn.
4. Draw a 'fair curve' through the 12 points so obtained to complete the required spiral.

Drawing a cycloid to a circle

1. **Drawing 2** – Figure 4.12. Draw a circle of centre O of 25 mm radius.
2. Draw diagonals across the circle at 30 degree intervals. Draw a horizontal line through centre.
3. Draw the line AB of circumference length:

$$\text{pi} \times d = 3.14 \times 50 = 157 \text{ mm}$$

4. Divide AB into 12 equal parts. At each division draw verticals to meet the horizontal through O at 1 to 12.
5. From each of the 30 degree division points on circle O draw horizontal lines.
6. With a compass centred at 1 to 12 on the line through O and with a radius of 25 mm, draw circles.
7. Points on the required cycloid are found at the intersections of these circles with the horizontal lines from the circle O. One example is given at the position of the circle from point 7.

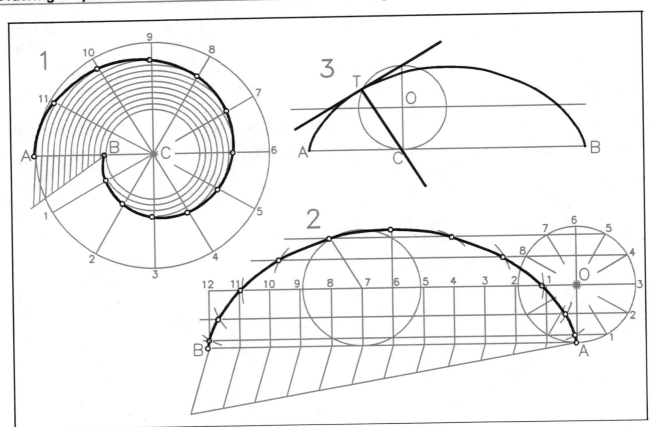

Figure 4.12 Archimedean spiral and cycloid

8. Draw a fair curve through the points so obtained to complete the required cycloid.

Tangent to a cycloid

1. **Drawing 3** – Figure 4.12. T is any point on the cycloid.
2. With centre T and radius of the cycloid's circle, strike an arc across the central line of the cycloid to give O.
3. Draw a circle of the cycloid circle radius at O.
4. Draw OC vertically through O. Then CT is the normal to the cycloid and a line at right angles to CT at T is the tangent to the cycloid at T.

Epicycloid and hypocycloid

Drawing an epicycloid

> An **epicycloid** is the locus of a point on a circle as it is revolved along the outside of an arc of another circle.

1. Figure 4.13. Draw an arc AB of centre C and radius 95 mm. This is the base circle of the epicycloid.
2. At A draw a semi-circle centre O of radius 20 mm tangential to the arc AB.
3. Divide the semi-circle into 6 equal parts.
4. With centre C draw arcs parallel to AB passing through the divisions of the semi-circle centred at O.
5. With a compass set to the length of one of the divisions of the semi-circle O step off 12 equal divisions along the arc AB.
6. Draw lines from C through the 12 points so obtained, to meet the arc through O at the points 1 to 12.
7. At each of these 12 points draw a circle of radius 20 mm (i.e. equal to the radius of O).
8. Points on the epicycloid are at the intersections of these circles with the arcs from the 6 divisions of the semi-circle O. One example is given – that of the circle centred at point 8.
9. Draw a fair curve through the points of the epicycloid.

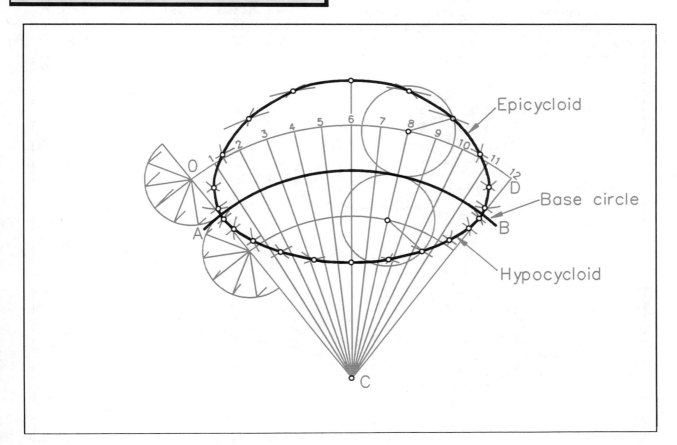

Figure 4.13 Epicycloid and hypocycloid

Drawing an hypocycloid

> A **hypocycloid** is the locus of a point on a circle as it is revolved along the inside of an arc of another circle.

The construction of the hypocycloid follows a similar routine as that for the epicycloid.

The same lines from C to the 12 points on the arc from semi-circle O can be used. A second circle of the same radius (20 mm) needs to be drawn tangential internally to A on the arc. This semi-circle is again divided into 6 equal parts, from which arcs, centred at C are drawn.

Loci of moving parts — 1

Most machines contain parts which rotate, parts which slide, parts which oscillate. To determine whether a machine with moving parts will function properly without clashes, the loci of points on the parts will need to be determined. The method of drawing the loci of points of moving parts is based on drawing the moving parts in a number of positions in relation to each other and then plotting the locus curves of a number of points on the parts.

DRAWING 1 — Figure 4.14.

The arm OA rotates in a full circle clockwise about its end O. The link AB, is pivoted at A to AO. The end B of AB is constrained to move by a slider, in a straight line along OC. To find the locus of point P on AB:

1. Draw a circle centre O of radius equal to the rotating arm AO.
2. From A with a compass set to AB (90 mm) strike an arc on OC.
3. Divide the circle of centre O into 12 equal parts (30,60 set square) to give the points 1 to 12 on the circle.
4. From each of the points 1 to 12 in turn, strike arcs of radius 90 mm along the line OC.
5. Along each line so drawn and with a compass set to 50 mm (AP), strike arcs to give 12 positions of P along each line.
6. Draw a fair curve through the 12 points so obtained to complete the locus of the point P.

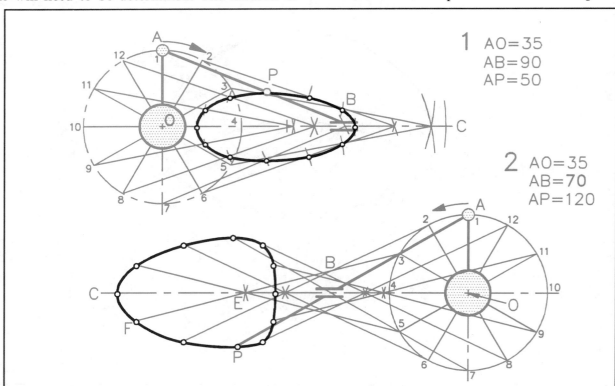

Figure 4.14 Loci of moving parts

DRAWING 2 – Figure 4.14.

This example can be constructed in a manner similar to that used in Drawing 1. An arm AO is constrained to rotate anti-clockwise around its end O. A link AP is pivoted at A to the arm AO. B, on the link AP is constrained by a slider to move in a straight line along OE. Draw the locus of the end P of the link AP.

The reader should be able to construct the required locus of the end P by following Drawing 2 of Figure 4.14 and basing the construction on the description of that given for Drawing 1.

Loci of moving parts – 2

DRAWING 1 – Figure 4.15.

A point moves between two circles of centres O and C so as to be equidistant from the circumferences of the two circles. Plot the locus of the point.

1. Draw the two circles of radii 20 mm and 5 mm with centres 55 mm apart.
2. With a compass set to 40 mm strike arcs from O between the two circles, above and below the line OC.
3. With a compass set to 25 mm strike arcs from C to cross the two arcs from O.
4. Continue striking arcs from O and C with the compass always set to 15 mm less for the arcs from C than they are from O. Two examples are shown.
5. Join the intersections (FE) to obtain the locus.

DRAWING 2 – Figure 4.15.

A point P moves steadily along a line OB as OB rotates around O. Plot the locus of P for one complete revolution of B around O.

1. Draw the circle of centre O and radius 45 mm.
2. Divide OB into 6 equal parts.
3. Divide the circle into 12 equal parts (30, 60 set square).
4. With centre O and radius O to the first division

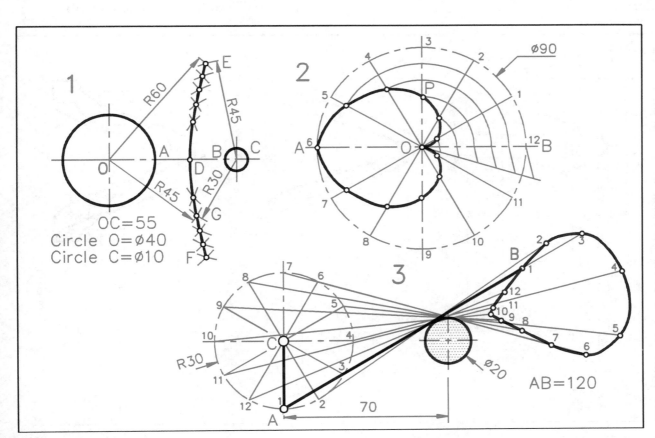

Figure 4.15 Loci of moving parts

along OB, draw an arc to meet radius line number 1.

5. Draw further arcs centred at O with radii of O to each division along OB, the arcs to meet the lines 2 to 6.
6. Repeat for the lower radii of the circle.
7. A fair curve through the points produces the locus.

DRAWING 3 – Figure 4.15.

An arm of length AC, 30 mm long rotates about a fixed pivot at C. A link AB rests on a drum of diameter 20 mm as shown. Plot the locus of B as the arm AC rotates.

1. Divide a circle, centre C, of radius 30 mm into 12 equal parts.
2. From each of the 12 points draw AB 120 mm long and tangential to the drum.
3. Set a compass to 120 mm and from each of the points 1 to 12 in turn, strike arcs along the lines AB.
4. A fair curve through the points produces the locus.

Helices

A **helix** is the locus of a point as it rotates around a cylinder and moves with regular velocity in the direction of the axis of the cylinder. Screw threads are helical in shape. **Helical springs** are another example of helices. Helices can also be drawn on cones. We are only concerned here with cylindrical helices.

Simple line helix

DRAWING 1 – Figure 4.16.

The helix to be of diameter 60 mm and pitch 60 mm.

1. Draw a circle of diameter 60 mm. Divide into 12.
2. Draw a line (1) above the circle. Draw 12 further lines parallel to line 1 at 5 mm intervals.

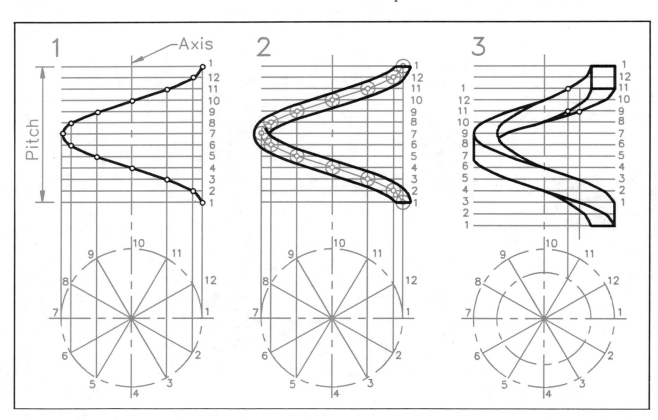

Figure 4.16 Helices

3. Draw verticals from each of the 12 points on the circle to meet each of the lines as shown.
4. A fair curve through the points of intersection of the vertical and the parallel lines gives the helix.

A helical spring

DRAWING 2 – Figure 4.16.

The helical axis through the spring is to be the same diameter and pitch as in Drawing 1. The spring material is to be of diameter 10 mm. To draw one pitch of the spring:

1. Draw the same helix as for Drawing 1.
2. At each point of intersection of vertical and parallel lines draw a circle of radius 5 mm.
3. Draw fair curves above and below and tangential to the 12 circles to complete the helical spring.

A square spring

DRAWING 3 – Figure 4.16.

To draw one pitch of a spring made from 10 mm square steel material of the same helical axis and pitch as Drawing 1:

1. Draw two circles – one of the inside diameter of the spring (40 mm), the other of the outside diameter of the spring (60 mm).
2. Divide the two circles into 12 equal parts.
3. Draw parallel lines as in the first two examples, but add 2 further parallels to take account of the square material of the spring.
4. Draw the helices for each circle as shown. Note that the inner and outer helices merge at various points in the final drawing. Points from diameter 11 are shown as small circles.

■ CHECK YOUR UNDERSTANDING

● Be careful that you do not confuse the scaling of a polygon in a given ratio to calculating the area of a polygon by 'reduction' to a triangle, rectangle or square.
● When reducing a polygon to a square of equal area, the order of construction will be – polygon to triangle; triangle to rectangle; rectangle to a square.

● There are 100 square millimetres in a square centimetre. There are 1,000,000 square millimetres in a square metre. There are 10,000 square centimetres in a square metre.
● The area of a triangle is

$$\frac{\text{base} \times \text{height}}{2}.$$

● The area of a rectangle is base × height.
● The area of a square is side².
● The area of a polygon with straight sides is found by drawing its diagonals and then adding the areas of the triangles formed by the sides and the diagonals.
● The area of an irregular outline can be calculated approximately by drawing centimetre squares within the outline and adding them together.
● Another method of calculating the area of an irregular polygon is by adding the 'ordinates' in the centre of 1 cm divisions along one side of the polygon.
● An **ellipse** can be regarded as the locus of a point which moves so that the addition of its distances from two fixed points is always the same.
● A **parabola** can be regarded as the locus of a point which moves so that it is always the same distance from a fixed point (the **focus**) as it is from a fixed line (the **directrix**).
● A **hyperbola** can be regarded as the locus of a point which moves so as to be at a distance from a fixed point in a ratio that it is from a fixed line. This ratio is known as the **eccentricity** of the hyperbola.
● The eccentricity of a parabola is unity (1).
● The eccentricity of an ellipse is less than unity (<1).
● The eccentricity of an hyperbola is greater than unity (>1).
● Rays from a light at the focus of a parabola will be reflected by the parabola parallel to its axis.
● The outlines of spur gears in engineering components are usually based on the **involute** to a circle.
● A **cycloid** is the locus of a point on a circle as it rolls in a straight line along a flat plane.
● An **epicycloid** is the locus of a point on a circle as it is revolved along the outside of an arc of another circle.
● A **hypocycloid** is the locus of a point on a circle as it is revolved along the inside of an arc of another circle.
● The basis for the construction of the loci of moving points in mechanisms is based on drawing the moving parts in a number of positions in relation to each other and then plotting the locus

curves of a number of points on the parts.
● Screw threads, conical and cylindrical springs are usually **helical** in form.

REVISION EXERCISES AND QUESTIONS

Exercises

---

1 Figure 4.17 is the floor plan of a building drawn to a scale of 1:200.

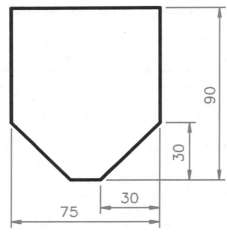

Figure 4.17 Exercise 1

  a) Copy the given drawing to the given dimensions.
  b) Reduce to a rectangle of the same area.
  c) Calculate its area in square millimetres.
  d) From your answer calculate the area of the floor of the building in square metres.

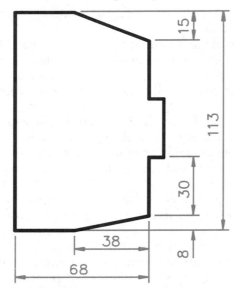

Figure 4.18 Exercise 2

2 Figure 4.18 is another floor plan of a building drawn to a scale of 1:200.
  a) Copy the given drawing to the given dimensions.
  b) Reduce your drawing to a rectangle of the same area.
  c) From your rectangle calculate its area in square millimetres.
  d) Calculate the area of the floor of the building in square metres.

3 Figure 4.19 shows two circles tangential to an ellipse.
  a) Draw the ellipse.
  b) Using a correct construction involving tangents to the ellipse, add the two circles to your drawing.

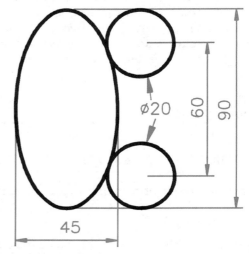

Figure 4.19 Exercise 3

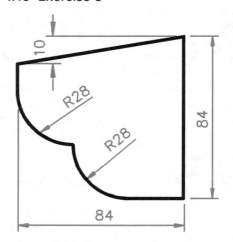

Figure 4.20 Exercise 4

4 a) Make an accurate copy of Figure 4.20 to the given dimensions.
  b) Copy your drawing to a scale of 3:7.

5 a) Make an accurate drawing of Figure 4.21 working full size. The straight lines to the ellipse should be accurately drawn using a correct construction.

b) Reduce your drawing to a scale of 3:5.

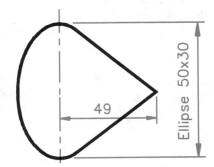

Figure 4.21 **Exercise 5**

6 Figure 4.22 is an outline drawing showing a section through a parabolic lamp and its parabolic reflector. The bulb of the lamp is at the focal point of both parabolas. Make an accurate drawing of the outline to a scale of 1:1 as follows:

a) Using the construction for a parabola given on page 58, construct the reflector outline.

b) Using the construction shown in the lower drawing of Figure 4.22 construct the parabolic lamp outline.

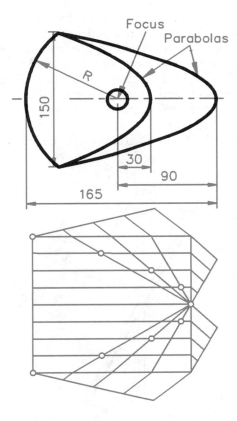

Figure 4.22 **Exercise 6**

Notes on parabolic reflectors
- The construction shown in Figure 4.22 is for drawing a parabola within a given rectangle.
- Reflectors for lamps are often made of a parabolic shape with the bulb for the lamp at the parabola's focus. This is because one of the characteristics of a parabola is that a ray of light from a light source at its focal point is reflected from the parabola in a line parallel to the axis of the parabola.

7 Figure 4.23 shows a crank AB which rotates in a full circle around its end A. A link BC is attached to the crank AB by a pin joint at B. The end C of link AB is constrained by a slider to move in a vertical straight line through C.

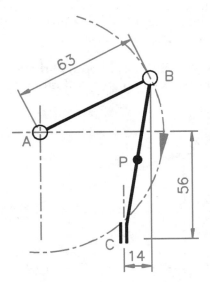

Figure 4.23 **Exercise 7**

Plot the locus of P on BC for one complete revolution of the crank AB.

8 Figure 4.24 is a diagrammatic outline through an 'up-and-over' door to a garage. As the bottom edge of the door C, is raised, the top edge A is constrained to slide horizontally as shown by an arrow, and the pivot at B is constrained to move vertically as shown by an arrow.

Plot the locus of the bottom edge, C of the door.

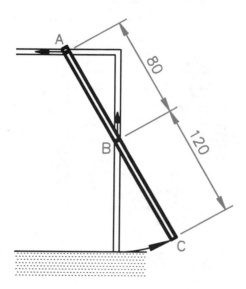

Figure 4.24 Exercise 8

9 Figure 4.25 shows a crank BA, of length 35 mm rotating around a fixed point at B. A link AC pin-jointed at A to AB and of length 100 mm is constrained at its end C by a slider, to move in a straight line along BC. The points P1 and P2 are 35 mm and 65 mm respectively from A along AC.

Construct the locus of both of the points P as AB makes one complete revolution about B.

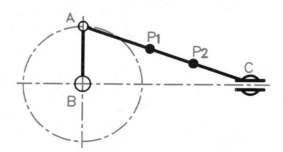

Figure 4.25 Exercise 9

10 Figure 4.26. The crank CD can rotate around a fixed point at D. The link AB is pin-jointed to the crank CD at C. The end A of the link AB is constrained to move along a quarter of an ellipse as shown in either direction.

Plot the locus of the end B as CD makes one complete revolution around D.

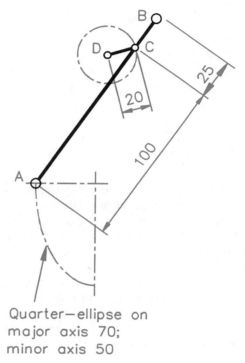

Quarter–ellipse on major axis 70; minor axis 50

Figure 4.26 Exercise 10

11 Construct the involute to a circle of diameter 20 mm. Take any point on the involute and draw a line tangential to the involute at that point.

12 Construct a cycloid to a circle of diameter 30 mm. At a point 40 mm from the left-hand end of your cycloid construct a straight line tangential to the cycloid.

13 Draw an arc of radius 100 mm. Construct an epicycloid for a circle of 15 mm radius along the arc.

14 Construct a regular hexagon of side length 35 mm. Calculate its area in square centimetres.

15 Construct a regular pentagon of edge length 45 mm. Reduce it to a square of equal area. From the square calculate the area of the pentagon in square centimetres.

16 What is the eccentricity of a parabola? Is the eccentricity of a hyperbola greater or smaller than that of a parabola?

17 Figure 4.27 shows the outline of a spanner head

for use with hexagonal nuts and bolts. The method of constructing the spanner head is indicated by arrows.

Construct the outline for a spanner head suitable for a nut whose across flats (AF) measurement is 40 mm.

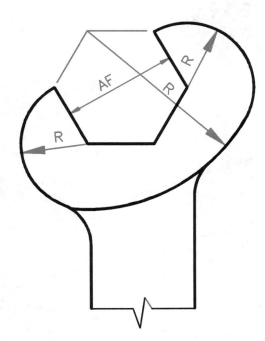

Figure 4.27 Exercise 17

18 Figure 4.28 is a diagrammatic outline of a crank connected to a piston by a link. The crank OA is constrained to move in a circular rotation at its fixed end O. A pin joint at A connects the link AB to the crank OA. The end B of the link AB is constrained to move in a straight line along OB.

Plot the locus of the point P on the link AB.

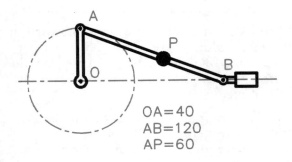

OA=40
AB=120
AP=60

Figure 4.28 Exercise 18

Questions

1 You have to give an estimate for the cost of tarmacing a school play area, which is in the form of an irregular polygon. How could you use the geometry learned in this chapter for this purpose?

2 You have an electric bicycle lamp which, when switched on gives a narrow beam of light. What is the most likely shape of its reflector and how does this affect the position of the bulb?

3 Wind a length of string around a cylindrical object – a cotton reel or some article such as a saucepan. Try to estimate the locus of the end of the string as you unwind it. What is the name given to this locus curve?

4 Name some article which is based upon the shape of an Archimedean spiral.

5 What are the differences between a cycloid, an epicycloid and a hypocycloid?

6 Examine as many screw threads of different sizes as you can find. They are all based on the helix curve.

7 Examine the working mechanism of an up-and-over garage door. How does the mechanism function?

8 Suspension bridges depend for their strength on the curve of the wires from which the bridge is suspended. What is the shape they form?

9 Examine arches – door, bridge and other forms of arch. What geometric shapes are they formed from?

10 Make sketches of some form of link mechanism seen in a machine. Then make drawings of the possible locus curves points along the link will form as the machine works.

Further applications of plane geometry

Introduction

This chapter includes some basic work on vectors, forces acting on objects and in structures and the moments of forces acting around points. This work is included because it is an important part of designing in engineering, building and architecture, involving technical drawing skills.

For further work in the area of forces acting on structures, you are advised to seek additional information in books specializing in this form of drawing construction. The mathematics of vectors, forces and moments is also of great interest to those wishing to follow a career in engineering, building or architecture.

Vectors

Force diagrams, consisting of **vectors** are constructed when designing structures, in order to assist the designer in calculating the forces loading the structure. The diagrams will assist the designer to make sure the structure being designed is safe to use.

Figure 5.1 shows two types of line:

- **Drawing 1** is a scalar – it has quantity – its length, but no magnitude or direction.
- **Drawings 2** and **3** are vectors – they have magnitude and direction.
- **Drawing 2** shows that something is moving with a velocity of 20 kilometres per hour in the direction shown by the angle of the line and the arrow on the line.
- **Drawing 3** shows that a force of 50 **Newtons** (see section on units of force below) is acting

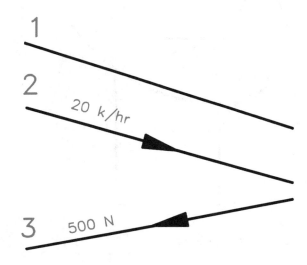

Figure 5.1 Scalars and vector lines

along the angle of the line in the direction shown by the arrow on the line.

Units of measurement

SI units (System International) are used in this book. SI units are metric. So far we have been using SI units of length, based on the metre. Prefixes showing fractions of multiples of metres are:

- *milli*metre (mm)   1,000th of a metre.
- *centi*metre (cm)   100th of a metre.
- *deci*metre (dm)   10th of a metre.
- *deca*metre (dam)   10 metres.
- *hecto*metre (hm)   100 metres.
- *kilo*metre (km)   1000 metres.

Units of force

The basic SI unit of force is the **Newton**.

> Isaac Newton's Third Law states that:
> - Reaction is always opposite and equal to action.

According to Newton's Third Law, if a mass of 1 kilogram (1kg) rests on a surface, it is exerting **1 kilogram force (1kgf)** downwards in a vertical direction. The surface must be exerting an opposite and equal force vertically upwards – otherwise the 1 kg mass would fall through the surface.

1 kilogram force (kgf) is approximately equal to 9.81 Newtons. This value varies slightly throughout the world. Because 9.81 is so near to 10, for practical purposes the value of 1 kgf is often taken as being equal to 10 Newtons. This practice will be followed in this book.

Forces in equilibrium

If a structure is stationary, without movement, it is said to be in **equilibrium**. If a structure is in equilibrium, then according to Newton's Third Law, each of the forces acting on the structure must be balanced by an opposite and equal force (**action** and **reaction**).

Moments about a point

In order to make an object move around a fixed point a force must be exerted on the object. The force can be stated in Newtons. As the force causes a rotation the **moment** of the movement is measured in **Newton metres (Nm)**, or in **Newton millimetres (Nmm)**.

Examples of vectors

> **DRAWING 1 – Figure 5.2.**

A and B start at the same time from the road junction J on straight roads. A travels at a constant 90 km/h, B travels at a constant of 60 km/h. How far apart will A be from B at the end of an hour?

1. Draw AB 60 mm long parallel to JR2. Draw AC 90 mm long parallel to JR1. AB and AC are vectors, drawn to a scale of 1 mm to 1km/h.
2. Join BC and measure its length and angle.

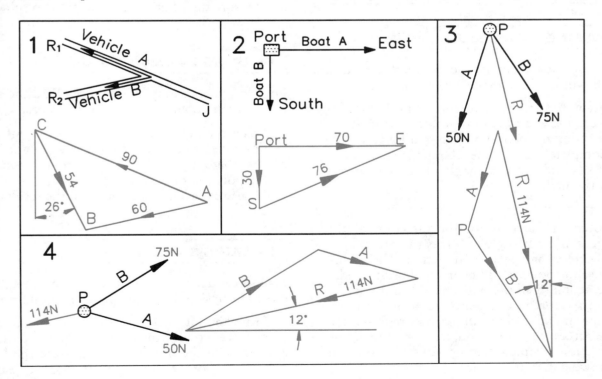

Figure 5.2 Vectors

DRAWING 2 – Figure 5.2.

Two boats leave Port at the same time. A sails east, B sails south. A travels 70 km and B 30 km. How far will A be from B and what is the bearing of B from A?

1. Draw Port/E 70 mm to the east. Draw line Port/S 30 mm long and parallel to the travel of boat B.
2. Join SE, measure its length and the angle SE/Port.

DRAWING 3 – Figure 5.2.

A mass P is attached to A and B. Find the single force which could replace the two forces A and B.

1. Draw parallels to forces A and B (50 and 75 mm).
2. Join the ends of the line (R).
3. A force of 114 N at P at 12 degrees to the vertical, could replace A and B.

Note: the 114 N is a **resultant** of A and B. The direction of the arrow for R in the **triangle of forces** runs in the **opposite** direction to A and B.

DRAWING 4 – Figure 5.2.

P can be moved by A and B. Find a **resultant** which will hold the mass P in equilibrium.

1. Draw A parallel to force A and 50 mm long. From the end of A draw a line B parallel to the direction of force B and 75 mm long.
2. Complete the triangle. R represents a force of 114 N and lies at an angle of 12 degrees to the horizontal.

Note: the arrows for the direction of the forces in the triangle of forces run around the triangle all in the same direction. This is because the point P will be in equilibrium under the action of all three forces. When the action of three forces at a point result in the point being in equilibrium, the arrows representing the forces run around the triangle in the same direction. Compare this with the results in Drawing 3.

Polygon of forces

When more than three forces act at a point, the same rules apply to vectors forming a **polygon of forces:**

- If the mass upon which the forces are acting is in equilibrium, the direction of forces in the polygon all run the same way around the polygon of forces.
- If a single force replaces the forces acting upon a mass, the direction of the **resultant** will be in an opposite direction to the other forces of the polygon.

DRAWING 1 – Figure 5.3.

Three forces are acting on the mass M as shown. Find the single force which could replace the three given forces.

1. Draw the polygon of forces from the information given to give the open quadrilateral abcd.
2. Join the open ends of the 3 vectors to complete the polygon of forces.
3. Measure the length and angle of the resultant R.

DRAWING 2 – Figure 5.3.

Four forces are acting at a point R. Find the single force which could replace the four forces.

1. Draw the polygon of forces from the information given to give the open pentagon abcde.
2. Join the open ends of the 4 vectors to complete the polygon of forces.
3. Measure the length and angle of the resultant R.

DRAWING 3 – Figure 5.3.

Five forces act at a point R. Find the strength and direction of R holding the point in equilibrium.

1. From the information given draw the polygon of forces to give the open hexagon abcdef.
2. Complete the polygon and measure the length and angle of the closing line to find the resultant R.

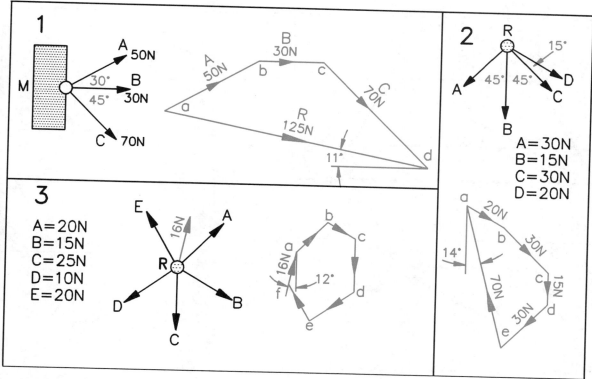

Figure 5.3 Polygon of forces

Note:
The similarity between the construction of a **polygon of forces** and a **triangle of forces**.
The construction of polygons of forces is the basic method involved in finding the forces acting in structures such as arrangements of girders.

Frame stress diagram

A pin-jointed frame is shown in **Drawing 1** of Figure 5.4 (see page 74). The frame is in equilibrium, resting on two girders. To find the forces acting in the five members of the frame and their reactions at the two supporting girders:

1. Copy **Drawing 1** full size.
2. Letter the drawing as shown – letters A to F. This form of lettering is known as **Bows Notation**. In this form of lettering of a frame a vector representing the 60 N force would be labelled *ab* – that is it lies between the letters A and B; the vector for the 150 N force would be labelled

bc – it lies between B and C. Note the use of lower case letters.
3. Draw the triangle of forces at the point of action of the 60 N force to a scale of 1 mm represents 2 N – **Drawing 2**. The vector *ab* of **Drawing 2** is thus 30 mm long. The vector *be* lies parallel to the frame member BE, the vector *ae* lies parallel to the frame member AE.
4. Draw the force polygon **Drawing 3**. The vector length of *be* is taken from **Drawing 2**; the vector for the 150 N force *bc* 75 mm long is drawn vertically; the vector *ef* is parallel to the frame member EF; the vector *cf* is parallel to the frame member CF. From this polygon of forces we now know the vector length of the forces acting in the frame members EF and CF.
5. Draw the polygon of forces – **Drawing 4**, starting with *ef* taken from **Drawing 3**, the other vectors drawn parallel to their respective frame members.
6. The triangle of forces **Drawing 5** can now be drawn commencing with the vector *fd* from **Drawing 4**. The other vectors *cf* and *cd* are parallel to CF and CD.
7. Finally add all the triangles and polygons of forces together – **Drawing 6**, to obtain the required stress diagram for the frame.

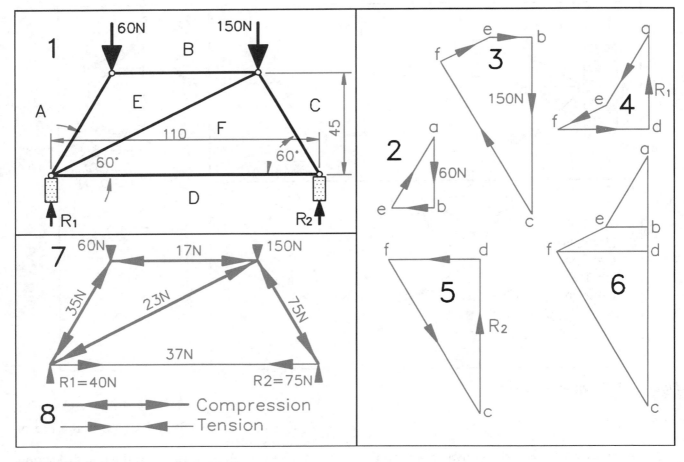

Figure 5.4 Frame stress diagram

8. From the stress diagram we can measure the sizes of the forces in the frame and the reactions at the two girders by measuring the vector lengths.

> **Note:** the frame is in equilibrium, thus at any point in the frame there must be action and reaction forces in opposite directions. This is the reason for the different directions of the arrows in the force diagram.

Moments about a point

DRAWING 1 – Figure 5.5.

M exerts a force 20 N downwards. M is held firmly by a beam PA. To find the moments about P:

1. The clockwise (cw) moment about P $55 \times 20 = 1100$ Nmm.
2. The anti-clockwise (acw) moment about P must also be $55 \times 20 = 1100$ Nmm.

DRAWING 2 – Figure 5.5.

A lever AB acts about a fulcrum C. A force F holds the mass M stationary. The system is in equilibrium. To find F:

1. The cw moment about C is $F \times 60 = 60F$ Nmm.
2. The acw force about C is $50 \times 30 = 1500$ Nmm.
3. The system is in equilibrium, therefore $60F$ Nmm $= 1500$.
   ∴ $F = 25$ Nmm.

DRAWING 3 — Figure 5.5.

To find the force F which would hold the system in equilibrium:

1. cw moment about P is 100 × 120 + 200F Nmm = 12,000 + 200F.
2. acw moment about P is 60 × 80 + 80 × 140 = 16,000 Nmm.
3. ∴ 200F = 16,000 − 12,000 = 4,000.
4. ∴ F = 4,000/200 = 20 N.

DRAWING 4 — Figure 5.5.

The system is in equilibrium. To find the reactions at D and at E:

1. cw moments about D = 80×10 = 800 Nmm.
2. acw moments about D:

$$= 4 \times 100 + 2 \times 40 + 40R_2$$
$$= 400 + 80 + 40R_2 = 40R_2 + 480 \text{ Nmm.}$$
$$\therefore 40R_2 = 800 - 480 = 320$$
$$R_2 = 320/40 = 8 \text{ N.}$$

3. The two reactions must be opposite and equal to the downward forces on the system:
$$R_1 \text{ at } D = 8 - R_1 = 4 + 2 + 10$$
$$\therefore R_1 = 16 - 8 = 8 \text{N.}$$

Centres of gravity

Drawings 1, 2 and 3 of Figure 5.6 (see page 76) show the methods of finding the centres of gravity (CoG) of some plane figures. In triangles, the CoG is where two medians of the triangle cross each other; in squares, rectangles, rhombuses and parallelograms, it is where the diagonals cross; in a circle, it is the centre of the circle.

To find the CoG of an irregular plane figure

1. **Drawing 4** of Figure 5.6. To find the CoG of the figure ABCDEF: draw the diagonals of the two rectangles making up the plane figure.
2. **Drawing 5**. Find the CoG of the two rectangles

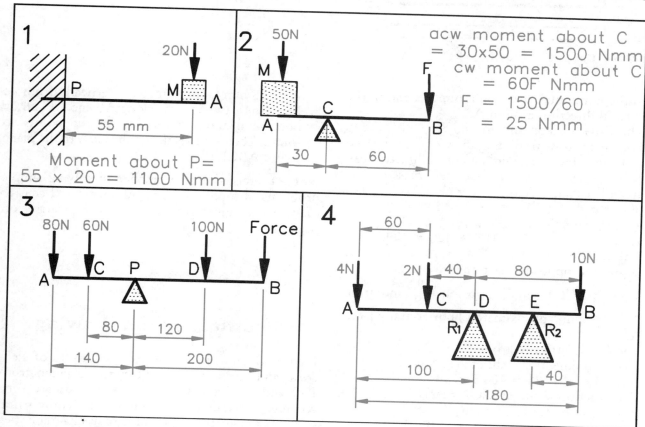

Figure 5.5 Moments about a point

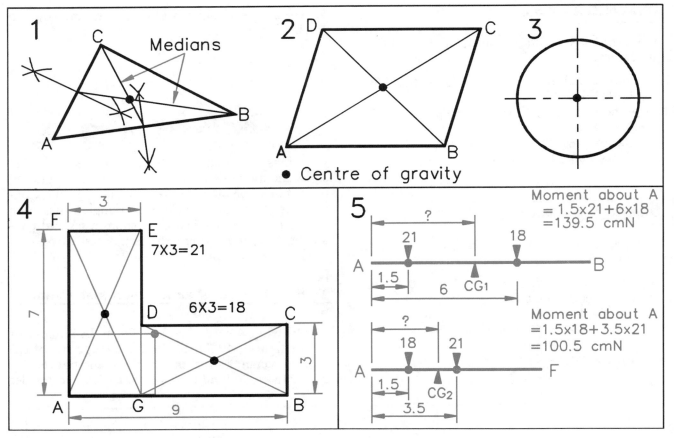

Figure 5.6 Centres of gravity

in the horizontal direction around A and in the vertical direction around A.

3. The CoG horizontally around A:
For the purpose of finding the CoGs of the two rectangles their areas in square millimetres can be regarded as representing their masses. The area of rectangle ABEF is 7 × 3 = 21 mm, and of rectangle GBCD is 6 × 3 = 18 mm.
Taking moments cw about A:
1.5 × 21 + 6 × 18 = 31.5 + 108 = 139.5.
The reaction value at CG1 = 21 + 18 = 39 (equal and opposite reaction).

Therefore CG1 is in the position $\frac{139.5}{39}$ mm from

A = 3.6 mm (approximately) horizontally from A.

4. The CoG vertically around A:
Taking moments cw about A:
1.5×18 + 3.5×21 = 100.5.
The reaction value at CG2 = 21 + 18 = 39 (equal and opposite reaction).

Therefore CG1 is in the position $\frac{100.5}{39}$ mm from

A = 2.6 mm (approximately) vertically from A.

5. Mark these two lengths along AB and AF. Draw horizontal and vertical lines at the points so found. Their intersection is the CoG of the plane figure ABCDEF.

Note: exercises to give practice in solving simple problems of force polygons, moments and centres of gravity are given later in this chapter, starting on page 81.

Electrical circuit drawing

Figure 5.7 and Figure 5.8 show examples of electrical and electronics circuit symbols taken from ISO and BS standards. These standards are very complex, containing thousands of symbols for components in the types of circuit diagrams becoming increasingly common in modern technolo-

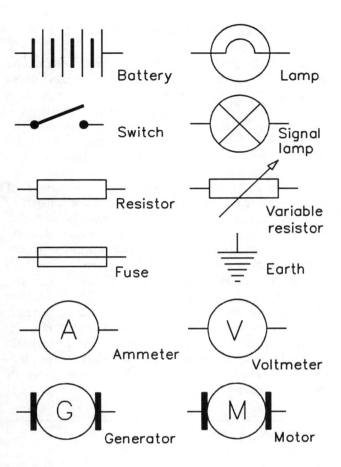

Figure 5.7 Standard electrical circuit symbols

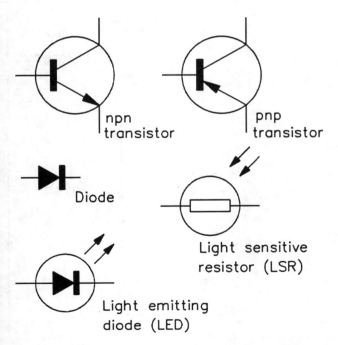

Figure 5.8 Standard electronic circuit symbols

gy. The given examples are just a sample from the standards. Those wishing to learn technical drawing should attempt to draw some simple circuits such as those in Figure 5.9. Simple electrical circuits such as the three shown are fairly easy to design. It is best to make drawings of the circuits before attempting to install the actual components in a circuit. The three circuits in Figure 5.9 are:

DRAWING 1 – Figure 5.9.

Two lamps connected **in series** to a battery, with a switch between the battery and the lamps. When the switch is on, the lamps light. When the switch is off (as shown) the lamps are not lit.

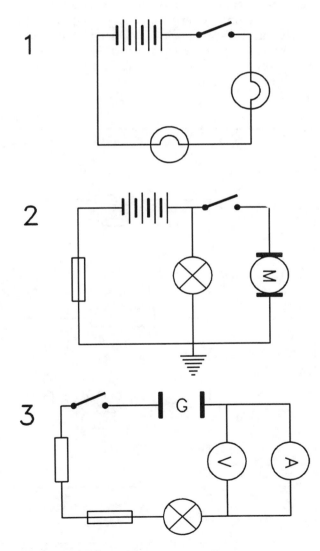

Figure 5.9 Electrical circuit drawing

DRAWING 2 – Figure 5.9.

A battery is connected to a motor with a switch and a fuse **in series** with the battery and the motor. A signal lamp is set in the circuit **parallel** to the motor. When the switch is on the motor is running. The signal lamp shows that the motor is active. If the motor is overloaded, the fuse will cut out, saving the possible burning out of the motor. The circuit is earthed.

DRAWING 3 – Figure 5.9.

A **generator** – a device for generating electricity, is set in a circuit with an **ammeter in series** to show how much current is being generated and a **voltmeter in parallel** to show the voltage at which the current is being generated. A signal lamp in series shows that the generator is working when the circuit switch is on. A fuse protects the components in the circuit from burning out. A **resistor** in the circuit prevents too much current running through the circuit.

An electronic circuit

Figure 5.10 is an example of a simple electronic circuit. The circuit is activated by pressing a press switch. When the circuit has been activated, if a light is shone on to the light-sensitive diode, the transistors in the circuit cause the relay to be switched on. The transistors act as amplifiers of the current surge produced when light shines on the light-sensitive diode. When light is no longer shining on the diode, the relay causes the surges of current to cease. The circuit is therefore known as a light-sensitive circuit, such as might be installed to activate systems for opening and closing doors, by shining (or not shining) a light onto the light sensitive diode.

Further examples of symbols for circuit drawing are given in Figure 5.11 and Figure 5.12. These two illustrations show just two **pneumatic circuit symbols** and a very simple **pneumatic circuit**. Although the numbers of symbols for pneumatic circuits are not anywhere near as many as for electrical and electronics circuits, the samples given in these two illustrations show the type of symbols

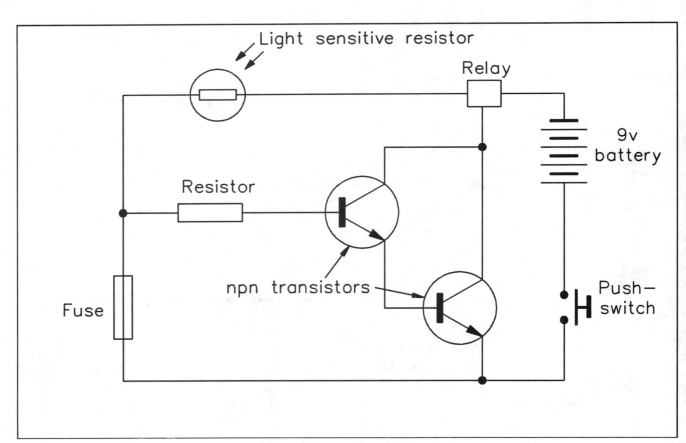

Figure 5.10 An electronic circuit

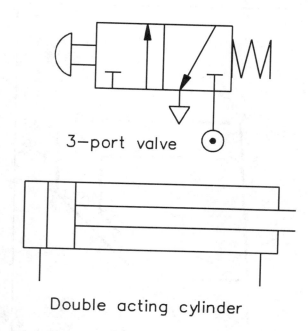

3—port valve

Double acting cylinder

Figure 5.11 Two pneumatic circuit symbols

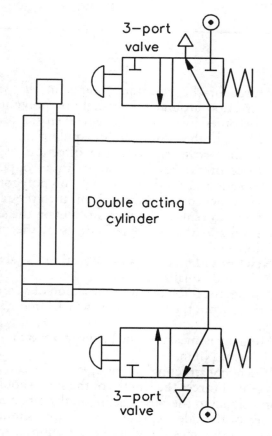

3—port valve

Double acting cylinder

3—port valve

Figure 5.12 A pneumatics circuit

for this form of circuit. The simple pneumatic circuit Figure 5.12 shows a double-acting cylinder which moves in when the plunger of one of the three-port valves is pushed and moves out when the plunger of the other three-port valve is pushed. Pneumatic circuits depend upon a compressed air supply system in order to function.

Scaling areas of polygons

This construction must not be confused with the construction for scaling polygons (page 50). That construction involved the drawing of polygons of the same shape but with side lengths drawn to a given ratio. The construction explained here is for drawing polygons similar in shape to given polygons but drawn so that their areas are a given ratio of the original polygons.

DRAWING 1 – Figure 5.13.

In this example (see page 80) the ratio of the required polygon of the same shape is 3:5 – i.e. less than 1:1.

1. Draw the polygon ABCDE to the dimensions given.
2. With A as centre draw a semi-circle of radius AB and produce BA to meet the semi-circle at F.
3. Divide AF into 5 equal parts. Take 3 of them – at G.
4. Bisect BG and draw a semi-circle on BG.
5. Draw a vertical at A meeting the semi-circle at H.
6. With centre A and radius AH, draw an arc to meet AB at J.
7. Then AJ is the base of the required polygon.
8. Draw JK, KL and LM parallel to their respective sides of the original polygon.
9. Then the polygon AJKLM is the required polygon whose area is 3/5 of the area of the polygon ABCDE.

DRAWING 2 – Figure 5.13.

This example, using the same method as for Drawing 1, is for constructing a polygon of the same

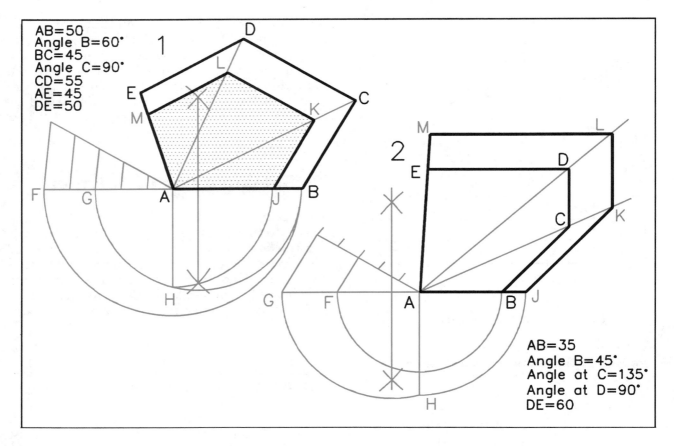

AB=50
Angle B=60°
BC=45
Angle C=90°
CD=55
AE=45
DE=50

AB=35
Angle B=45°
Angle at C=135°
Angle at D=90°
DE=60

Figure 5.13 Scaling areas of polygons

shape as a given polygon but with its area in a ratio greater than 1:1.

1. Draw the polygon ABCDE to the given dimensions.
2. Following the same procedure as for Drawing 1 construct the polygon AJKLM which is 5:3 the area of polygon ABCDE.

Note: the only difference in the two constructions is that the line AF is divided into 3 equal parts of which 5 are taken to produce the ratio 5:3.

■ CHECK YOUR UNDERSTANDING

● A **scalar** has length but no magnitude or direction.
● A **vector** has magnitude and direction.
● If a system is stationary under the action of forces acting in or on it, then the system is said to be in **equilibrium**.
● In a **triangle of forces** or a **polygon of forces:**
 a) If the arrow showing the direction of the

force of the **resultant** points in the same direction around the triangle or polygon as the other forces in a system, then the forces acting in the system are in equilibrium.
 b) If the arrow showing the direction of the force of the resultant points in an opposite direction around the triangle or polygon as the other forces in the system, then the resultant can replace the forces to obtain the same results as the combined effects of the other forces.
● **Newton's Third Law** – Reaction is always opposite and equal to action.
● A **moment** is the result of the action of a force at a distance from the point about which a moment is taken.
● Moment is measured in **Newton metres** – e.g. Nm, Ncm, Nmm.
● When constructing a **triangle of forces** or a **polygon of forces** the lengths of the sides should be proportional to the forces acting in the direction of the vector the sides represent and arrows should be placed on the lines showing the direction in which the forces are acting.

● Forces acting on a lever about its **fulcrum** can be found by taking moments about the fulcrum.

● Forces acting on a beam can be found by taking moments about any point on the beam.

● At any point on a beam, the clockwise moments must be equal to the anti-clockwise moments if the beam is to be in equilibrium.

● **Centres of gravity:**

A triangle – at the point where two medians cross.

A parallelogram, square, rectangle or rhombus – where the diagonals cross.

A circle – at its centre.

Plates made up from plane figures – by taking moments horizontally and vertically about one corner of the plate.

● **Scaling a polygon** to obtain an area in a given ratio to the area of an original polygon is more complicated than scaling the side lengths of a polygon.

REVISION EXERCISES AND QUESTIONS

Exercises

1 Figure 5.14. A mass exerts a 600 N force downwards at B of the pin-jointed triangular framework ABC. The member AC of the frame is fixed firmly to a wall. By drawing a triangle of forces, calculate the forces acting in AB and in AC and the directions in which they are acting. Also state which of the members AB and AC is in compression and which in tension.

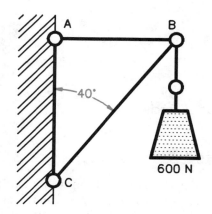

Figure 5.14 Exercise 1

2 Figure 5.15. Four cables attached to a ring are exerting forces as shown. The forces are all acting in the same plane. By drawing a polygon of

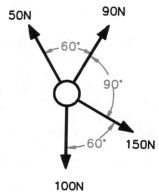

Figure 5.15 Exercise 2

forces, calculate the force and its direction which is needed to hold the ring in equilibrium.

3 Figure 5.16 shows a look-out cabin raised on a framework. The cabin is designed for travellers to take photographs of animals in the wild.

The framework consists of two pin-jointed frames mounted underneath each side of the cabin. The mass of the cabin is exerting a downwards force on the frames of 1000 Newtons, distributed evenly at the four pin joints at the tops of the frames. Thus the joints C and D are each being acted upon by downward forces of 250 Newtons.

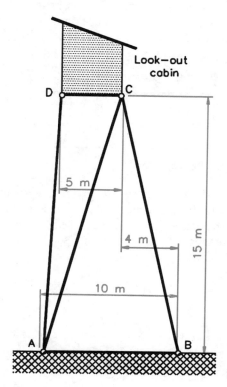

Figure 5.16 Exercise 3

By constructing a stress diagram for the frame ABCD:

a) Calculate the forces acting in each of its members.

b) From your stress diagram show the direction in which forces are acting in the members.

c) State which members are in compression and which are in tension.

d) Find the reactions at ground level at A and B.

4 Figure 5.17. The drawing shows a flat plate of even thickness. Calculate the centre of gravity of the plate.

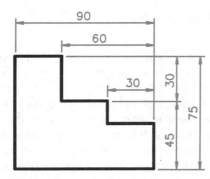

Figure 5.17 Exercise 4

5 Figure 5.18. Three downwards forces are acting on a beam, which is held in equilibrium by a single force acting vertically upwards.

Calculate the force F necessary to hold the beam in equilibrium.

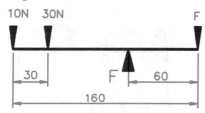

Figure 5.18 Exercise 5

6 Figure 5.19. Construct the given irregular hexagon to the dimensions shown. Construct a hexagon of the same shape with an area 4/9 that of the given hexagon.

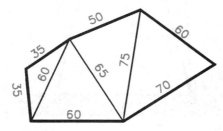

Figure 5.19 Exercise 6

7 Figure 5.20. Complete the electrical circuit shown by replacing the boxes containing the names of the components with correct symbols taken from Figure 5.7 on page 77.

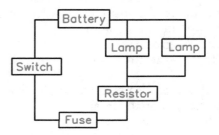

Figure 5.20 Exercise 7

8 Figure 5.21. Complete the electronics circuit shown by replacing the letters denoting the symbols with correct symbols taken from Figure 5.8 on page 77.

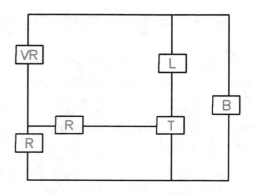

VR — variable resistor
R — resistor
L — lamp
B — battery
T — npn transistor
S — switch

Figure 5.21 Exercise 8

Design exercises

The four design exercises on the next page are included here for revising the geometry and design ideas in earlier chapters. When answering the four design exercises:

a) Make neat freehand sketches on spare pieces of paper of as many ideas to solve the design as you can.

b) Select the design sketch which you think is the best of your sketched solutions.
c) Make an accurate drawing of your selected solution with the aid of drawing instruments.

1 Figure 5.22. The given drawing is a suggestion for a logo to advertise the starting up of a university college which is to be called the Local University College.

Do not copy the given design, but make several sketches of other designs which you think are suitable for the logo. When you are satisfied you have a good design idea, make an accurate drawing of your design with the aid of instruments.

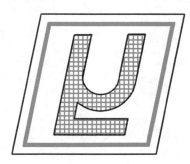

Figure 5.22 Design Exercise 1

2 Figure 5.23 is part of a pictorial graph showing the possible increase in the sale of men's clothes by a clothing firm during the years 1995 to 1997.

Design and draw a similar type of graph which shows the following possible increases in the sales of women's clothes over the same period:

• In 1995 – 58,000 garments
• In 1996 – 75,000 garments
• In 1997 – 125,000 garments.

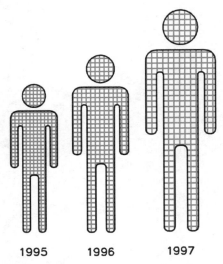

1995   1996   1997

Figure 5.23 Design Exercise 2

3 Figure 5.24. A petrol station manager has asked you to design a sign showing that his station sells petrol. The given drawing is a suggestion for the sign, but the manager does not like it.

Make a number of sketches of suitable designs. Select that which you think is the most suitable and make an accurate drawing of your selected design with the aid of instruments.

Figure 5.24 Design Exercise 3

4 Figure 5.25. A plan of a small house in its grounds is shown.
Copy the given plan working to a scale of 1:200. The following are to be added to the plan:
a) A part of the road which passes the front of the house. The road is to be 4 metres wide.
b) A name for the road.
c) A path to the door of the house.
d) A path to the store shed from the rear of the house.
e) An area with a sand-pit for children to play. Make sketches of ideas for these additions and when satisfied with one of your ideas, add the details to your plan.

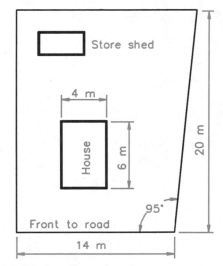

Figure 5.25 Design Exercise 4

Questions

1 When you next see a pylon, try to estimate the forces acting on it. Think in terms of Newtons and not in terms of kilograms of force. Make a sketch of part of the pylon and try estimating the forces acting in those parts you have sketched.

2 When you are out walking and somebody passes you estimate the comparative speed with which you have been passed.

3 Why are there so many triangles in a steel girder bridge?

4 Pick up any fairly heavy object. Can you tell where its centre of gravity is?

5 Cut any shape out from a piece of cardboard. Make holes in three places near the edge of the shape. Hang the card from a pin with a piece of string or cotton in each hole in turn. How can the centre of gravity of the carboard shape be found by carrying out this experiment?

6 Look at an electric torch. Sketch the circuit diagram for the torch.

7 Try to sketch the electric circuit for the classroom you usually use.

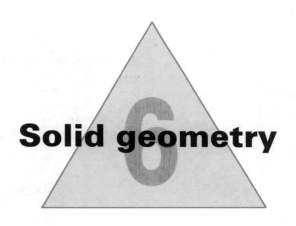

Solid geometry

Introduction

Many technical drawings will be **orthographic projections**. These allow a draughtsman to show the exact form, shape and sizes of solid objects. If you wish to learn how to construct good technical drawings, learn the theory underlying orthographic projection.

Horizontal and vertical planes

If a horizontal plane is crossed by a vertical plane, they must be at right angles to each other – they are **orthogonal** to each other. Orthographic projection is based upon orthogonal planes. A **horizontal plane** is usually called an H.P. A **vertical plane** is usually known as a V.P. Figure 6.1 shows an H.P. crossing a V.P. These planes form four angles –

known as the First angle, the Second angle, the Third angle and the Fourth angle. In orthographic projection, only the First and Third angles are used.

First angle orthographic projection

Figure 6.2 to Figure 6.4 describe the theory of First angle projection.

1. The object to be drawn is placed on the H.P. in the First angle – Figure 6.2.
2. Looking at the object directly from the front, what can be seen is drawn onto the V.P. This is a **Front view**. Looking at the object directly from above, gives a **Plan**.

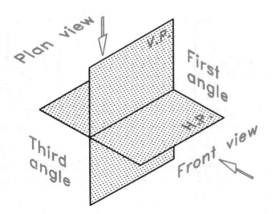

Figure 6.1 The two orthogonal planes H.P. and V.P

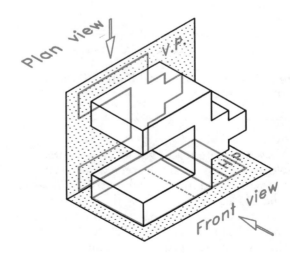

Figure 6.2 An object placed between the V.P. and the H.P.

85

3. The object is removed from its place between the two planes – Figure 6.3.
4. The H.P. is rotated through 90 degrees to lie in line with the V.P. This gives a Front view and Plan of the object in First angle projection – Figure 6.4.

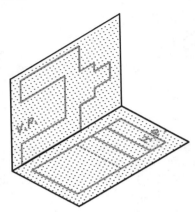

Figure 6.3 Front view and Plan drawn onto the V.P. and the H.P.

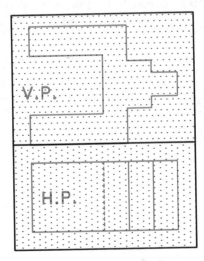

Figure 6.4 A Front view and Plan in First angle orthographic projection

Notes:
- **Views** are often known as **elevations**. The word view is to be preferred because it is the word used in ISO and British Standards.
- The **Plan** is drawn **below** the **Front view**.
- Because of the way in which the two views were obtained from a V.P. and an H.P., they must be vertically in line with each other.

An example of a First angle orthographic projection

- Figure 6.5 is a '**pictorial**' view of a pipe clip made from plastic for clipping a pipe to a wall.

Figure 6.5 A pipe clip

- Figure 6.6 is a Front view and a Plan in First angle projection of the pipe clip.

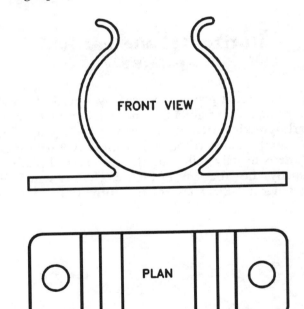

Figure 6.6 First angle projection of the pipe clip

- Figure 6.7 shows the orthographic projection of the pipe clip in the form the orthographic projection would be drawn for use by those engaged in making the clip. Many more drawings of this type appear later in this book.

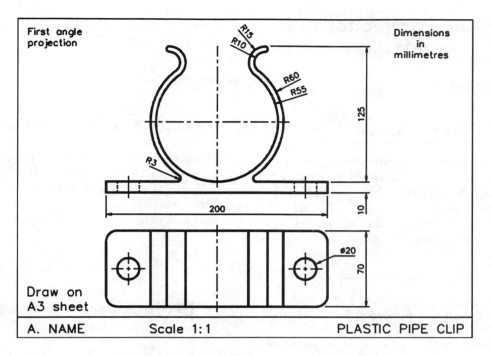

Figure 6.7 A dimensioned drawing of the pipe clip drawn on an A3 sheet of paper

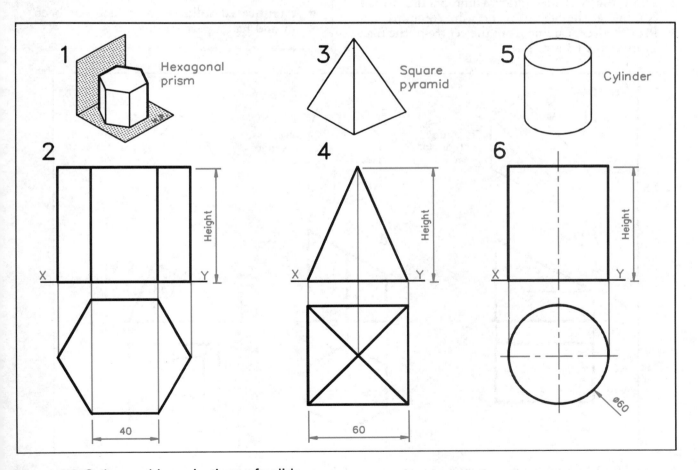

Figure 6.8 Orthographic projections of solids

Orthographic projections of solids

A hexagonal prism

DRAWINGS 1 and 2 – Figure 6.8.

1. Construct the plan – a regular hexagon of 40 mm side lengths – with the aid of a set square.
2. Draw the line XY. Draw a line parallel to the XY line at the height of the solid (70 mm).
3. Project vertical lines from the corners of the plan to meet the 70 mm line above XY.

A square pyramid

DRAWINGS 3 and 4 – Figure 6.8.

1. Draw the plan – a square of sides 40 mm with its diagonals.
2. Draw the XY line. Draw a line parallel to the XY line at the height of the solid (65 mm).
3. Project a vertical line from the centre of the plan to meet the 65 mm line.

Project vertical lines from the corners of the plan to meet the XY line.

A cylinder

DRAWINGS 5 and 6 – Figure 6.8.

1. Draw the plan – a circle of diameter 60 mm.
2. Draw the XY line. Draw a line parallel to the XY line at the height of the solid (60 mm).
3. Draw vertical lines from the plan to the height line and complete the projection as shown.

Projections – truncated solids

- A **truncated solid** is one which has been cut and had a part removed.

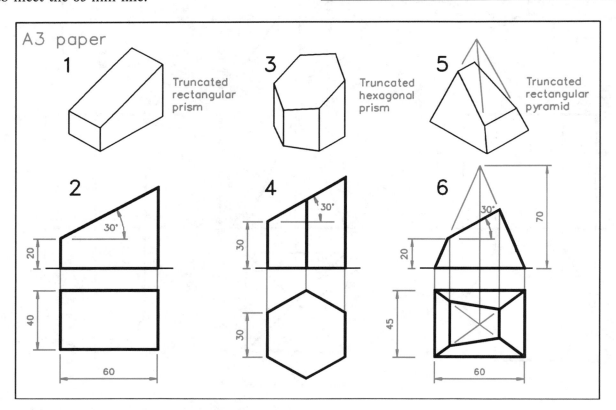

Figure 6.9 Orthographic projections of truncated solids

Truncated rectangular prism

DRAWINGS 1 and 2 – Figure 6.9.

1. Draw the plan – a rectangle 60 mm × 40 mm. Draw an XY line.
2. From the plan project verticals across the XY line.
3. At 20 mm above the XY line from the left hand line draw a line at 30 degrees.
4. Complete the front view as shown. Do not include dimensions.

Truncated hexagonal prism

DRAWINGS 3 and 4 – Figure 6.9.

1. Draw the plan – a regular hexagon of 30 mm sides.
2. Draw an XY line. Project verticals from the corners of the plan across the XY line.
3. At 30 mm above the XY line from the left hand vertical line, draw a line at 30 degrees.
4. Complete the Front view as shown. Do not include dimensions.

Truncated rectangular pyramid

DRAWINGS 5 and 6 – Figure 6.9.

1. Draw the plan of the pyramid before truncation.
2. Draw an XY line and draw a Front view of the pyramid before truncation, 70 mm high.
3. Draw a 30 degree line of truncation 20 mm above the XY line. Complete the Front view as shown.
4. Where the 30 degree line crosses the Front view of the pyramid before truncation, project lines vertically down across the Plan.
5. Complete the Plan as shown. Do not include dimensions.

Revision – Dimensions

Some information about the inclusion of dimensions in technical drawings was given on page 6 and in Figure 1.16. When adding dimensions to a tech-

nical drawing, note the following as shown in Figure 6.10:

- Dimension and extension lines are thin lines.
- A gap of about 3 mm should be left between the outline and an extension line.
- Extension lines should extend about 3 mm beyond the dimension line to which they refer.
- The diameter and radius symbols should be placed before the figure of the diameter or radius to which they refer.
- Arrow heads should be about 3 mm long.
- Smaller dimensions should be placed between larger dimensions and the drawing outline to which they refer.
- Figures should be clearly readable. The following heights are suitable for use with different sizes of sheets of paper:

  A4 – 3 mm high
  A3 – 4 mm high
  A2 – 5 mm high

- Although not necessarily associated with dimensions, all circles or parts of circles should have centre lines passing through their centre points in both directions.

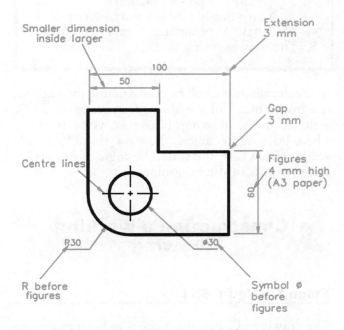

Figure 6.10 Details about simple dimensioning

A 'working drawing'

Drawings of items in orthographic projection which have been designed for use by those who will actually manufacture the item are often referred to as **working drawings**. Working drawings usually include:

1. One, two or more views in orthographic projection.
2. Dimensions of the item, unless the drawing is for assembly purposes, but even then they may require dimensioning in parts.
3. A title block in which the following may be printed:
   a) A title for the item described in the drawing.
   b) The name of the draughtsman or woman.
   c) The scale to which the drawing has been made.
   d) Other details such as:
      • the date the drawing was completed
      • the materials from which the item is made
      • the initials of the person who checked the drawing for accuracy
      • any possible tolerances to which the item should be machined
      • any finishes which may be required
4. The angle of projection – First or Third.
5. The dimensioning units.

In the drawings we will be constructing throughout this book, many of the above features may not be included in the drawing. However, your drawings when learning technical drawing should include your name, a title, the scale, the angle of projection and the units of dimensioning.

Constructing a working drawing

Stage 1 – Figure 6.11.

The drawing of a *bearing block* is to be drawn on an A3 sheet of paper. An A3 sheet is 420 mm by

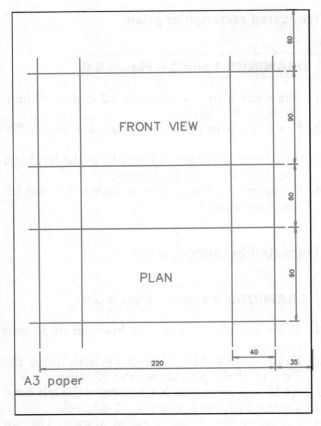

Figure 6.11 Stage 1

297 mm. The drawing is to be placed vertically on the paper – in a 'portrait' position. A border line is drawn all around the paper 15 mm in from its edges. This leaves a working area of 390 mm by 267 mm. We shall be drawing a line 20 mm up from the bottom border line to provide space for a title block – this leaves a working area of 370 mm by 267 mm.

Taking dimensions vertically:

• The height of the Front view is 90 mm.
• The height of the plan is 90 mm.
• These two heights leave a vertical space of

    370 − 180 = 190 mm.

  which allows us to position the top of the Front view 60 mm down from the top border line and allows a space of 60 mm between the two views.
• To position the views in the width of the paper

    267 − 220 = 47.

If the right hand space is made 35 mm, this leaves room to place the dimensions on the right hand side of the views.
• Figure 6.11 shows the construction lines based on the above arithmetic.

> **Note:** You should always work out the positions of the views for your drawings on scrap paper because the better the layout of your drawing, the easier it is to read. Badly laid out drawings can be difficult to understand clearly.

> **Remember** that outline lines should be thicker than other lines in your drawings. Thus the outline lines should stand out against centre lines, hidden detail lines and, later dimension lines.

Stage 2 – Figure 6.12.

Now fill in all details of the outlines of the Front view and plan.

- Add centre lines through all circles and arcs.
- Add hidden detail lines showing details which cannot be seen in the outside view of the item.
- Radii at corners can be added with the aid of a radius curve (see page 4).
- Erase all unwanted lines such as construction lines.

Stage 3 – Figure 6.13.

To complete the drawing add the following:

- Your name in neat capital letters 8 mm high.
- The title of the item which has been drawn – also in neat capital letters 8 mm high.
- All dimensions – use figures which are about 4 mm high.
- The phrases – 'First angle projection' and 'Dimensions in millimetres' – 6 mm high lettering would be suitable for these.

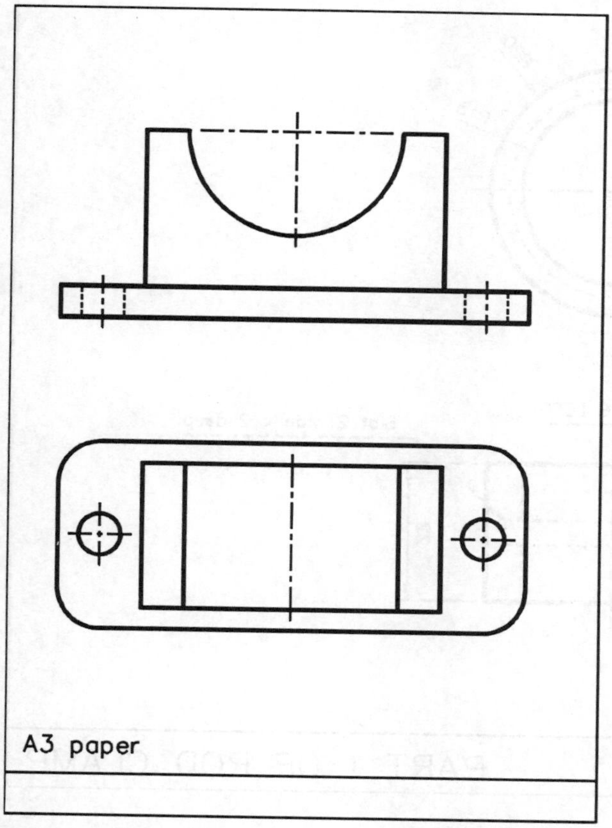

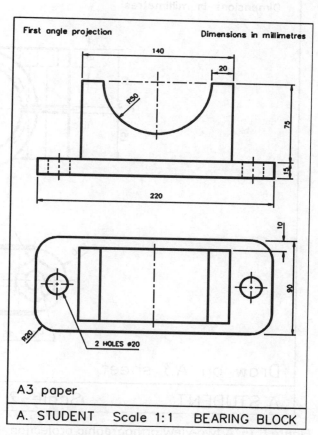

Figure 6.12 Stage 2

Figure 6.13 Stage 3 – the finished projection

Part 1 of a *rod clamp*

Figure 6.14 is a photograph of a *rod clamp* and Figure 6.15 a two-view First angle orthographic projection of the clamp. Working on an A3 size sheet of paper in a 'landscape' layout copy Figure 6.15. Follow the same procedures as were followed when drawing the *bearing block* (page 90):

1. Draw a border around the sheet edges and a line for the upper edge of a title block.
2. Work out a good layout on scrap paper.
3. Draw faint construction lines for the positions of the two views.
4. Draw the outlines of Front View and Plan in firm, black thick lines.
5. Add centre lines and hidden detail.
6. Add your name, a title, First angle projection and Dimensions in millimetres in suitably sized, neat lettering.
7. Carefully erase unwanted lines with a rubber.

Figure 6.14 A photograph of the *rod clamp*

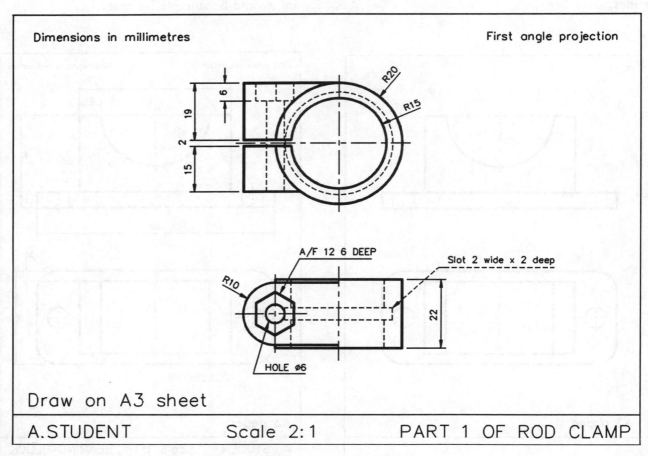

Figure 6.15 A two-view orthographic projection of the *rod clamp*

End views in First angle projection

1. Figure 6.16 shows the result of adding a second V.P. to the H.P. and V.P. shown in Figure 6.1 and projecting what is seen from looking in the direction labelled End view in Figure 6.16.

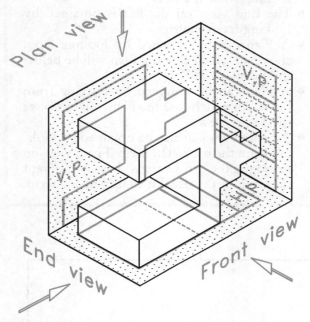

Figure 6.16 Adding a second V.P.

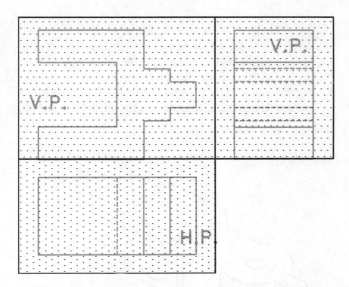

Figure 6.17 The three First angle views obtained from Figure 6.16

2. Figure 6.17 shows the results of rotating both V.Ps so that they lie flat with the H.P. The result is that a new view – an End view has been added to the Front view and Plan.

3. Figure 6.17 shows how an end view can be included in a First angle orthographic projection. Taking the theory further, Figure 6.18 shows that it is possible, by adding further imaginary V.Ps and H.Ps to include two End views and two plans in a First angle projec-

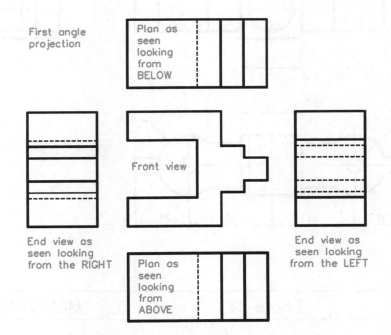

Figure 6.18 Five views in First angle orthographic projection

tion. Note that the term 'Plan' is used here in a different sense to its normal meaning. In orthographic projection a Plan can be drawn by looking upwards at an object from below.

4. Figure 6.19 is a pictorial view of a *mounting rubber* from a motor car engine and Figure 6.20

is an example of a First angle orthographic projection which includes a Front view and End view and a Plan.

Notes:
- The End view on the right is obtained by looking from the left.
- The End view on the left is obtained by looking from the right.
- A Plan can be obtained by looking from above, in which case the Plan will be below the Front view.
- A Plan can be obtained by looking from below, in which case the Plan will be above the Front view.
- A Front view can also be obtained by looking from the back. The term 'Front view' in orthographic projections has a different meaning to the usual meaning of the term.

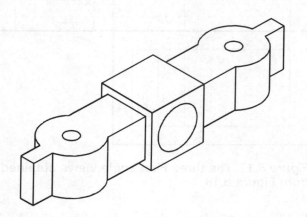

Figure 6.19 A pictorial view of a *mounting rubber*

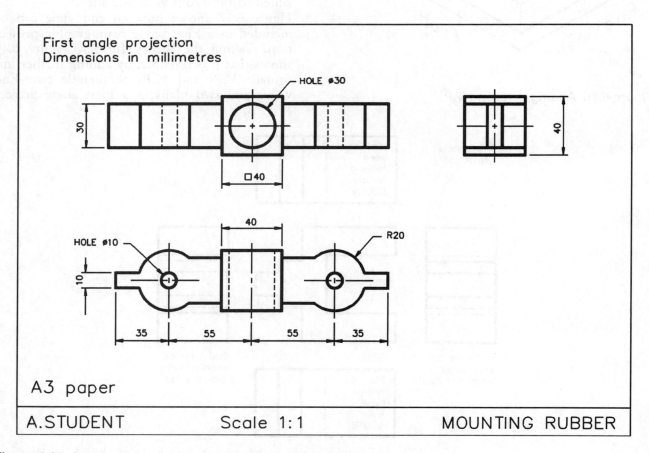

Figure 6.20 An example of a three-view First angle orthographic projection

A support bracket

Figure 6.21 is a photograph of a *support bracket* and Figure 6.22 a three-view First angle orthographic projection of the bracket. Working on an A3 size sheet of paper in a 'landscape' layout copy the Figure 6.22. Follow the same procedures as were followed when drawing the *bearing block* (page 90).

1. Draw a border around the sheet edges and a line for the upper edge of a title block.
2. Work out a good layout on scrap paper.
3. Draw faint construction lines for the positions of the two views.
4. Draw the outlines of Front View, End view and Plan in firm, black thick lines.
5. Add centre lines and hidden detail.
6. Add your name, a title, First angle projection and Dimensions in millimetres in suitably sized, neat lettering.
7. Carefully erase unwanted lines with a rubber.

Figure 6.21 A photograph of a *support bracket*

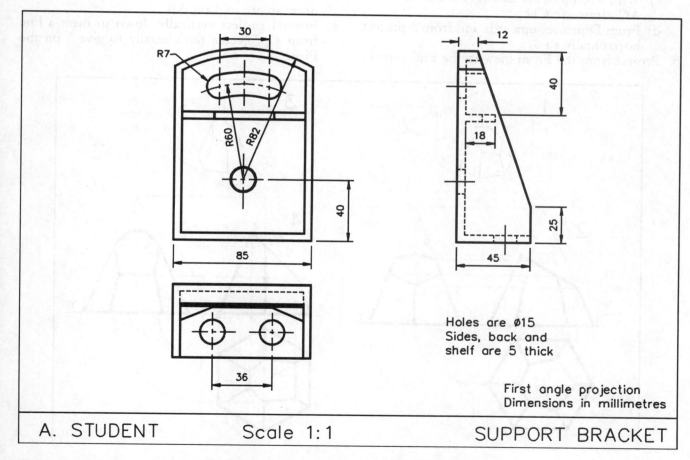

Figure 6.22 A three-view orthographic projection of the *support bracket*

Orthographic projections of pyramids

DRAWINGS 1 and 2 – Figure 6.23.

Drawing 1 shows a truncated hexagonal pyramid lying on a H.P. together with two V.Ps. To construct a three-view orthographic projection of the truncated hexagonal pyramid – **Drawing 2**:

1. Draw a Plan, Front view and End view of the pyramid before truncation.
2. Draw the truncation line at 30 degrees.
3. Draw AB at right angles to the XY line.
4. To complete the Plan and End View project as shown for the projections of points 1 to 3 for each intersection of the truncation lines with the sloping lines of the Front view:
   a) From 1 project to 2;
   b) From 2 project to C on AB.
   c) With a compass centred at A and with radius AC, draw arc CD.
   d) From D project upwards and from 1 project horizontally to 3.
5. Project from the Front view to the End view in

the same manner from each point on the truncation line to complete both Plan and End view.

DRAWINGS 3 and 4 – Figure 6.23.

Drawing 3 shows a truncated hexagonal pyramid resting on an H.P. together with two V.Ps. In this example the hexagonal pyramid is placed so that the solid has been turned through 90 degrees as compared with Drawing 1. As a result, the truncated surface is of a different shape.

To construct the Front view, End view and Plan, proceed as in **Drawing 4**. The same method is used as in Drawing 2 and an example of the method of construction follows the projections:

1. Draw a Front view, and End view and a Plan of the solid before truncation.
2. Draw AB at right angles to XY.
3. From point 1 on the Front view project to 2 on the End view.
4. From 2 project to 3 on the XY line.
5. With a compass centred at A and radius A3, draw an arc to 4 on AB.
6. From 1 project vertically down to meet a line from 4 projected horizontally to give 5 on the Plan.

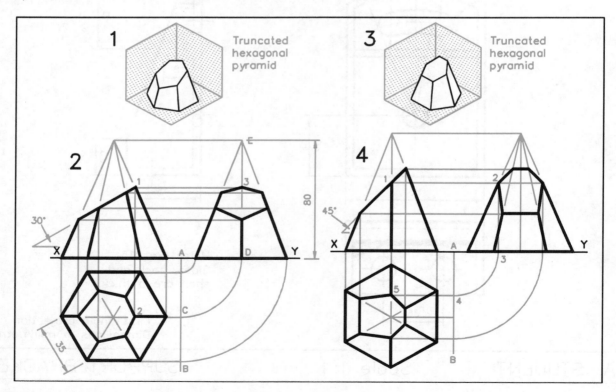

Figure 6.23 Orthographic projections of pyramids

Projections of lines and triangles

To find the True length of a line and its True angles to H.P. and the V.P.:

1. **Drawing 2** – Figure 6.24. Draw the Front view and Plan of the line AB to the dimensions given.
2. From A in the plan draw a horizontal line.
3. With a compass centred at A and radius AB, draw arc to meet the horizontal line from A at 1.
4. From B₁ in the Front view draw horizontal line.
5. From 1 in the plan project a vertical to meet the horizontal from B₁ at 2.
6. Then A₁2 is the True length of line AB.
7. Measure the angle which A₁2 makes with the XY line. The line lies at a True angle of 20 degrees to the H.P.
8. **Drawing 3** – to find the True angle of the line to the V.P., project to find the true length in the Plan. Then measure the angle the line of the True length makes with XY to give the True angle to the H.P.

To find the True shape of a triangle in space

1. **Drawing 5** – Figure 6.24. Draw the Front view and Plan of the triangle.
2. AC lies parallel to XY in both Front view and Plan – AC must therefore be the True length of the side AC of the triangle.
3. Find the True lengths of AB and BC by construction, using the method given in Drawing 2.
4. The True length of each side of the triangle is now known and its True shape can now be drawn – **Drawing 6**.

Note: when working in orthographic projection, the True lengths, True angles and True shapes of details within the projections may have to be constructed. This form of construction is particularly important when constructing the developments of surfaces of a solid – examples of developments are given in Chapter 7.

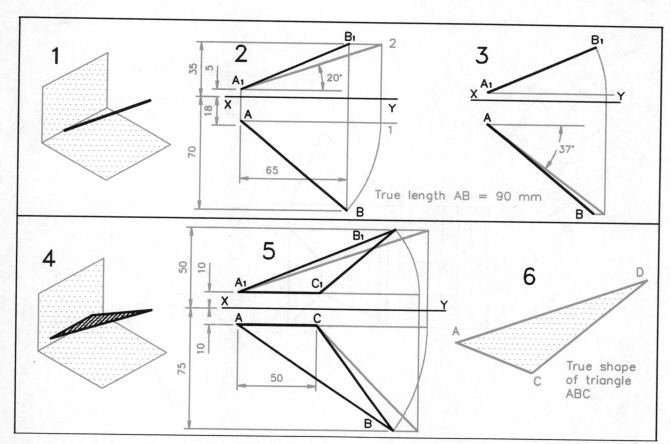

Figure 6.24 Projections of lines and triangles

An auxiliary view

- An **auxiliary view** is a view in orthographic as seen when looking at an object from an angle to the H.P. or V.P. (or both).

To draw an **auxiliary view** of a truncated square pyramid which includes the True shape of the truncated surface:

1. Draw the Front view and Plan of the truncated square pyramid to the details given in Figure 6.25.
2. Draw X_1Y_1 parallel to the sloping face as seen in the Front view.
3. Project at right angles to the sloping face from the points A, B, and where the base of the pyramid rests on XY.
4. Draw lines parallel to X_1Y_1 at the distances shown by the dimensions 1 to 6 on the plan.
5. Points on the required auxiliary view are where the parallels to X_1Y_1 intersect the projected lines at right angles to the sloping face.
6. The auxiliary view can now be drawn through the points so found. This view includes the True shape of the surface AB of the Front view.

Notes
- An **auxiliary view** may be referred to as a **new view**.
- **Auxiliary views** (or **new views**) are often of value when constructing the developments of surfaces of solids.
- **Auxiliary views** (or **new views**) are sometimes required when drawing orthographic projections for engineering and building drawings.
- The **True shape** of surfaces which are at right angles to the direction of the viewing point will be included in an **auxiliary view**.

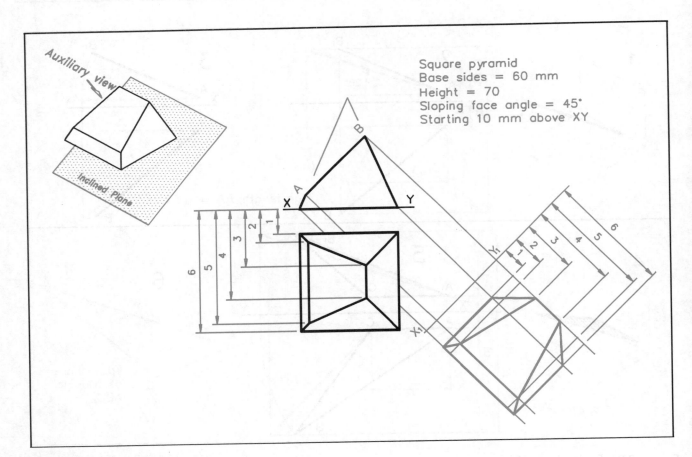

Square pyramid
Base sides = 60 mm
Height = 70
Sloping face angle = 45°
Starting 10 mm above XY

Figure 6.25 An auxiliary view

Circle and hyperbola as conic sections

The circle has been frequently used in examples given in earlier pages of this book. A construction for a hyperbola was given on page 58. These two curves are often described as conic sections. Sections and sectional views will be described in later pages (pages 131 to 133). The method of constructing the two curves as conic sections is described in Drawings 2 and 4 of Figure 6.26.

The circle as a conic section

1. **Drawing 2** – Figure 6.26. Draw a Front view, End view and Plan of a truncated cone to the dimensions given with **Drawing 1**.
2. Project vertically down from 1 in the Front view on to the centre line of the plan to give 2.
3. In the plan, with a compass centred at 3 and set to the radius from 3 to 2, draw a circle.
4. The plan of the truncated cone is now complete, the circle being part of that plan.

The hyperbola as a conic section

1. **Drawing 4** – Figure 6.26. Draw a Front view and a Plan of the truncated cone to the details given with **Drawing 3**. Note that the cut surface is vertical.
2. Draw a line at 45 degrees to XY as shown.
3. Take a point 1 on the slope line of the cone in the Front view.
4. Project vertically down to 2 on the centre line of the Plan.
5. With a compass centred at the centre of the Plan, and set to the point 2, draw a circle.
6. The circle cuts the vertical face in the Plan at 3.
7. From 3 project on to the 45 degree line from XY to 4.
8. From 4 project vertically upwards to meet a horizontal line projected from 1 at 5.
9. 5 is a point on the required hyperbola.
10. Construct a number of points in the same manner as for 1 to 5 and draw a fair curve through the points so constructed to complete the hyperbola.

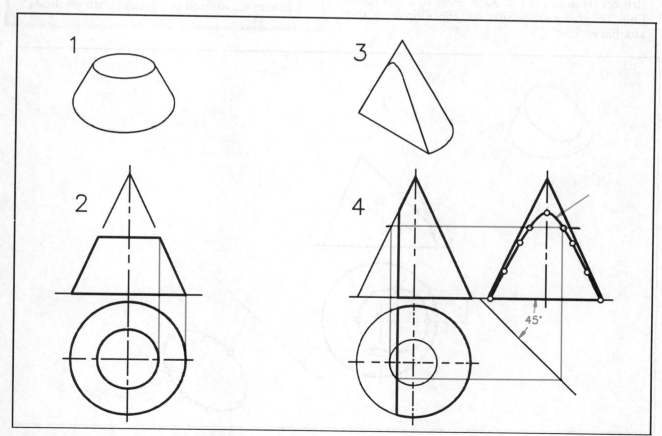

Figure 6.26 Circle and hyperbola as conic sections

The ellipse as a conic section

Constructions for ellipses have been described earlier (pages 43 to 44). Figure 6.27 describes the construction of an ellipse as a conic section.

1. Draw a Front view and a Plan of a cone to the dimensions given in Figure 6.27.
2. Draw X_1Y_1 parallel to the sloping face of the Front view. Draw the centre line of the auxiliary view at the same distance from X_1Y_1 as the centre line of the plan is from XY.
3. From 1 on the sloping face line of the Front view, project to 2 on the slope, line of the cone.
4. From 2 project vertically down to the centre line of the Plan to 3 and draw a circle, centred at the centre of the plan (4) and set to the point 3.
5. The circle 3 passes through a vertical from 1 on the Front view at 5 in the plan.
6. Measure the distance of 5 from the centre line of the plan with a compass and draw lines parallel to and at that distance each side of the centre line in the auxiliary view.
7. Project from point 1 at 90 degrees to cross these lines to give two points on the ellipse in the auxiliary view.

8. Plot other points in the same manner and draw a fair curve through the points so obtained to complete the ellipse.

Note: In this example, only the **True shape** of the sloping surface of the truncated cone has been constructed.

Notes:
- A **circle** is formed when a right cone is cut by a plane at right angles to the axis of the cone.
- A **hyperbola** is formed when a right cone is cut by a plane parallel to the axis of a cone.
- An **ellipse** is formed when a right cone is cut by a plane at an angle between 0 and 90 degrees to the axis of the cone.
- Projections from Front view to Plan to End view can be made by drawing either arcs from a point on the XY line or by projecting on to a line at 45 degrees to XY. The choice is left to the reader, who is, however, advised to practise both methods.

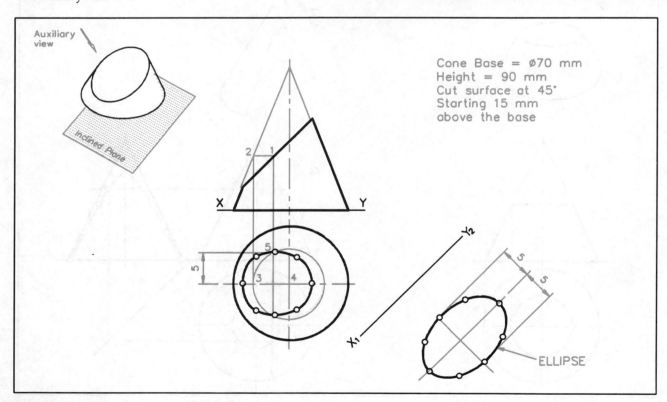

Cone Base = ⌀70 mm
Height = 90 mm
Cut surface at 45°
Starting 15 mm
above the base

Figure 6.27 Ellipse as a conic section

True shapes of sloping surfaces

The parabola as a conic section

Constructions for parabolas have been described earlier (pages 57 to 58). **Drawing 2** of Figure 6.28 describes the construction of a parabola as a conic section.

1. Draw the Front view and Plan of a cone to the dimensions given with **Drawing 1**.
2. Draw an X_1Y_1 line parallel to the sloping face of the cone in the Front view and draw a centre line parallel to X_1Y_1 and at the same distance from X_1Y_1 as the Plan centre line is from XY.
3. Draw a number of lines, A, B, C parallel to XY in the Front view. Taking the line A as an example, from 1 on the slope line of the cone, project down to 2 on the centre line in the Plan.
4. With a compass centred at the centre of the Plan and set to the point 2, draw a circle.
5. From 3 in the Front view project vertically down on to the circle to give point 4.
6. Set a compass to the length 5 and transfer the

length on to either side of the centre line in the auxiliary view, to give points 6 and 7.
7. Plot a number of other points in the same manner from the lines A, B and C and draw a fair curve through the points so obtained to complete the True shape of the sloping surface of the truncated cone. This true shape is a parabola.

Auxiliary view of a truncated hexagonal pyramid

Drawing 3 of Figure 6.28 is an orthographic projection of a truncated hexagonal pyramid showing a Front view, a Plan and an auxiliary view. The method of constructing the three views follows procedures already explained in recent pages. The reader is advised to draw the given three views using the descriptions given in earlier pages.

Note: A fourth conic section is a parabola. We therefore have described four conic sections – the circle, hyperbola, ellipse and parabola.

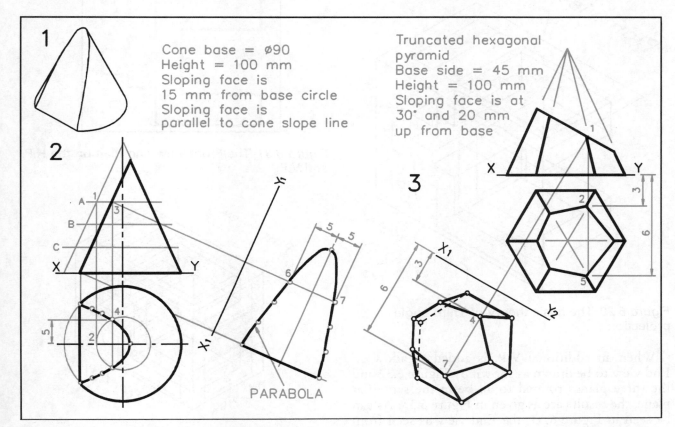

Cone base = ∅90
Height = 100 mm
Sloping face is 15 mm from base circle
Sloping face is parallel to cone slope line

Truncated hexagonal pyramid
Base side = 45 mm
Height = 100 mm
Sloping face is at 30° and 20 mm up from base

PARABOLA

Figure 6.28 True shapes of sloping surfaces

Third angle orthographic projection

Third angle orthographic projection was mentioned on page 85. Although nearly all the orthographic projections in this book will be in First angle, it is important the reader can recognise Third angle projections when he/she comes across them. The theory of planes behind Third angle projection is the same as for First angle, except the object to be drawn is placed in the Third angle of the H.P. and V.P. crossing planes. This results in the planes being placed in front of the object being drawn.

Figure 6.29 shows an object placed in the Third angle formed by an H.P. and a V.P. and the directions of viewing to see the Front view and Plan. In Figure 6.30, the object has been removed, leaving the outlines of a Front view on the V.P. and of a Plan on the H.P. When one of the two planes is rotated through 90 degrees so that both planes are lying flat together, the result is as shown in Figure 6.31 – with the Plan above the Front view.

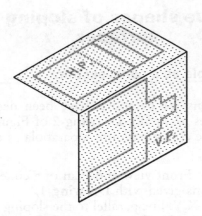

Figure 6.30 The H.P. and V.P. with the object removed

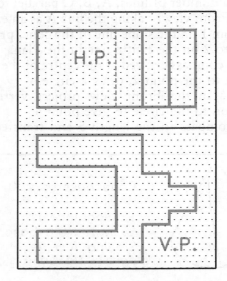

Figure 6.31 The Front view and Plan on the H.P. and V.P.

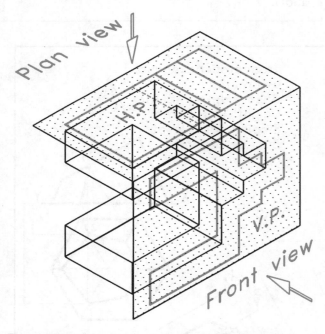

Figure 6.29 The basic theory of Third angle projection

When an additional V.P. is added to allow an End view to be drawn as shown by Figure 6.32 and the three planes rotated to all be in the same flat plane, the results are as given in Figure 6.33. As can be seen in Figure 6.33, the End view as seen from the **left** is drawn on the **left** of the Front view.

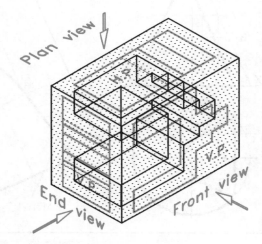

Figure 6.32 Adding a second V.P.

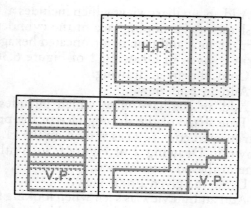

Figure 6.33 Three views in Third angle projection

Thus in Third angle orthographic projection:
- The Plan is **above** the Front view.
- An End view as seen when looking from the left is drawn to the **left** of the Front view.
- An End view as seen when looking from the right of the Front view is drawn to the **right** of the Front view.

■ CHECK YOUR UNDERSTANDING

● The theory of orthographic projection is based upon the object to be drawn being placed in space with a horizontal plane (H.P.) below the object and other planes – vertical (V.P.) and inclined – being placed behind, to the sides of or at angles to, the object.

● Two angles of orthographic projection are in use – First angle and Third angle projection.

● In orthographic projection the Front view is not necessarily the front of the object, but the view chosen to give the best information about the object as seen in a Front view.

● In First angle projection:
  a) The Plan is placed below the Front view.
  b) An End view as seen from the left is placed on the right of the Front view.
  c) An End view as seen from the right is placed on the left of the Front view.
  d) The front faces of End views and Plans face outwards away from the Front view.

● In Third Angle projection:
  a) The Plan is placed above the Front view.
  b) An End view as seen from the left is placed on the left of the Front view.

  c) An End view as seen from the right is placed on the right of the Front view.
  d) The front faces of End views and Plans face inwards towards the Front view.

● Other views are possible, e.g. a Plan as seen from below; a Front view as seen from behind.

● A truncated solid is one that has been cut by a plane and had part of the solid removed.

● When laying out drawings in orthographic projections:
  a) Drawing sheets may be placed vertically – 'portrait' layout, or horizontally – 'landscape' layout.
  b) Add a border (margin) line all around the sheet of drawing paper:
      ● 10 mm for A4 sheets.
      ● 15 mm for A3 sheets.
      ● 20 mm for A2 sheets.
  c) Include a title block with printing, mostly in capital letters:
      ● 6 mm high for A4 sheets.
      ● 8 mm high for A3 sheets.
      ● 10 mm high for A2 sheets.

REVISION EXERCISES AND QUESTIONS

Exercises

1 A Front view and a Plan of a truncated rectangular prism is given in **Drawing 1** of Figure 6.34. Copy the given two views and add an End view on the right of the Front view and an auxiliary view which includes the True shape of the sloping surface of the prism.

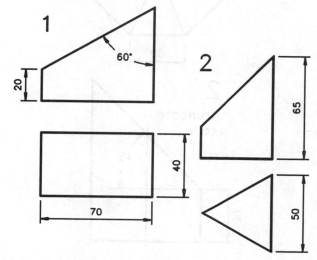

Figure 6.34 Exercises 1 and 2

2 A Front view and a Plan of a truncated equilateral triangular prism is given in **Drawing 2** of Figure 6.34. Draw the two given views and add an End view to the right of the Front view and an auxiliary view which includes the True shape of the sloping surface of the prism.

3 A Front view and a partly completed Plan of a truncated octagonal pyramid is given in **Drawing 1** of Figure 6.35.
a) Copy the two given views.
b) Complete the Plan.
c) Add an End view.
d) Add an auxiliary view which includes the True shape of the sloping surface of the pyramid.

4 A Front view of a truncated cylinder is given in **Drawing 2** of Figure 6.35.
a) Copy the given Front view.
b) Add a Plan.
c) Add an End view which includes the truncated surface.

d) Add an auxiliary view which includes a True shape of the sloping face of the cylinder.

5 A Front view and Plan of a truncated hexagonal prism is given in **Drawing 1** of Figure 6.36.
a) Copy the given drawing.
b) Add an End view.
c) Add an auxiliary view which includes the True shape of the sloping face of the prism.

6 A truncated cone rests as shown on the H.P. as shown in **Drawing 2** of Figure 6.36. With the cone in the position shown:
a) Draw the given Front view.
b) Add an End view as seen when looking from the right – this End view should therefore be drawn on the left of the given Front view.
c) Add a Plan.
d) Add an auxiliary view which includes the True shape of the truncated face of the cone.

7 **Drawing 1** of Figure 6.37 is a pictorial view of a *fork connector* within a grid of lines drawn at 20 mm intervals. To determine the lengths of

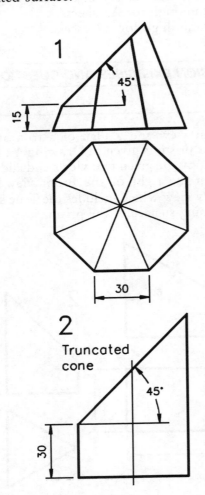

Figure 6.35 Exercises 3 and 4

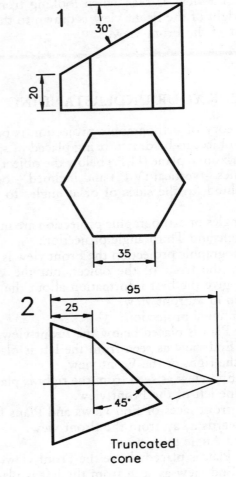

Figure 6.36 Exercises 5 and 6

any part of the *fork connector*, count along the grid lines and multiply by 20.
a) Draw a Front View, an End View and a Plan of the *fork connector*.
b) Fully dimension your views.

8 Drawing 2 of Figure 6.37 is a pictorial view on a grid of lines of a *clip*. The grid lines are at 20 mm intervals.
a) Draw a full size orthographic three-view projection of the *clip*.
b) Fully dimension your views.

Top 100 x 45
Thickness of top = 5
Back = 20 x 10
Holes = ⌀20

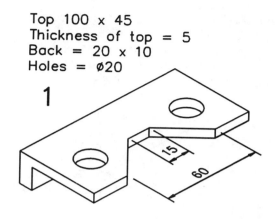

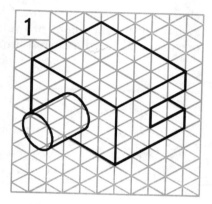

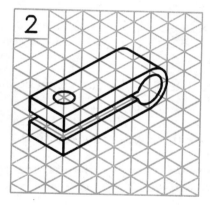

Figure 6.37 Exercises 7 and 8

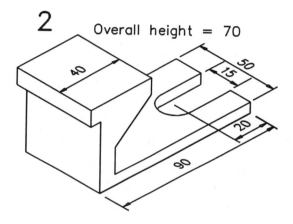

Figure 6.38 Exercises 9 and 10

11 Figure 6.39 is a pictorial dimensioned drawing of a *tee connector*.
a) Construct an accurate three-view orthographic projection of the *connector*.
b) Fully dimension your views.

9 A pictorial, dimensioned drawing of a *radius location plate* is shown in **Drawing 1** of Figure 6.38.
a) Draw an accurate three-view orthographic projection of the *plate*.
b) Fully dimension your views.

10 Drawing 2 of Figure 6.38 is a pictorial dimensioned drawing of a *switch contact*.
a) Construct an accurate three-view orthographic projection of the CONTACT.
b) Fully dimension your views.

Outer cylinder
= 140 x ⌀80
Hole = ⌀60

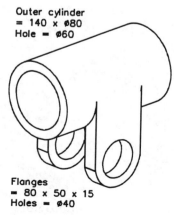

Flanges
= 80 x 50 x 15
Holes = ⌀40

Figure 6.39 Exercises 11

12 Figure 6.40 is a pictorial dimensioned drawing of a *slide block*.
   a) Construct an accurate three-view orthographic projection of the *slide block*.
   b) Fully dimension your views.

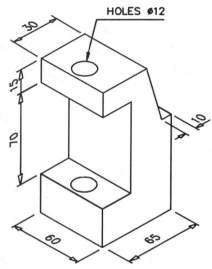

HOLES ⌀12

Overall height = 110 mm

Figure 6.40 Exercises 12

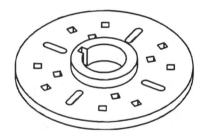

Figure 6.41 Exercise 13 – pictorial view of lathe face plate

Figure 6.42 Exercise 13 – photograph of the face plate

13 There are three illustrations to support this exercise:
   • Figure 6.41 is a pictorial drawing of a *lathe face plate*.
   • Figure 6.42 is a photograph of the *face plate*.
   • Figure 6.43 shows the dimensions of the *face plate* and its various parts.
   a) Draw suitable borders and title block on an A3 sheet of paper.
   b) Construct an accurate three-view orthographic projection of the *face plate*.
   c) Include hidden lines and centre lines to your views.
   d) Fully dimension your drawing.
   e) Include suitable lettering in the title block, together with a statement of the angle of projection and the dimension units.

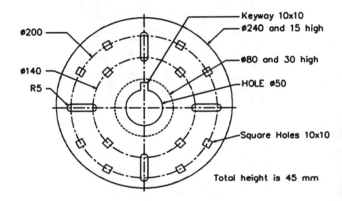

Keyway 10x10
⌀240 and 15 high
⌀80 and 30 high
HOLE ⌀50
Square Holes 10x10
Total height is 45 mm
⌀200
⌀140
R5

Figure 6.43 Exercise 13 – dimension details of the face plate

14 There are three illustrations to support this exercise:
   • Figure 6.44 is a pictorial drawing of a *pivot from a robot*.

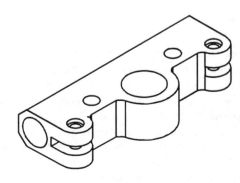

Figure 6.44 Exercise 14 – pictorial view of a joint link

- Figure 6.45 is a photograph of the *pivot*.
- Figure 6.46 shows the dimensions of the *pivot* and its various parts.
  a) Draw suitable borders and title block on an A3 sheet of paper.

Figure 6.45 Exercise 14 – a photograph of the joint link

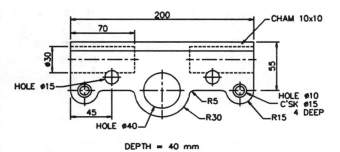

DEPTH = 40 mm

Figure 6.46 Exercise 14 – Dimension details of the joint link

b) Construct an accurate three-view orthographic projection of the *pivot*.
c) Include hidden lines and centre lines to your views.
d) Fully dimension your drawing.
e) Include suitable lettering in the title block, together with a statement of the angle of projection and the dimension units.

Questions

1 Make a freehand sketch of any article and draw a front view of the article you have sketched.
2 Many articles are made up of geometrical solids – cubes, cuboids, cones, cylinders, pyramids. Make freehand sketches of an article which is constructed mainly from such solids and draw the Front view and End view of the article.
3 Sketch a three-view orthographic projection of a part from a car or lorry. Then attempt a drawing from your sketch using technical drawing equipment.
4 What do you think was the use of the *rod clamp* shown in a photograph on page 92?
5 State a use for the *support bracket* shown in the photograph on page 95.
6 Drawing 1 of Figure 6.38 is a drawing of a *radius plate*. State a use for this plate.

Surface development

Introduction

In order to manufacture articles from sheet materials, such as cardboard, tinplate, sheet steel, sheet copper, etc., drawings showing the development of the surfaces of the articles will be required. The methods of surface developments rely upon:

> 1. Constructing the true lengths of edges of parts of the development.
> 2. Constructing the true shapes of surfaces of the development.

In this chapter you will learn how to construct the surface developments of some common solids – prisms, pyramids, cylinders and cones, and how to develop the surfaces of articles made from sheet materials – paper, cardboard, sheet metal.

When constructing surface developments it is very important to make sure that you have found correct true lengths of edges and true shapes of surfaces.

Pictorial views and the surface developments of three rectangular prisms, such as might be parts of packaging made from sheet cardboard, are shown in Figure 7.1. The dimensions of the prisms are:

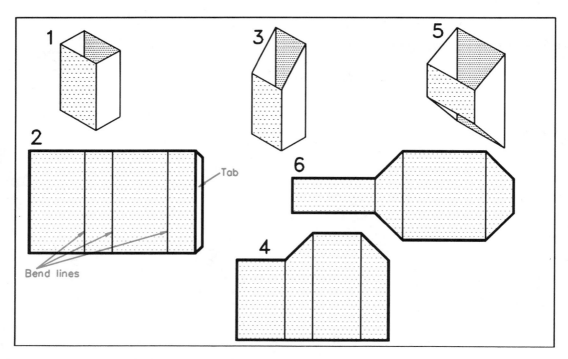

Figure 7.1 Developments of rectangular prisms

Drawings **1** and **2** – Base rectangle 20 mm ×
   12 mm; height 70 mm.
Drawings **3** and **4** – Base rectangle 20 mm ×
   12 mm; height 75 mm; truncated at 45 degrees.
Drawings **5** and **6** – Base rectangle 60 mm ×
   12 mm; height 65 mm; truncated top and bottom
   at 45 degrees.

Cardboard packages require gluing tabs to allow
them to be held together. Drawing 2 includes a
gluing tab. However it is unusual to include tabs in
development drawings because many will be for
sheet metal articles, the edges of which may be
soldered or brazed or welded. In such cases the
person making the articles must decide whether
tabs (or other forms of additions) are required to
manufacture the article from the development
drawing.

The surface developments of the three prisms in
Figure 7.1 are straightforward, requiring no ex-
planations. The lines along which the parts of the
developments are to be bent should be included in
the drawings.

You are advised to work the three examples to
the dimensions already given.

Developments of surfaces of rectangular prisms

DRAWINGS 1 and 2 – Figure 7.2.

1. Draw the Front view and Plan of the truncated
   prism to the given sizes.
2. Construct the development of the four sides of
   the prism.
3. Construct the true shape of the upper face (the
   top) of the truncated prism.
4. Complete the surface development of the sides
   and top of the prism as shown, including all
   bend lines.

DRAWINGS 3 and 4 – Figure 7.2.

1. Draw the Front view and Plan of the truncated
   prism to the given sizes.
2. Construct the development of the four sides of
   the prism.

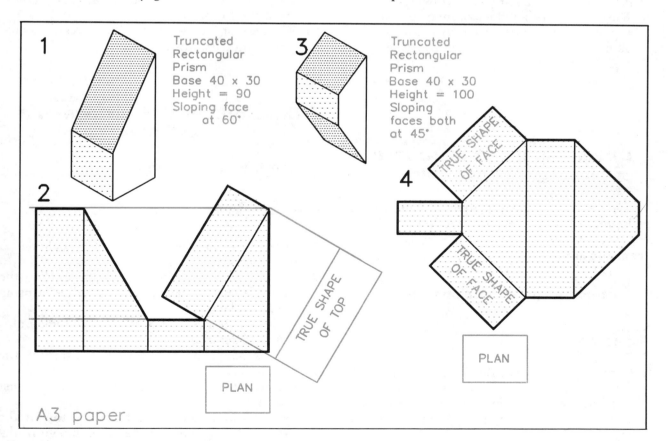

Figure 7.2 Developments of surfaces of rectangular prisms

3. Construct the true shape of the two sloping faces of the truncated prism.
4. Complete the surface development of the sides and top of the prism as shown, including all bend lines.

Notes:
- Before constructing a surface development it is usually necessary to draw orthographic projections of the article and to project from the views in the projection to obtain the required true lengths and true shapes for the development. In these two examples Front view and Plans have been drawn. The Front views have been included as part of the finished development.
- In these two examples, the true shapes of the vertical faces of the prisms are easily constructed from the Front view and Plan.
- Surface developments are usually referred to as 'developments'.
- All bend lines are included in the two developments.
- No tabs are included in the drawings.
- The term **parallel development** is often applied to this type of construction – for obvious reasons – lines within the development are drawn parallel to each other.

Development of truncated hexagonal pyramid

This type of development is often known as **radial development** because many of the lines in the development are radial from a point, requiring the use of compass arcs.

To construct the given development

Figure 7.3.

1. Draw the Front view, End view and Plan of the truncated pyramid to the given dimensions. The End view and Plan of the truncated surface are constructed following the example given on page 96.
2. Note that the Front view does not include any

true lengths or true shapes of any edges or faces. Thus the development is worked from the End view because the edge A1 and the lengths AB, AC and AD are true lengths.
3. With a compass centred at A and with a radius A1 draw an arc.
4. Set a compass to the edge length of the octagonal base of the pyramid (30 mm) and starting at 1, strike arcs along the arc centred at A to give the points 2, 3, 4, 5, 6 and 1. The two lines A1 are the edges which would be joined together to form the pyramid from the development.
5. Join A to the divisions along the arc centred at A with straight lines.
6. Draw horizontal lines from intersecting points in the End view of the truncation surface to give B, C and D along line A1.
7. With a compass centred at A and set to AB, AC and AD in turn, draw arcs to the lines between A and the divisions along the arc centred at A.
8. Complete the development of the sides of the pyramid as shown.
9. Construct the true shape of the sloping face from the Front view.
10. The base of the pyramid will be a regular octagon of side lengths 30 mm.

Development of surface of a cylinder

To construct the development

Figure 7.4.

1. Draw the Front view and Plan of the cylinder to the dimensions given in Figure 7.4.
2. Draw a horizontal line of length equal to the circumference of the circle of the cylinder, using the formula:
   Circumference $= 2 \times \pi \times R$ – in which:
   π is taken as being 3.14,
   R is 35 – the radius of the circle of the cylinder.
3. Project verticals from each end of the line just drawn.
4. Project a horizontal line from the top of the Front view to complete the development of the vertical surface of the cylinder.

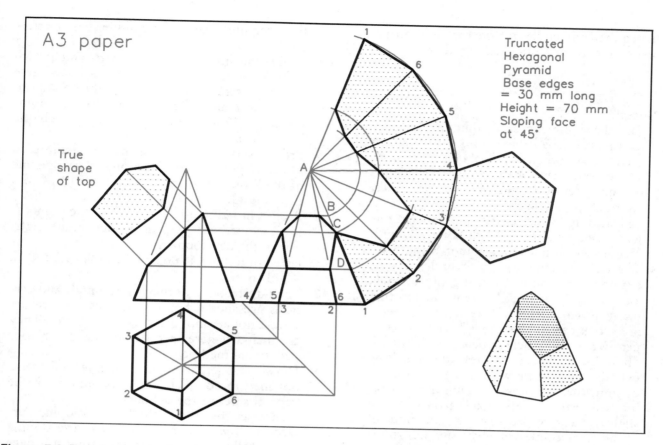

Figure 7.3 Development of truncated hexagonal pyramid

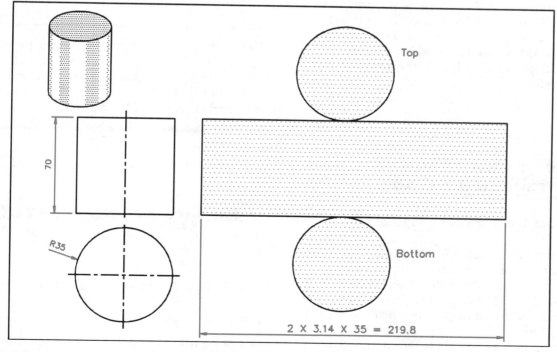

Figure 7.4 Development of surface of a cylinder

5. If required add circles for the top and bottom of the cylinder, each of cylinder radius.

> **Notes:**
> - The developments shown in this chapter have all been shaded in colour to distinguish them from other parts of the drawings. There is no need for the reader to shade his or her developments in this manner, although it is a fairly common practice to add shading to surface developments in this way – either shading with a pencil, with crayons or with a water colour wash.
> - The circumference of the cylinder in this example was found by using the formula $2\pi R$ (or πD). It must be remembered that many developments will be drawn for making articles from sheet metals such as copper. When the article is being made, it will often be necessary to beat the resulting cylinder into shape with mallets, hammers or some form of press machine. This working will cause some materials to stretch slightly. The more accurate method of finding a circumference by using a formula may not be as suitable as stepping off one twelfth of the circle in the Plan 12 times along a line forming the base line of the development. This in effect is stepping off 12 chord lengths and not 12 arc lengths and, as a result, is not as accurate as using the formula to find the required base length – a chord length being slightly shorter than an arc length.

Development of surfaces of truncated cylinder

To construct the example – Figure 7.5:

1. Draw the Front view and Plan of the truncated cylinder to the given sizes.
2. Divide the Plan circle into 12 equal parts with the aid of a 30, 60 set square – to give the divisions on the circumference marked 1 to 12 in the Plan.
3. Project a line horizontally from the base of the Front view and mark off along its length the circumference of the cylinder base circle – $2\pi R$.
4. Divide this line into 12 equal parts and at each point so obtained draw a vertical line. These lines represent the verticals from the points 1 to 12 in the Plan – they can therefore be numbered 1 to 12 in the same way as they are in the Plan circle.
5. Project vertically up from the Plan from each of the 12 points in the Plan onto the slope line of the Front view – to give points A, B, C, D, E, F and G.
6. Project horizontally from each of the points A to G to intersect with their appropriate verticals in the development – thus point A is projected onto lines 1; point B onto lines 2 and 12 – and so on.
7. The intersections of these horizontals and verticals are shown by small circles. The reader should not attempt drawing these circles. They are included here in order to make the constructional method clear.
8. Draw a fair curve through the points so obtained to complete the development of the vertical sides of the cylinder.
9. Construct the true shape for the sloping surface to obtain the development of the sloping face – following the methods shown on page 101.
10. If a base is required it will be a circle of the cylinder base diameter.

> **Note:** When cylinders and/or cones are to be developed, common practice is to divide the base circle into 12 equal parts with the aid of a 30,60 set square. The reader will come across this method again in later pages.

Surface development of cones

DRAWINGS 1 and 2 – Figure 7.6.

Another radial development.

1. Draw a Front view and a Plan of the cone to the given sizes (see page 114).

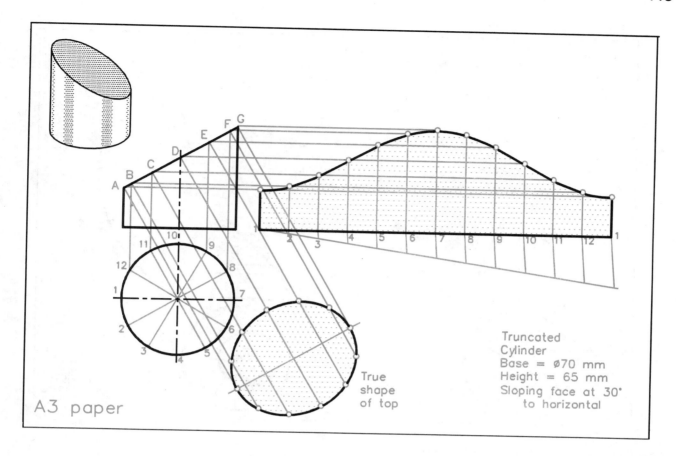

Figure 7.5 Development of surfaces of truncated cylinder

2. Divide the base circle into 12 equal parts with the aid of a 30,60 set square.

3. Project from each of the 12 points on the circumference of the Plan onto the base line of the Front view.

4. From each of the points on the base of the Front view draw lines to the apex of the cone A.

5. With a compass centred at A and of radius A1 draw an arc.

6. Set a compass to the chord length of one of the divisions in the Plan circumference – such as from 1 to 2.

7. Step off the length 12 times along the arc centre A.

8. Draw a line from the 12th division (marked 1) to the apex A to complete the development.

DRAWINGS 3 and 4 – Figure 7.6.

1. Draw the Front view and Plan to the given sizes.

2. Divide the circle in the Plan, draw an arc from A and step off divisions along the arc as in Drawing 2.

3. Join each of the points numbered 1 to 12 to 1 on the arc to A.

4. Project from the 12 points in the Plan onto the base in the Front view. Join each point to the apex A.

5. Where these lines meet the slope line of the cone in the Front view project lines horizontally.

6. Taking the point C as an example – it is on lines 3 and 11. From C project horizontally on to the slope line of the cone.

7. With a compass set to the length from A to where the horizontal from C meets the slope line, draw an arc centred at A to meet lines 3 and 11 from the arc of the development.

8. Find the other points from the horizontals in the same way.

9. Draw a fair curve through the points to complete the development.

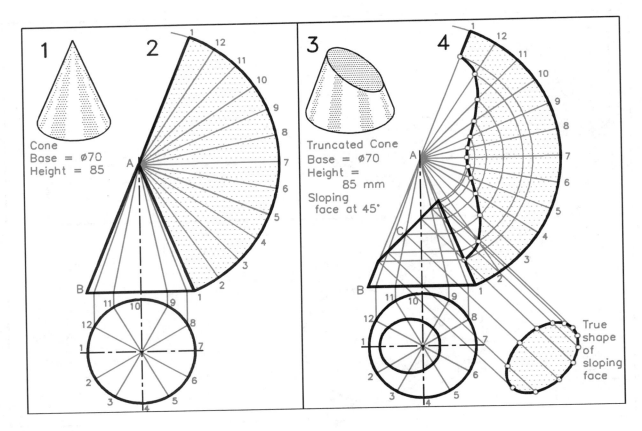

Figure 7.6 Surface development of cones

10. The development of the sloping face of the cone is found by constructing its true shape, following the procedure given on page 101. If a development of the base is required, it will be a circle of base diameter.

Lines of intersection and developments – 1

Two examples are shown here of the lines where two equally shaped solids meet at an angle of 90 degrees. The two examples are a joint of two square pipes and another of two hexagonal pipes. In both cases, the **line of intersection** (as it is called) is a straight line at 45 degrees to each of the solids. No matter what the shape (the 'sectional' shape) of the solids, if they are both equal, the line of intersection will be at 45 degrees if the solids meet at 90 degrees. If two solids of equal shape section meet at angles other than 90 degrees, the line of intersection forms an angle of half the angle at which the two parts meet.

DRAWINGS 1 and 2 – Figure 7.7.

1. Draw the Front view and Plan of the intersecting pipes to the dimensions given in Figure 7.7.
2. Draw a base line for the development of one of the pipes and mark 4 equal divisions of 35 mm (the pipe edge length) along the line. Draw verticals at these points.
3. Project from the Front view as shown to obtain the true shape of each of the sides.

DRAWINGS 3 and 4 – Figure 7.7.

1. Draw a Front view and the End view of the hexagonal section of the pipe as shown. Work to the given dimensions.
2. Project a line from the base and step off six 20 mm divisions along this line – six hexagon edge lengths.
3. Project from the Front view downwards on to each line in turn.
4. Draw lines between the points so obtained to complete the development.

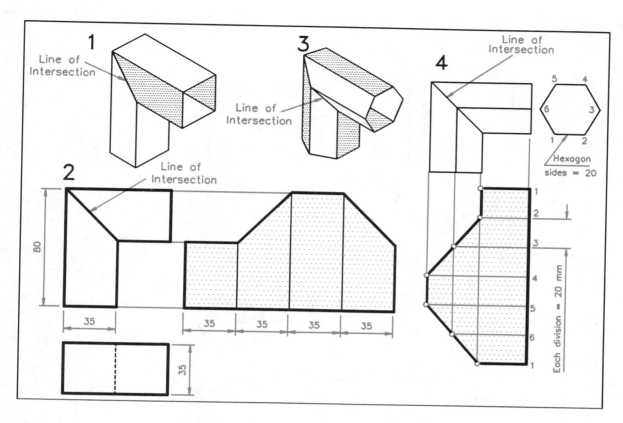

Figure 7.7 Lines of intersection and developments – 1

Note: In each example only one part of the two making up the intersecting joints has been developed. This is because the second development in each case would be the same as the first.

Lines of intersection and developments – 2

Two further examples of pipes of equal section meeting at 90 degrees are shown here. In the first, the two pipes are equal size cylinders. In the second the two pipes are equal size hexagonal pipes. The second example is not the same as that given on page 114 – because the hexagons of the pipes have been turned through 60 degrees.

DRAWINGS 1 and 2 – Figure 7.8.

1. Draw the Front view and Plan of the joining cylinders to the given sizes (see page 116).
2. Divide the circle of the pipe in the Plan into 12 equal parts.
3. From the Front view project the base line of the vertical cylinder and mark off along it the length of the cylinder circumference to obtain the base for the development of one of the pipes.
4. Divide this base line into 12 equal parts and draw verticals at each division point – points 1 to 12 to 1.
5. Project from the 12 points in the Plan circle up to the intersection line of the pipes.
6. Project from each of the points so obtained onto their respective vertical lines in the development.
7. Draw a fair curve through the points so obtained to complete the development.

DRAWINGS 3 and 4 – Figure 7.8.

1. Draw the Front view and the outline of the

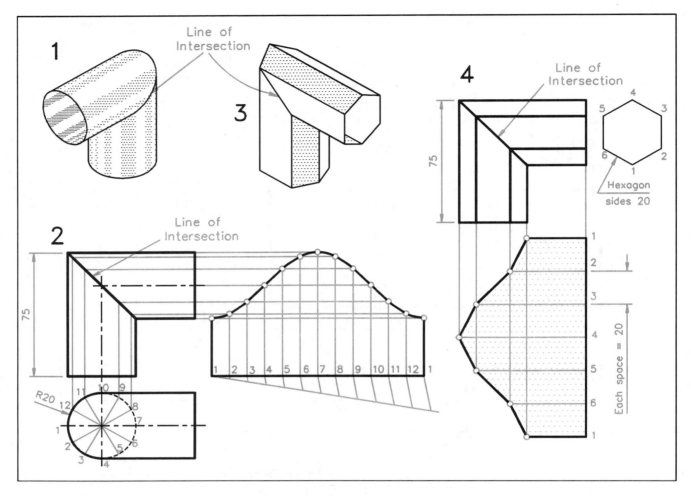

Figure 7.8 Lines of intersection and developments – 2

hexagon of the pipe in its proper position in relation to the Front view.

2. Following the methods given with Example 2 in Drawings 3 and 4 (Figure 7.7) page 115, complete the development as shown.
3. Draw a base line for the development – six equal 20 mm spaces.
4. Project from the Front view onto the horizontals from the 20 mm points.
5. Join the points so obtained in the development with straight lines.

Note: Once again when dealing with a cylinder, the circumference has been divided into 12 equal parts.

Developments of intersecting pipes

In the previous examples of intersections, the pipes have joined at right angles. In this example one 60 mm diameter cylindrical pipe is meeting another at an angle forming 60 degrees between the two cylinders. Because the developments of the two parts of the join are not the same, both have been constructed.

1. Draw a Front view and a Plan of the intersecting pipes (Figure 7.9). In the Plan, the upper circle of the sloping pipe is seen as an ellipse.
2. Draw the development of the vertical cone before the hole for the intersecting pipe is constructed – its base is 3.14 × 60 mm long.
3. Divide half of the Plan circle into 6 equal parts and project from the divisions onto the lines of intersection in the Front view.

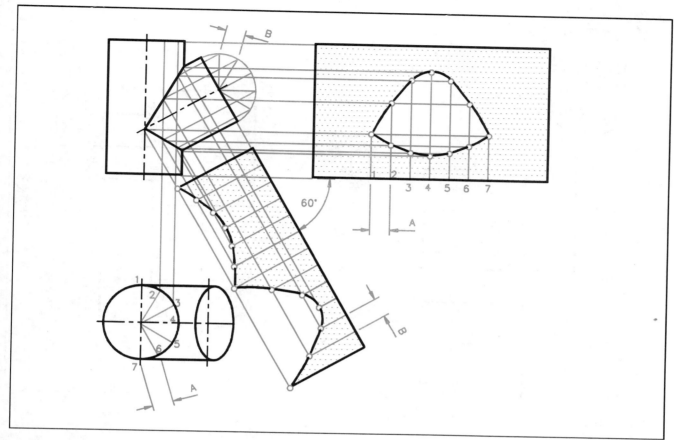

Figure 7.9 Developments of intersecting pipes

4. The hole for the intersecting pipe is cut in only one side of the vertical cylinder. Thus only 6 of the 12 divisions – 3 each side of a vertical line through the middle of the pipe are required. The spacings between these divisions is taken from A in the Plan.

5. Project horizontally from the points on the lines of intersection in the Front view onto their respective verticals in the development.

6. Draw a fair curve through the points so obtained to complete the hole in the development.

7. Working in a similar manner construct the development of the sloping pipe.

8. Start by drawing a semi-circle on the end of the pipe in the Front view.

9. Mark off the length B from the semi-circle in the Front view 12 times along a line projected at 60 degrees from the end of the sloping pipe.

10. Project lines from the 6 divisions of the semi-circle on to the lines of intersection.

11. Where these lines meet the lines of intersection project at 60 degrees on to the 12 spaced lines in the development.

12. Draw a fair curve through the points so obtained to complete the required development.

Lines of intersection between cylinders — 1

The previous examples of lines of intersection between cylinders dealt with cylinders of the same diameter. The two examples detailed below are of lines of intersection between cylinders of different diameters.

DRAWINGS 1 and 2 – Figure 7.10.

1. Draw the Front view and Plan of the two intersecting cylinders to the sizes given in Figure 7.10 (see page 118).

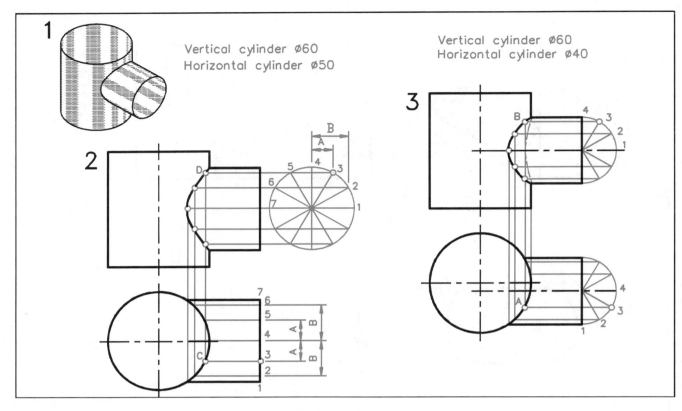

Figure 7.10 Lines of intersection between cylinders – 1

2. Draw a circle in line with the smaller cylinder in the Front view and divide it into 12 equal parts. Only the points 1 to 7 are numbered.
3. Project horizontal lines from these divisions on the circle.
4. Set a compass to the distances A and B in turn and transfer them to A and B in the plan to determine points 1 to 7 in the Plan.
5. Project from 2 to 6 in the Plan onto the circumference of the larger circle. One such point is labelled C.
6. Project from the points so obtained onto the lines projected from the circle at the end of the Front view. One such point is labelled C in the Front view.
7. Draw a fair curve through the points to complete the line of intersection between the two cylinders.

DRAWING 3 – Figure 7.10.

The procedure follows the same steps as for Drawings 1 and 2:

1. The two cylinders do not meet on a common centre line, part of the line of intersection will show as a hidden detail line.
2. Distances between Front view and Plan were determined from semi-circles divided into 6 equal parts.
3. Follow the projection of lines from the two points labelled 3.
4. From 3 in the semi-circle in the Front view project a line horizontally.
5. From 3 in the Plan project a line onto the larger circle to give A.
6. From A project vertically up to give the point B on the line from 3 in the Front view. B is on the line of intersection.

Lines of intersection between cylinders – 2

In this example the line of intersection between two cylinders of different diameters, with the smaller cylinder meeting the large at an angle of 60 degrees is shown. Only the development of the larger cylinder is shown (Figure 7.11).

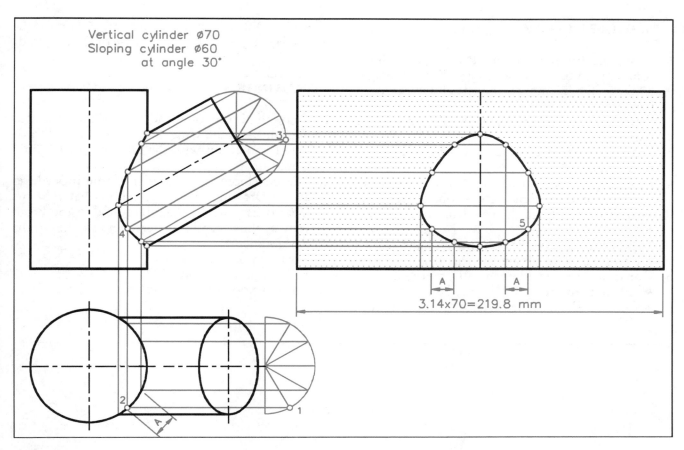

Figure 7.11 Lines of intersection between cylinders – 2

1. Draw a Front view and Plan of the two cylinders.
2. Draw a semi-circle in line with the smaller cylinder in both Front view and Plan.
3. Divide the semi-circles into 6 equal parts.
4. The method of plotting points on the lines of intersection between the two cylinders is demonstrated by the sequence from 1 to 4.
5. From 1 on the semi-circle in the Plan, project to 2 on the larger circle in the Plan. From 2 project a line vertically upwards. From 3 on the semi-circle in the Front view project a line to meet the line from 2 at 4. The point 4 is on the required line of intersection.
6. Plot other points in the same manner and draw a fair curve through the points to obtain the line of intersection.
7. Construct the development of the larger cylinder before plotting points for the hole in its surface.
8. Transfer distances from the larger circle in the Plan onto the development – as the example A.
9. To plot points on the hole outline follow the example given by point 5 projected from point

4 on the line of intersection onto a line drawn vertically from the measured distance A.
10. Plot other points in a similar manner and draw a fair curve through the points so obtained to complete the hole outline.

Development by triangulation – 1

Examples of surface developments involving parallel line development and radial development have been described in the previous pages of this chapter. One of the more important methods of constructing developments is by **triangulation**. Three simple examples are given here. It should be noted that sheet metal workers use development by triangulation methods more frequently than other methods, but triangulation can involve complex constructions beyond the scope of a book of this nature.

DRAWINGS 1 and 2 – Figure 7.12.

1. Draw the Front view and Plan of an oblique square pyramid – base edges 60 mm; height 80 mm; apex 25 mm to the left above centre of base.
2. Draw a horizontal line through the centre of the plan.
3. With a compass centred at E and radius EA draw the arc AF.
4. From F project vertically up on to a line from the base of the Front view – join to E in the Front view to obtain the true length of the edge EA.
5. Repeat for the edge ED on the left hand side of the two views, to obtain the true length of ED.
6. Construct the development – **Drawing 2**:
   • EA and EB are each the true length of EA.
   • EC and ED are taken from the true length of ED.

• CA, AB, BD and DC are each 60 mm – the edge length of the square base of the pyramid.

DRAWINGS 3 and 4 – Figure 7.12.

1. Draw the Front view and Plan of the truncated pyramid – to the same dimensions as for Drawings 1 and 2, but with the top truncated 30 mm from the apex.
2. The development follows the same procedures as for Drawings 1 and 2, except that the true lengths EH and EJ must be found in the Front view as shown and transferred on to lines in the development:
   • EH on lines EA and EB.
   • EJ on lines EC and ED.
3. The development can now be completed.

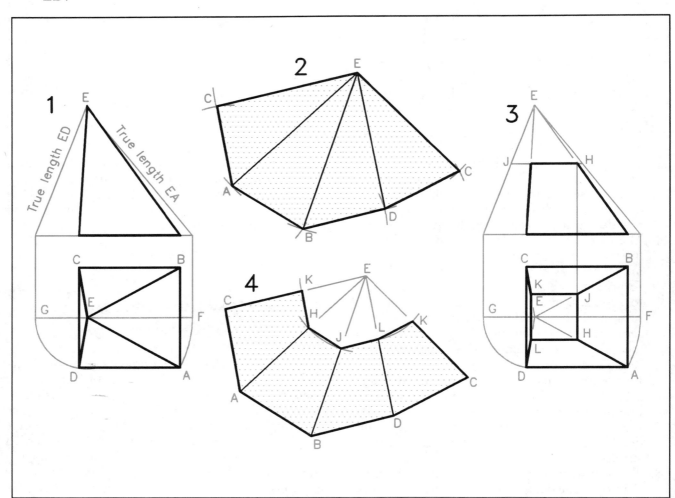

Figure 7.12 Development by triangulation – 1

Development by triangulation – 2

Figure 7.13.

This example shows the development of a transition piece – a sheet metal device which is placed between other sheet metal devices to change the shape of an outlet to an inlet or vice versa. The example could be used to change the inlet from a square of 60 mm sides (ABCD) to the smaller square (EFGH), or vice versa.

1. Draw the Front view and Plan of the transition piece to the given dimensions.
2. The development consists of a series of triangles of side lengths the same as the true lengths of the parts of the transition piece. Thus EF in the development is equal to EF in the plan; JB is equal to JB in the Front view; BE is equal to BE as seen in the Front view; BC is equal to BC in the Plan and so on.

Figure 7.14 is a photograph of a transition piece

made from sheet steel. The inlet side – the square top, is changed to a circular outlet at the bottom.

Figure 7.14 A photograph of a typical transition piece which would require developing by triangulation

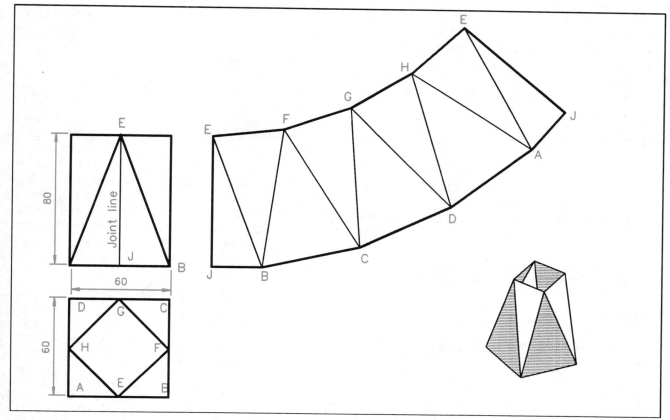

Figure 7.13 Development by triangulation – 2

CHECK YOUR UNDERSTANDING

● All surface development constructions depend upon finding:
  a) **True lengths** of edges.
  b) **True shapes** of surfaces.
    Always make sure that you have found correct true lengths and true shapes. It is very easy to make mistakes about these two important features of surface developments.
● There are three types of construction used in surface development method:
  a) **Parallel line development.**
  b) **Radial development.**
  c) **Development by triangulation.**
● The **circumference of a circle** is found by:
  Circumference = 2πR (or πD)
● Common practice when constructing developments of circular parts is to divide the circle circumference into 12 equal parts with the aid of a 30,60 set square.
● The **line of intersection** between two identical solids will be a straight line.
● The line of two identical solids meeting at 90 degrees will be a line at 45 degrees to either of the axes of either solid.
● The line of intersection between two identical solids meeting at angles other than 90 degrees will still be a straight line, but will slope at an angle bisecting the angle at which the solids meet.
● The line of intersection between two unequal solids will have to be plotted by taking plot lines through the solids.
● When constructing developments for articles made from cardboard, gluing tabs may be necessary.
● When constructing developments for articles to be made from sheet metals or plastics, common practice is to ignore gluing or jointing tabs and to leave such features to the judgement of those who will be making the article from the development.

REVISION EXERCISES AND QUESTIONS

Exercises

1 Figure 7.15 is a pictorial drawing of a cardboard package box. Construct a development of the surfaces of the box, including suitable tabs for gluing the development together.
2 Figure 7.16 is a Front view of a lamp shade fitted to a wall, together with a pictorial view of the shade. The shade consists of a truncated

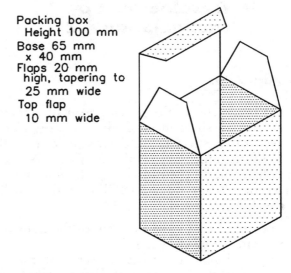

Packing box
Height 100 mm
Base 65 mm
 x 40 mm
Flaps 20 mm
 high, tapering to
 25 mm wide
Top flap
 10 mm wide

Figure 7.15 Exercise 1

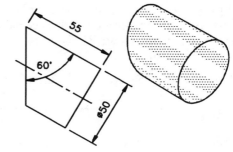

Figure 7.16 Exercise 2

cylinder made from plastic sheet. The light fitting for the bulb for the light shade is held in a hole of 25 mm diameter cut in the centre of the elliptical part of the shade which fits against the wall.
  Construct a full size development for the shade to include the elliptical part with its hole.
3 Figure 7.17 is a pictorial view of the sides of a stand to be made from plywood. Construct a full-scale development of each of the four parts of the stand.

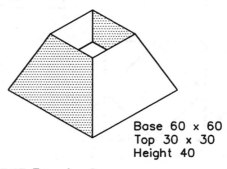

Base 60 x 60
Top 30 x 30
Height 40

Figure 7.17 Exercise 3

4 Figure 7.18 is a pictorial drawing of a funnel to be made from tinplate. It consist of three parts:
a) The funnel – in the form of a truncated cone.
b) A lipping in the form of a cylinder.
c) A spout in the form of another truncated cone.

Construct a full size development for each part of the funnel. You will find difficulty in constructing a development for the spout if you try to treat it as a cone. It is better to assume the spout is made up from a series of triangles and construct the development by triangulation.

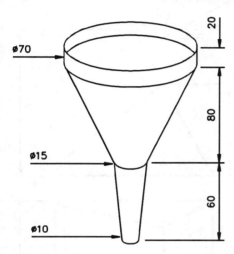

Figure 7.18 Exercise 4

5 Figure 7.19 shows two views in orthographic projection of a cylinder truncated at both top and bottom as shown. Construct a full size development of the sides of the cylinder and add a base and a top.

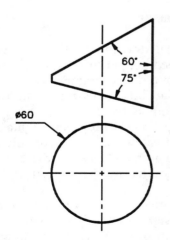

Figure 7.19 Exercise 5

6 Two regular hexagonal pipes meet at right angles as shown in Figure 7.20. Construct a full size development of both parts of the assembly.

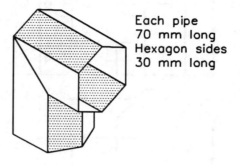

Each pipe
70 mm long
Hexagon sides
30 mm long

Figure 7.20 Exercise 6

7 Figure 7.21 shows a Front view and a Plan of two cylinders meeting at right angles, but with their centre lines in different planes. The line of intersection between the two cylinders in the Front view has not been included.

Copy the two views full size and add the line of intersection accurately constructed.

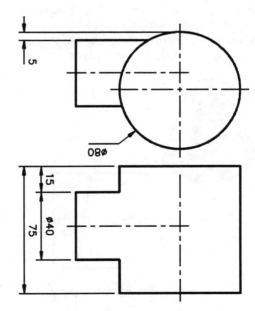

Figure 7.21 Exercise 7

8 Figure 7.22 (page 124) is a Front view and Plan of a cylinder jointed to a hexagonal prism at right angles. The line of intersection between the two solids has not been included in the Front view.

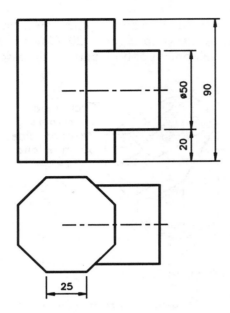

Figure 7.22 Exercise 8

Copy the two given views and include the line of intersection in the Front view.

9 An intersection piece for fixing between a circular opening and a square one is shown in Figure 7.23, together with a Front view and Plan of the intersection piece.

Construct a full-scale development of the surface of the intersection piece.

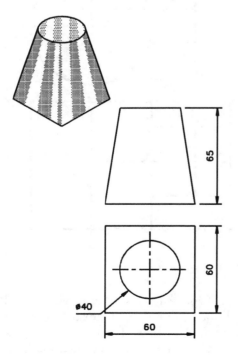

Figure 7.23 Exercise 9

10 A rectangular pyramid has been cut by a sloping face as shown in the pictorial drawing of Figure 7.24. A Front view and a Plan of the solid is included.

Copy the given two views and construct a full development of all parts of the surfaces of the solid, including its top and its bottom faces.

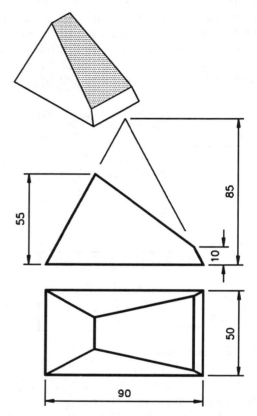

Figure 7.24 Exercise 10

Design exercises

1 The pictorial drawing of Figure 7.25 shows a funnel shaped hopper into which plastic granules are to be poured. The granules are to be stored in a rectangular box into which an open-ended truncated cone is fixed.
a) Working on scrap paper make several freehand sketches of a suitable transition piece for joining between the bottom of the hopper outlet to the top of the truncated cone.
b) When satisfied that you have a reasonably good design, draw a three-view orthographic projection of your design working to a scale of 1:5.

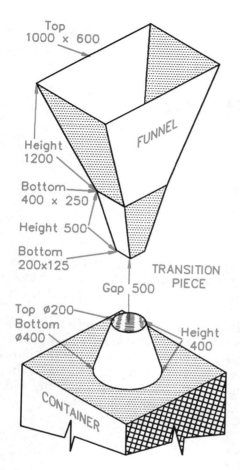

Top
1000 × 600

FUNNEL

Height
1200

Bottom
400 × 250

Height 500

Bottom
200×125

TRANSITION
PIECE

Gap 500

Top ⌀200
Bottom
⌀400

Height
400

CONTAINER

Figure 7.25 Design Exercise 1

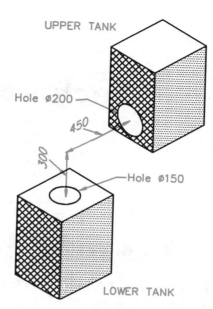

UPPER TANK

Hole ⌀200

450

300

Hole ⌀150

LOWER TANK

Figure 7.26 Design Exercise 2

c) Make an accurate development of the transition piece you have designed.

Note: because of the sizes of the parts for this exercise, you will have to choose a scale smaller than 1:1. The scale you choose is left to your judgement.

Questions

1 Construct the development of a cube of 60 mm edge lengths. Cut out the development from strong paper. Include gluing tabs and join the sides of your cut-out to form the cube.

2 Construct the development of a hexagonal pyramid with base edge lengths 40 mm and height 80 mm. Cut out the development from strong paper and build up the pyramid.

3 If you can find a cardboard cylindrical tube, saw, or cut across the tube at 45 degrees and join the two parts together to form intersecting cylinders at right angles.

4 Try making a simple small-scale model of a single storey house from cardboard.

c) Construct three surface developments as follows:
   i) Of your design – to a scale of 1:5.
   ii) Of the two parts of the hopper funnel, working to a scale of 1:10.
   iii) Of the open-ended truncated cone fixed to the rectangular box – working to a scale of 1:5.

2 A tank for holding fuel oil (the upper tank of Figure 7.26) is to be connected to another tank (the lower tank of Figure 7.26) by a transition piece which has not yet been made.

a) Working on scrap paper, make freehand sketches of suitable designs for the connecting transition piece.

b) Make an accurate orthographic projection of the best of the designs you have sketched.

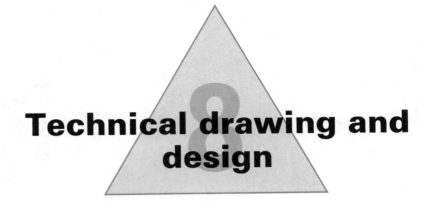

Technical drawing and design

Introduction

Technical drawing is a major method of communicating and exchanging design ideas in industry. Before looking at more aspects of technical drawing we will look at designing in general, but it must be remembered that this book is about technical drawing. The purpose here is to show how technical drawing fits into the overall design process. A number of design processes can be seen in various books. Although other design processes may appear different to those described here, if you look at others carefully, you will see a general pattern in them all.

Figure 8.1 describes a design process in a circular flow chart form. Why is it circular? This is because unless a completed design is suitable for the purpose for which it has been designed and made, the designer will have to go back to the beginning and start all over again. In the given flow chart:

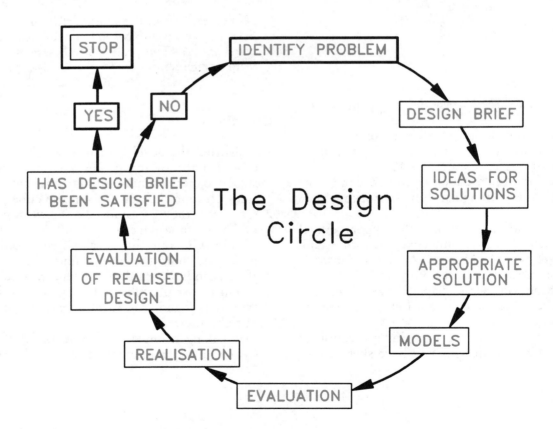

Figure 8.1 A flow chart describing a design process

- **Identify problem**: what is it that the design is supposed to do? Why is the design being thought out and made? When starting to design anything, it is a good idea to state the problem which the design is supposed to be solving in a few brief notes.
- **Design brief**: having noted what the problem is, state in a few brief sentences what it is that is to be designed. Everything that is to be designed should start with such a design brief. The brief gives the terms of reference for the design. When the design has been completed, one should be able to check back to the design brief to see if the brief has been satisfied.
- **Ideas for solutions**: this is where technical drawing becomes an important part of designing. At this stage, any ideas about how the design brief can be tackled should be written down and also drawn – technical drawings are the best method of showing design ideas in a graphical form.
- **Appropriate solution**: again, technical drawing is an important part at this stage. The best of the solutions is chosen and accurate technical drawings of this chosen solution are made.
- **Models**: it may be necessary at this stage to make a model from the drawings of the chosen solution. These may be full size or scale.
- **Evaluation**: check whether the drawings are correct; check the model for suitability for solving the design brief. If the model is a working device, it may be given a whole range of tests to check whether its working parts are satisfactory.
- **Realisation**: make the design.
- **Evaluation of realised design**: does the completed design answer the design brief? Does the design solve the problem for which it has been made. If it is a device which moves or has moving parts, a range of tests may also be needed as part of the evaluation.
- **Has the design brief been satisfied**: if the answer is NO, then start again. If the answer is YES, the design process will stop. At this stage the design may go forward for manufacture in quantity. If it is a one-off design, the design process stops.

Note: in manufacturing industries, once a design has gone into manufacture, improvements of its design may well be needed from time to time. If faults show up in the design when it has been put to use, further work may be needed in order to solve the problems shown up by the faults.

The place of technical drawing in designing

As seen above, technical drawings play an important part in design problem-solving. In this book we are not dealing with the designing and making of articles, but only with the drawing skills so important in the design process. Because of this, the examples and exercises contained in its pages are based on:

1. Sufficient examples, exercises and practice for the reader to learn the skills necessary for constructing technical drawings.
2. A number of exercises which will give the reader some practice in designing graphics using the technical drawing skills which have been learned in the preceding chapters.

Some examples of simple graphics design

The following exercises are examples in the designing of simple graphics using technical drawing skills. The reader should be able to construct the answers to these exercises but if help is needed, references are included with each exercise stating the page(s) on which the technical drawing knowledge for constructing the answers can be found.

Design Exercise 1

Figure 8.2 (page 128) gives the sizes of an A4 sheet of drawing paper in a portrait layout position. Figure 8.3 (page 128) is a design for a folder or folio cover for storing A4 size sheets of drawings made during technical drawing classes. The cover could be made from stiff paper or card, from manila card or from paper glued to cardboard. It could also be the cover of a stiff A4 file holder envelope.

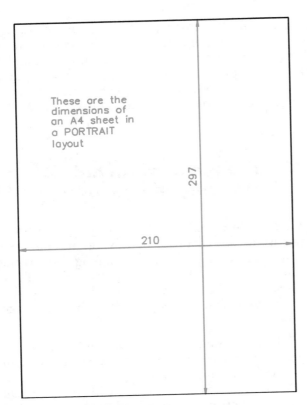

Figure 8.2 Design Exercise 1 – sheet sizes

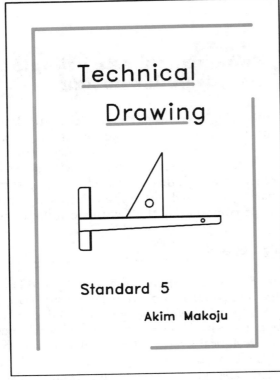

Figure 8.3 Design Exercise 1 – an example of an answer

1. Copy Figure 8.3 with your own name in place of the name on the given cover design.
2. Then, on spare sheets of paper and working freehand, sketch a number of designs you think would be suitable for a cover of a folio for your own drawings.
3. When you are satisfied you have a good design for the cover, working with instruments, make a full size accurate drawing of your design. Colour may be included in your design if you think fit. Refer to pages 10 to 12.

If you usually work on A3 size drawing sheets, make your cover designs to a size suitable for that size of sheet. What are the dimensions of an A3 size sheet of drawing paper?

Design Exercise 2

The left hand drawing in Figure 8.4 shows a design for a car wheel trim based on a regular pentagon. When a car wheel trim is clipped into place, it must be remembered that a flow of air is needed to cool down the brake drums or discs and this requires holes in the trims.

1. Working to the details given in the left hand drawing of Figure 8.4, construct the given drawing.
2. In the right hand drawing of Figure 8.4, a start has been made on a second design for a wheel trim based on a regular hexagon.
3. Working freehand on a spare piece of paper make freehand sketches for suitable designs for the right hand drawing of Figure 8.4. When satisfied you have a satisfactory design, and

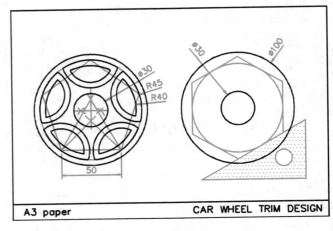

Figure 8.4 Design Exercise 2

working with instruments, complete the right hand drawing.

Design Exercise 3

Figure 8.5 shows three regular polygons – a square, a pentagon and a hexagon. The drawings include a method of dividing the base sides of the square and pentagon into three equal parts. An interleaved pattern of bands has been included in the square and hexagon.

Copy the given drawings of Figure 8.5 and add a similar interleaved set of bands in the pentagonal polygon.

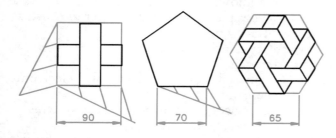

Figure 8.5 Design Exercise 3

Design Exercise 4

Figure 8.6 shows the initials of the author of this book intertwined to form a monogram.

1. Working freehand on spare pieces of paper design similar monograms for the three examples included in Figure 8.6.

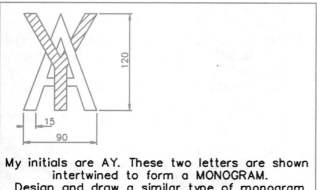

My initials are AY. These two letters are shown intertwined to form a MONOGRAM.
Design and draw a similar type of monogram for the initials of:
1. West Africa 2. E.Africa 3. Your own name

Figure 8.6 Design Exercise 4

2. When satisfied you have good designs for each of the monograms, working with instruments, make accurate drawings of your designs.
3. Colour or shading may be added to your designs if you think fit.

Design Exercise 5

Figure 8.7 is a sketch map drawn with technical drawing instruments. The map is not particularly accurate, but was drawn to describe the route from the town A to the offices and headquarters of an engineering company.

1. Copy the given map as accurately as you can. Remember it is a sketch map so, providing it clearly informs whoever is using it of a good route, its accuracy as to scale or distance does not matter.
2. Now draw a sketch map of your own district showing a route between your own town or village to some other destination. First sketch out your ideas freehand on spare paper, then make an accurate drawing, with instruments, of the design chosen from your freehand sketches.

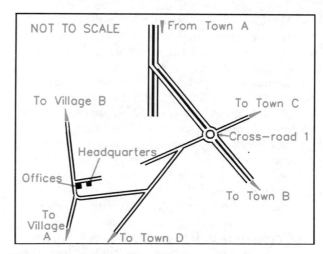

Figure 8.7 Design Exercise 5

Other aspects of the design process

An essential part of all design work is the investigation which must take place into features such as safety, control systems, materials, structures, energy usage, how a design is to be powered, its final appearance, its shape and form and its aesthetic quality (its beauty).

When a draughtsman is required to produce drawings for a design, the information on which the design is based will usually be included with the instructions for producing the drawings. Nevertheless, the following aspects of designing may have to be considered by the person making the drawings:

- **Safety**: an important consideration – particularly if a design includes control systems such as electrical, electronic, pneumatic or other circuits. The safety of structures must be considered; any fire hazards must be taken into account. The necessary safety devices which need to be incorporated in such designs will need to be shown in the drawings for the design.
- **Energy and power**: if the design is one which is to be driven by some form of power, which is the best and most efficient form?
- **Control system circuits**: circuits involving electrical, electronic or pneumatic components may be included in some designs. Mechanisms – controls by pulleys, gears, and bearings, may also be part of a design. A knowledge of the symbols and methods of drawing these is required.
- **Structures**: technical drawings often include structures of various types. The draughtsman may have to know safety limits under a variety of conditions.
- **Materials**: a knowledge of the materials most suitable for the design being drawn will be necessary. Features such as strength, durability, hardness, workability, colour, appearance, finishes, fire resistance, etc. will need to be considered.
- **Speed and noise**: problems may exist regarding these features as they affect the design.

■ CHECK YOUR UNDERSTANDING

- Technical drawing plays an important part in the design process.
- Although we are concerned with technical drawing, the problems involved in designing must be borne in mind.
- The design process involves:

a) Stating the problem to be solved.
b) A design brief.
c) An investigation on which sketches and drawings of possible solutions can be made.
d) Select best solution.
e) If necessary make a model.
f) Evaluate the chosen solution.
g) Make (realise) the chosen solution.
h) Evaluate the realised design.
i) Test the model (if made).
j) Has the design brief been satisfied?
k) If NOT, start from the beginning.
l) If YES the design is satisfactory.

- Even a satisfactory design may need redesigning.
- Although not primarily technical drawing problems some knowledge of the following features as they affect designing is needed in order to construct successful drawings:

a) Safety considerations.
b) Materials.
c) Circuit design – electrical, electronic, pneumatic.
d) A knowledge of pulley and gear systems.
e) A knowledge of bearings.
f) An appreciation of problems caused by fire, speed and noise.
g) Some knowledge of problems affecting structures.
h) Energy and power.

REVISION QUESTIONS

1 Figure 8.1 shows a flow chart in circular form describing the design process. Redraw the flow chart in a vertical form.
2 Explain the term in the flow chart *identify problem*.
3 What is a *design brief*?
4 Why do you think it is often necessary to make a model of a proposed design when designing any article?
5 Describe the term *realisation* when used in connection with designing.
6 Why is technical drawing important in the design process?
7 Name some features other than the actual drawing involved which you must consider when designing an article.
8 Why must so much consideration be given to safety during the designing of an article?
9 What is meant by shape and form?
10 What is the *Golden Mean*?

Working drawings

Introduction

Every article made in industry requires that technical drawings (most often orthographic projections) are required before the article can be manufactured. These drawings give details of the shape, form and sizes of the article to be made. These drawings are **working drawings**. They are the drawings from which engineers, builders, architects and other such people work. In this chapter we will be dealing with the many types of working drawing which are commonly used in industries.

Sectional views

Sectional views, or **sections** (as they are usually described), are frequently found in orthographic projections. Sections allow the draughtsman to show the inside shape of the objects being drawn. Figure 9.1 shows the basic idea behind sections.

In Figure 9.1, **Drawing 1** is a pictorial view of a *post support* – a device for holding a cylindrical post firmly upright. In order to see the shape of its internal parts, it is imagined that the support has been cut in half by a plane passing vertically through its centre – as shown in **Drawing 2**, fol-

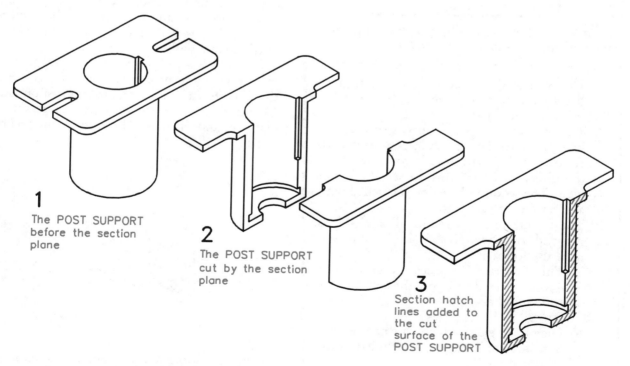

1
The POST SUPPORT before the section plane

2
The POST SUPPORT cut by the section plane

3
Section hatch lines added to the cut surface of the POST SUPPORT

Figure 9.1 The basic idea of sectioning

131

lowed by the front half being removed – **Drawing 3**. The shape of the cut surface is emphasised by a series of parallel lines drawn at an angle – usually at 45 degrees – **hatch lines**.

Figure 9.2 below is a two-view, First angle orthographic projection of the *post support*. The two views are a Plan and a sectional Front view. Note the following features in the two views of Figure 9.2:

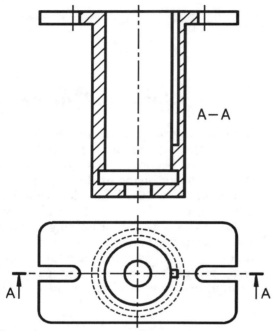

Figure 9.2 A First angle orthographic projection which includes a sectional view A-A

1. The plan of the section plane which gives rise to the sectional view is shown by a section plane line.
2. The section plane line consists of a centre line with two short thick lines at each end. Arrows against the thick end lines show the direction of viewing to see the Front view. The section plane line is labelled with a letter (A) at each end.
3. The Front view is a sectional view – it is referred to as Section AA. In Section AA, note the following:
   a) Thin lines at 45 degrees and either 3 or 4 mm apart drawn on the cut surface showing the section cut. These lines are known as **hatch lines**.
   b) Details of parts which can be seen behind the cut surface are included in the sectional view.
   c) The section is labelled with the same letters as the section plane line in the plan as A-A.
4. In this example, the section plane line is in the Plan. Section planes can be placed in any view, depending upon which is the best way in which to show the internal shape of the object being drawn. Thus one can have a sectional Front view, a sectional End view or a sectional Plan. Examples of each type of sectional view will be given in later pages of this book.

Exceptions to the general rules of sectioning

The following features within sectional views are always shown by outside views within a section:

- Bolts, nuts, washers, screws, spindles, webs and ribs, spokes of wheels, fasteners of any type.

Two examples of these exceptions are given in Figures 9.3 to 9.6. Figure 9.3 is a pictorial view of a plate holding a cylindrical locking spindle with a square base. As can be seen in the Plan and Section A-A of Figure 9.4, the spindle is shown by an outside view within the sectioned base.

Figure 9.5 is a photograph of a *tool grinding rest* from a grinding machine. The platform on which the tool rests as it is being ground is supported by a 10 mm thick web, between the underside of the platform and the parts of the rest, which is fixed to

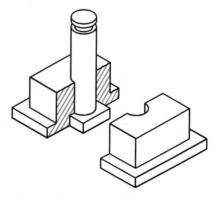

Figure 9.3 Some features within a section are shown by outside views

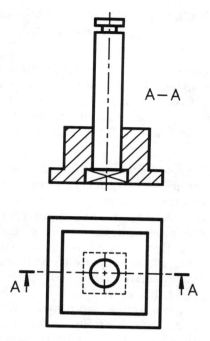

A–A

Figure 9.4 A feature shown by an outside view within a section

the machine. Figure 9.6 is a three-view First angle orthographic projection of the *tool grinding rest*. Note the following in Figure 9.6:

Figure 9.5 A photograph of a *tool grinding rest*

1. The section plane line A-A cuts the End view.
2. The End view is on the left of the Front view – it is therefore the view as seen when looking from the right of the Front view.
3. The Front view is the Section A-A.
4. In Section A-A, the web is shown by an outside view – it is not hatched.

Figure 9.6 Webs and ribs in sections are shown by outside views

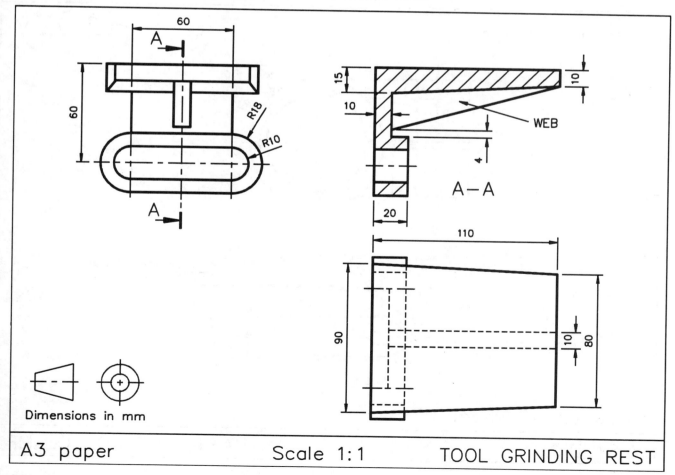

Dimensions in mm

A3 paper   Scale 1:1   TOOL GRINDING REST

ISO symbols of orthographic projection

Many orthographic projections will include ISO symbols for First or Third angle projection instead of stating the angle in words. The two symbols are shown in Figure 9.7. Each of the symbols are two-view First or Third angle projections of a truncated cone.

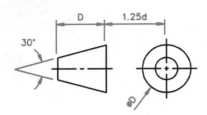

First angle projection

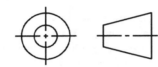

Third angle projection

Figure 9.7 ISO symbols of orthographic projection
Figure 9.8 Part drawing of Part 1 of a *rod clamp*

Part drawings and assembly drawings

The three-view orthographic projection Figure 9.10 is an **assembly drawing** of a *rod clamp*. It is assembled from five parts, each of which require its own orthographic projection **part drawing** – these are shown in Figure 9.8 and Figure 9.9.

Notes:
1. The part drawings Figure 9.8 and Figure 9.9 are dimensioned – in order that the parts can be manufactured to their correct sizes.
2. Figure 9.9 is an **exploded** orthographic drawing. The four parts it describes are placed in positions as if they were removed in line with the places into which they are to be fitted.
3. The draughtsman making the parts drawings may decide that parts 2, 3, 4 and 5 (Figure 9.9) should each have its own drawing sheet.
4. The assembly drawing Figure 9.10 does not include dimensions – it has been drawn to show how the parts are to be assembled.
5. The assembly drawing Figure 9.10 includes a **Parts list**. This states the materials used and the finishes to be applied.
6. The assembly drawing includes the statement DO NOT SCALE THIS DRAWING. This

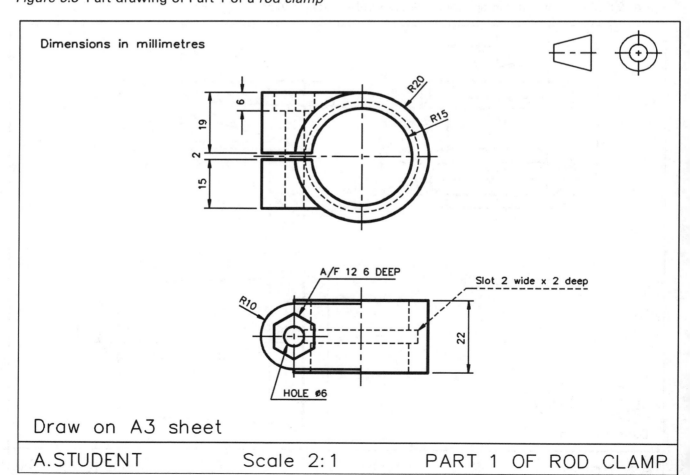

Dimensions in millimetres

Draw on A3 sheet

A.STUDENT   Scale 2:1   PART 1 OF ROD CLAMP

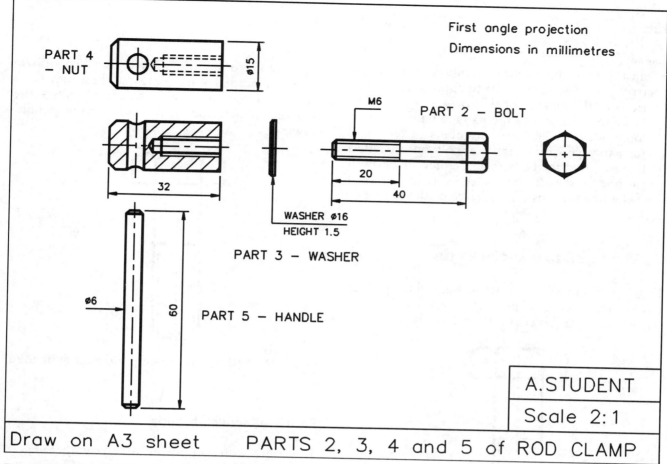

PART 4 – NUT

⌀15

PART 2 – BOLT

M6

20

40

32

WASHER ⌀16
HEIGHT 1.5

PART 3 – WASHER

⌀6

60

PART 5 – HANDLE

A.STUDENT

Scale 2:1

Draw on A3 sheet   PARTS 2, 3, 4 and 5 of ROD CLAMP

Figure 9.9 Part drawing of Parts 2, 3, 4 and 5 of the *rod clamp*
Figure 9.10 An assembly drawing of the *rod clamp*

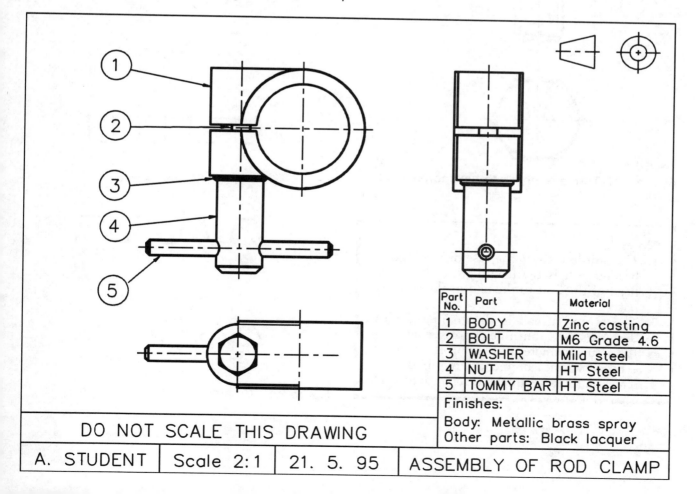

Part No.	Part	Material
1	BODY	Zinc casting
2	BOLT	M6 Grade 4.6
3	WASHER	Mild steel
4	NUT	HT Steel
5	TOMMY BAR	HT Steel

Finishes:

Body: Metallic brass spray
Other parts: Black lacquer

DO NOT SCALE THIS DRAWING

| A. STUDENT | Scale 2:1 | 21. 5. 95 | ASSEMBLY OF ROD CLAMP |

means that dimensions should not be taken from the drawing in order to apply such dimensions to the making of the parts.

Note the numbers of the parts in **balloons**. Balloons – circles enclosing numbers or letters to refer to parts of the drawing. Balloons include a line pointing to the part and either an arrow if the line finishes at a line on the drawing, or a dot if the line finishes on a surface of the drawing.

Screw threads

Figure 9.9 and Figure 9.10 included bolts which have screw threads. Figure 9.11 gives details of the terms used with bolts and their threads.

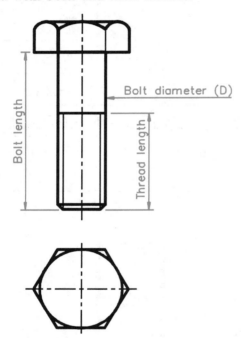

Figure 9.11 Terms referring to hexagonal headed bolts

Notes:
1. The **bolt length**, in the case of a hexagonal headed bolt is the length from under the head of the bolt to the end of the screwed part.
2. The **screw thread** is shown in technical drawings as a thin line. Its distance from the actual diameter of the bolt is estimated – no actual measurement is required.
3. The bolt thread diameter is referred to as D.

Figure 9.12 shows the sizes used when drawing hexagonal headed bolts. Note that these may not be the sizes if compared with the actual bolts – they are sizes for constructing the bolts within technical drawings.

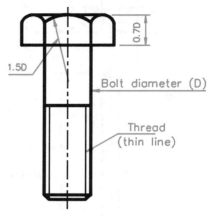

Figure 9.12 Sizes for drawing hexagonal headed bolts

Forms of screw threads

There are different forms of screw threads, the most common are shown in Figure 9.13.

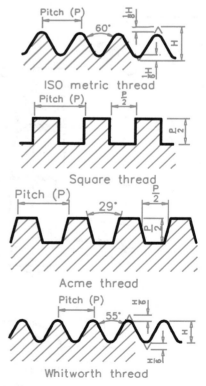

Figure 9.13 Common forms of screw threads

ISO metric thread

Possibly the most common screw thread in use at present. ISO metric threads are designated by the letter M preceding the diameter of the screw. There are three classes of fit for ISO metric threads, but the reader need only concern himself with the Medium class of fit which is by far the most commonly used in general engineering.

Other classes such as Close and Free are only used for specific purposes. Depending upon the diameter of the screw thread the Pitch of the screw varies – the larger the diameter the greater the Pitch.

Some examples of the Pitch relationship with the diameter in ISO metric Medium threads are:

Diameter	Pitch
6 mm	1.0 mm
8 mm	1.25 mm
12 mm	1.75 mm
20 mm	2.5 mm
24 mm	3 mm

Occasionally a different thread pitch is required for a special purpose, in which case the thread would be specified as e.g. M20 × 3.5. If, however, no Pitch is shown the ISO metric screw M20 would be assumed as having a Pitch of 2.5 mm. An example is given in Figure 9.14 (**Drawing 2**).

If a screw thread is not ISO metric, its description should be included in its dimensions, as shown in **Drawing 3** of Figure 9.14.

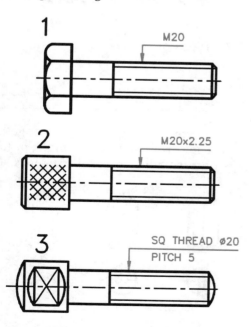

Figure 9.14 Dimensioning screw threads

Lock-nuts

In order to ensure that nuts do not work loose through vibration under working conditions of the machine of which they are a part, lock-nuts of various types are often used for engineering purposes. A number of these are shown in the following illustrations. These only show a few of the large number of different types of locking devices for making sure that nuts stay in place.

- Figure 9.15 is a Plan and sectional Front view of a locking tab. The tab is placed under the nut, which is tightened. The tab is then bent to retain the nut in place.

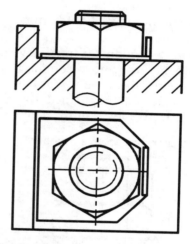

Figure 9.15 A nut locking tab

- Figure 9.16 is another form of tab, held in position with a small locking screw.

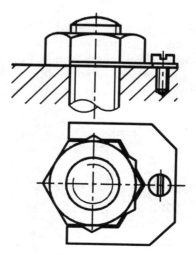

Figure 9.16 Another form of nut locking tab

- Figure 9.17 consists of a Front sectional view and an End sectional view. A hammer blow each side of the lock-nut bends the projection on the nut slightly, locking the nut against the screw.

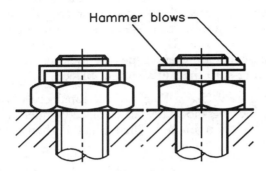

Figure 9.17 A nut locked by light hammer blows

- Figure 9.18 is a sectional Front view through what is probably the most common form of lock-nut. Note the thicker nut is above the thinner. The two nuts are tightened together and form a very effective lock on the screw thread.

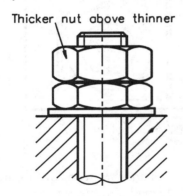

Figure 9.18 The commonest form of lock-nut

- Figure 9.19 is a sectional Front view of a Simmonds lock nut. This nut is very often found in modern motor vehicle engines in positions where vibration of movement of the vehicle is liable to loosen a nut.

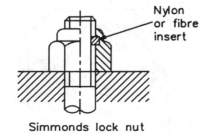

Figure 9.19 A Simmonds lock nut

Screws

Many types of screws are used for engineering purposes. A few of the more common screws are shown in Figure 9.20. Note that the screw length depends upon the shape of the screw head. In fact the screw length is the effective length for holding two parts together with the screw. Figure 9.20 also includes the drawing sizes when drawing these forms of screws. Again these sizes are for drawing purposes only and may not be the same as those found when measuring the actual screw.

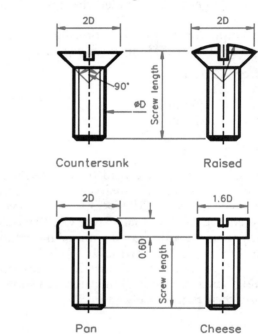

Figure 9.20 Types of screws

Set screws

Set screws are for holding small parts together in assemblies. They are found, for example, in fittings of pulleys onto spindles in small machines. Many

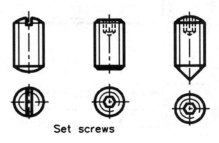

Figure 9.21 Three types of set screws

types of set screws are available, three of which are shown in Figure 9.21 in Front views and Plans. Some set screws are tightened with the aid of a screwdriver. Some are tightened with a hexagonal Allan key.

Studs

Figure 9.22 is a Front view of a stud. **Studs** are usually found for such features as bolting the parts of a petrol engine together.

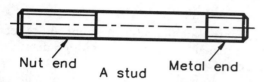

Nut end   A stud   Metal end

Figure 9.22 A stud

Drawing a hexagonal bolt and its nut

Figure 9.23 describes the sequence for drawing an

ISO metric hexagonal bolt and a hexagonal nut of diameter 20 mm. Follow the procedure:

Stage 1

Draw the outlines of the bolt and nut to the given sizes. The position of the nut does not matter a great deal, but make sure it will be on the screw thread when your drawing is completed.

Stage 2

Set a compass to 1.5D (60 mm in this example), and with the compass centred in an appropriate position on the bolt centre line draw the arcs as shown. The arcs for the nut are the same as those for the bolt head.

Stage 3

To complete the drawing of the bolt and nut:

1. Set a compass to about 0.5D and draw the smaller arcs on the bolt head and nut. Some experimenting with the size may be needed. If you have a radius curve, it is much easier to use this piece of equipment to draw the small arcs.
2. Draw the end of thread line.
3. Draw the thread lines. Although these can be drawn at the suggested 5 mm from the bolt

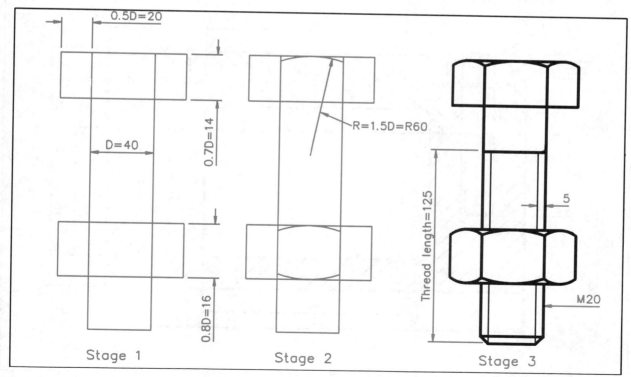

Figure 9.23 Drawing a hexagonal bolt and its nut

edges, this size is not very important, but your thread should 'look right' and not be too far away from the bolt lines or too near to them.

4. Add the chamfer lines at the bottom of the bolt.
5. Line in your drawing and erase any unwanted lines.
6. Add a title which includes your name and the title A BOLT AND NUT. Use capital letters in your title.

Notes:
- Remember that the sizes in this drawing are not the actual sizes of the bolt and nut. They are only the drawing sizes.
- Not all nuts are chamfered top and bottom as in this example.

An example of the use of studs

Figure 9.24 is a sectional Front view through a cast iron container to which a top has been bolted with the aid of studs.

- Working to the sizes included with the drawing make a full size copy of the sectional Front view.

Types of sections

A number of different types of sections will be seen in technical drawings.

Half sections

Figure 9.25 is a Plan and a half sectional Front view of a collar. In **half sections**:

1. The centre line defines the extent of the section.
2. It is unusual to include any hidden detail in half sections.
3. Half sections should only be drawn where both sides of the sectional view are symmetrical – i.e. the same shape as each other.

Half sections avoid having to draw two or more views. All information about the shape of an object can often be contained in a half sectional view.

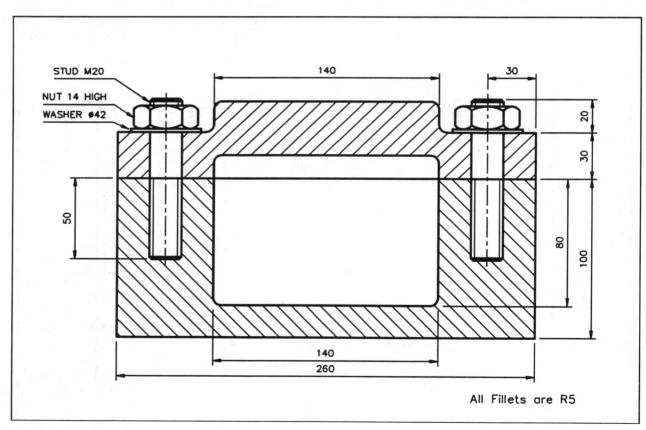

Figure 9.24 A sectional Front view to include studs

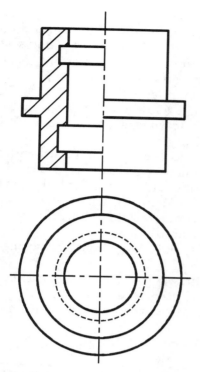

Figure 9.25 A half section

Figure 9.26 is another half sectional view. As can be seen in this example, it is really unnecessary to include further views of this article.

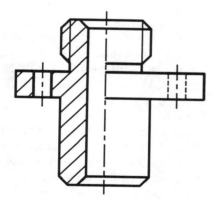

Figure 9.26 A half section

Revolved sections

Figure 9.27 is an example of a **revolved section**. Note that the outline of the section is in thin lines. The reason for the revolved section in this example is that, from the given Front view, it is not clear that the article is elliptical in section and not circular. The elliptical revolved section makes this detail quite clear.

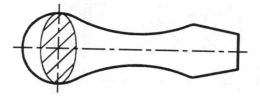

Figure 9.27 A revolved section

Removed sections

Figure 9.28 is an example of a **removed section**. It shows that the recess in the arm of the crank is cut into both the top and bottom of the arm. Note the centre line through the section and also that the outline of a removed section is in thick lines.

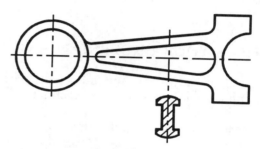

Figure 9.28 A removed section

Part sections

Figure 9.29 is an example of a **part section**. The part which has been section hatched is enclosed by a thin line drawn freehand.

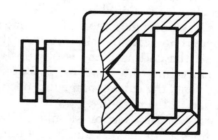

Figure 9.29 A part section

Section on parallel cutting planes

Figure 9.30 (page 142) is an example of a section made along parallel cutting planes. Note the thickening of the section plane line at its angles and that there is no indication in the sectional view that the section is on two parallel planes.

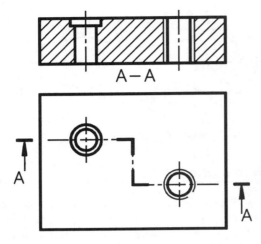

Figure 9.30 A section on parallel cutting planes

■ CHECK YOUR UNDERSTANDING

● Sectional views form an important part of orthographic projections in many technical drawings.

● Sectional views are generally referred to as **sections**.

● Sections may be in Front views, End views or Plans.

● The general rules for sections are:
  a) The edge of the section **cutting plane** should be shown in the relevant view. The cutting plane consists of a centre line with a thick short line each end and arrows pointing in the direction of viewing. Letters at each end of the section line should be included.
  b) If it is obvious where the cutting plane should be there is no need to include it in the drawing – e.g. if the cutting plane is obviously along the centre line of a Plan for a section in the Front view, the cutting plane line need not be included in the drawing.
  c) The cut face of a section should be 'hatched' with lines at 45 degrees and 3 or 4 mm apart.
  d) If there are two adjacent cut faces in a section, the hatching of one should be at a different angle to that of the other. Angles other than 45 degrees and spacings different to 3 or 4 mm may be used when several faces are adjacent to each other.

● Features such as bolts, washers, nuts, spindles, webs, ribs and similar features are shown by outside views in a section.

● A **part drawing** describes a part. **Assembly drawings** describe how parts fit together. Assembly drawings may not include dimensions.

● Other forms of sections are – **half sections, revolved sections, removed sections, part sections** and **sections on parallel cutting planes**.

● Common screw threads are the **ISO metric thread** (angle 60 degrees), **Square thread** (90 degrees), **Acme thread** (29 degrees), **Whitworth thread** (55 degrees).

● ISO metric threads are indicated with the prefix letter M followed by the thread diameter. Where the screw pitch is not standard, the pitch may be added to the M and diameter.

● All types of screw threads are shown in technical drawings with thin lines.

● A variety of lock nuts and nut locking devices is available.

● When drawing views of hexagonal heads of bolts or nuts, the sizes of the parts in the drawing may not be the same as those of the actual bolt head or nut.

REVISION EXERCISES AND QUESTIONS

Exercises

The exercises on the following pages are based on engineering examples and are included here to allow you to practise constructing First angle orthographic projections, including sections. All the exercises in this chapter are set at a fairly simple standard. More difficult exercises will be included later in the book. Some of the exercises which follow include design elements.

1 This exercise allows you to practise geometrical constructions involving circles and arcs and the geometry of tangential arcs and circles.
   A two-view First angle orthographic projection of a *brake cable compensation clip* is given in Figure 9.31. On an A3 size sheet of paper make accurate drawings of the two views. Add all the given dimensions.

2 A *clip* made from sheet mild steel is shown in a pictorial view in Figure 9.32. An end view of the clip is included to show sizes not included in the pictorial view.
   Construct a three-view, full size First angle orthographic projection of the *clip*. Fully dimension your drawing, add a title block in which the title, your name and the scale are printed. Add the two statements First angle projection and Dimensions in millimetres in

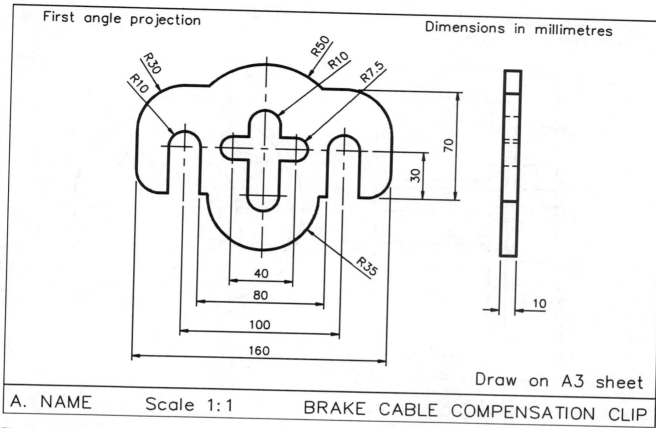

First angle projection   Dimensions in millimetres

R50
R10
R30
R10
R7.5

R35

70

30

40

80

100

160

10

Draw on A3 sheet

A. NAME   Scale 1:1   BRAKE CABLE COMPENSATION CLIP

Figure 9.31 Exercise 1

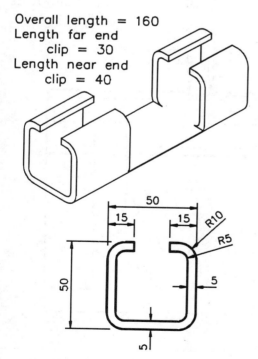

Overall length = 160
Length far end
    clip = 30
Length near end
    clip = 40

50
15
15
R10
R5
50
5
5

Figure 9.32 Exercise 2

suitable places on your drawing sheet.

3 A two-view orthographic projection of a *hub support* drawn to a scale of 1:2 (half full size) is given in Figure 9.33 (see page 144). The four screwed parts are studs, set into the face of the hub support face. Working to a scale of 1:2, make the following drawings of the *hub support*:
a) The given Front view (the right hand view of Figure 9.33).
b) The sectional End view B-B, showing the studs as outside views within the section.
c) Fully dimension your views and add a title block which includes:
  i) Your name.
  ii) The title of the drawing.
  iii) The scale of your drawing.
Add statements giving the angle of projection and the dimensioning units.

4 Figure 9.34 (see page 144) shows a *gear selection fork* from the gearbox of a heavy lorry engine. Figure 9.35 is a pictorial view of the spindle which fits into the diameter 30 mm hole in the sleeve of the fork.
    Working to a scale of full size make the following drawings of the *gear selection fork* with

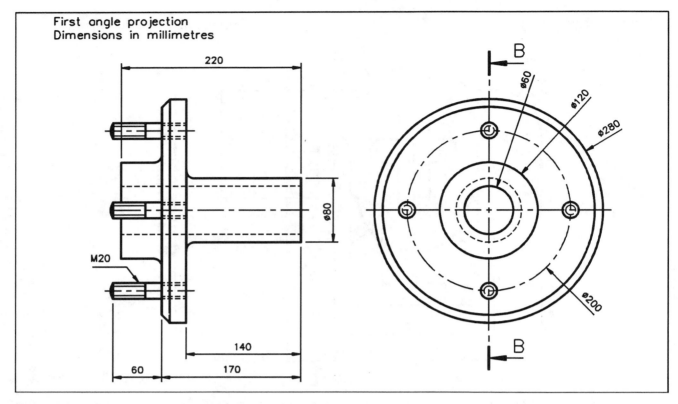

Figure 9.33 Exercise 3

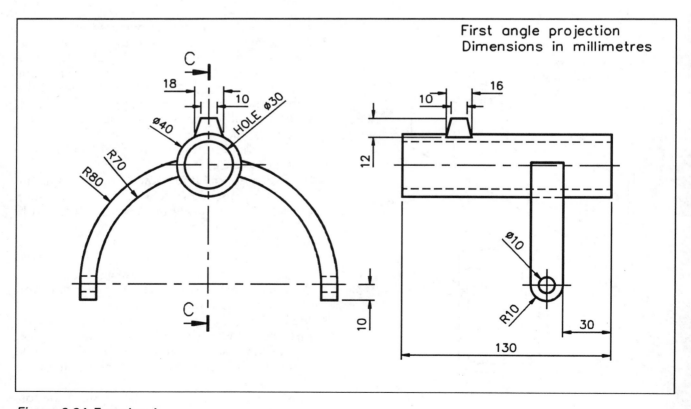

Figure 9.34 Exercise 4

its spindle fitted in place and with the clip shown in Figure 9.35 holding the spindle in position.

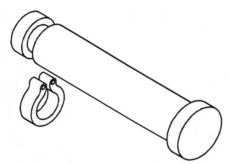

Figure 9.35 Part of Exercise 4 – the *gear selection fork* spindle and its holding clip

a) The given Front view (the view on the left in Figure 9.34).
b) A sectional End view on C-C with the spindle and its clip in place.
c) Fully dimension your views.
d) Add a title block with your name, the title and the scale printed in 8 mm high capital letters.

5 Two orthographic views of an *engagement fork* from the same lorry gear box as the fork of Exercise 4 are given in Figure 9.36. The part moved by the fork is shown in a pictorial view in Figure 9.37.

Construct accurate drawings of the *engagement fork*, with the part which moves in position between the 'claws' of the fork, as follows:
a) The given Front view (the view on the left of Figure 9.36).

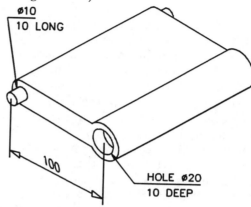

Figure 9.37 Exercise 5 – the part moved by the engagement fork

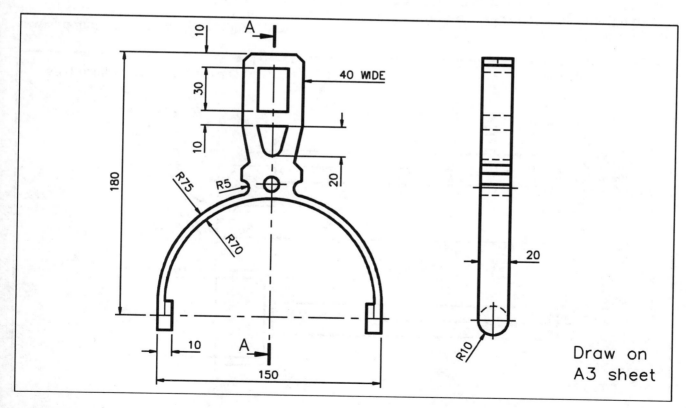

Figure 9.36 Exercise 5

b) A sectional End view on A-A, which includes the movable part in its correct position within the fork with the flat surface of the part horizontal.
c) Fully dimension your drawings.
d) Add a title block in which is printed in 8 mm high capital letters:
   i) Your name.
   ii) The title *engagement fork*.
   iii) The scale to which the drawing has been constructed.
Add statements giving the angle of projection and the units of dimensioning in suitable positions on the drawing sheet. Dimensions not given are left to your own judgement.

6 Figure 9.38 is a two-view First angle orthographic projection of a *damper fork* from the suspension unit of a small motor car. Figure 9.39 is a part held in the 'jaws' of the fork.

On an A3 sheet of drawing paper and working to a scale of 1:1, make the following accurate drawings of the *damper fork* with the part shown in Figure 9.39 held in position in the fork. Your drawings are to include a hexagonal head bolt, nut and washer in position holding the part in the fork jaws.

a) The given Front view (the upper view of Figure 9.38), with the part, the bolt, nut and washer in place.

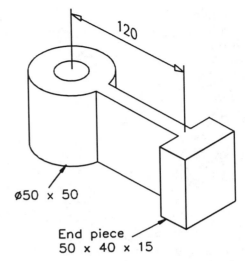

Ø50 × 50

End piece
50 × 40 × 15

Figure 9.39 Exercise 6 – the part held in the jaws of the *damper fork*

b) A sectional Plan. The section plane line is to be central to the Front view.
c) Fully dimension your views.
d) Add a title block in which the following are printed in neat 8 mm high capital letters: Your name, a title, the scale.

7 Figure 9.40 is a pictorial view of the base from a tyre pump. It is made from cast iron and the screwed spindle at the back of the pump base is

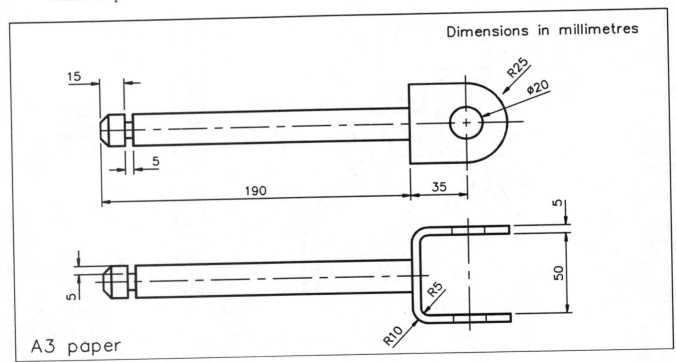

Dimensions in millimetres

A3 paper

Figure 9.38 Exercise 6

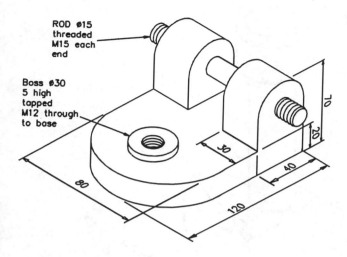

ROD ⌀15
threaded
M15 each
end

Boss ⌀30
5 high
tapped
M12 through
to base

Figure 9.40 Exercise 7

made from high tension carbon steel. Your drawings are to include a hexagonal nut and a washer on each end of the threaded spindle ready for bolting the part held on to the base in place (this part is not shown and is not to be attempted.

Make the following First angle orthographic projection of the pump base:

a) A Front view, choosing a suitable viewing position.
b) An End view.
c) A Plan.
d) Add a title block in which your name, the title and the scale are printed in neat 8 mm high capital letters.
e) Add a Parts list, which includes the materials the parts are to be made from.

8 Figure 9.41 is a pictorial view of a V-block, together with a Plan giving details of the slots in the base of the V-block. The slots in the base of the block are designed to allow the block to be bolted on to a surface with the aid of cheese headed screws. V-blocks are designed for holding cylindrical rods in position (in the Vs) while the rods are being worked or marked. Your drawings are to include two M8 cheese headed screws, 40 mm long in position ready to bolt the block to a surface. A length of rod, 40 mm diameter, 100 mm long is to be shown resting in the Vs of the block.

Make the following full size First angle orthographic views of the V-block:

a) An End view looking from the right-hand side of the block as shown in the given drawing.

b) A sectional Front view, the section plane to be central to the End view.
c) A Plan.
d) Add a title block to your drawing which includes.
   i) Your name.
   ii) The title V-BLOCK.
   iii) The scale to which the drawing has been made.

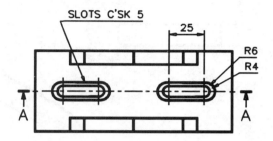

SLOTS C'SK 5

25

R6
R4

A   A

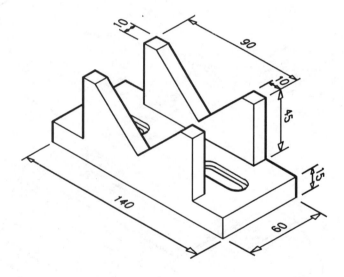

Figure 9.41 Exercise 8

9 Figure 9.42 (see page 148) is a pictorial drawing, together with a dimensioned End view of a *towing bracket*, such as can be bolted onto the rear of a lorry for towing a trailer or a caravan. A spindle drops vertically down into holes in the two horizontal parts of the bracket. The back of the bracket is 220 mm long overall. Other sizes are included in Figure 9.42.

With the spindle in position but with a thread added on its lower end and with a washer and

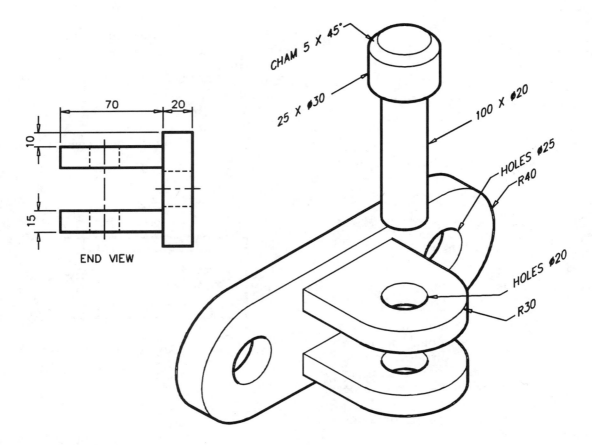

END VIEW

Figure 9.42 Exercise 9

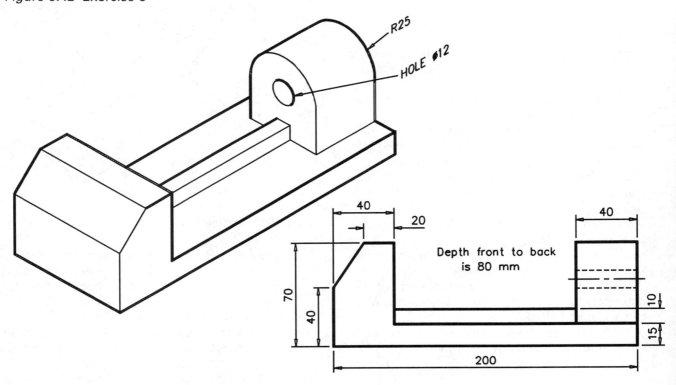

Depth front to back
is 80 mm

Figure 9.43 Exercise 10

nut screwed into position on the thread, draw the following orthographic projection of the *towing bracket*:

a) The given End view in section, with the spindle, its nut and washer included.

b) A Front view, with a section plane line running through the centre of the spindle in the End view.

c) A Plan.

d) Include a title block in which the following details are printed in neat 8 mm high capital letters:

   i) Your name.

   ii) The title – A TOWING BRACKET.

   iii) The scale.

e) Include the statements First angle projection and Dimensions in millimetres on your drawing sheet in suitable positions.

10 Figure 9.43 is a pictorial view of a cast-iron base for a small *drill vice*, with a fixed vice jaw at the front end and a boss, in which a threaded screw is to be fitted, at the rear end. The vice is designed to hold small pieces of material firmly on a drilling machine bench, as holes are drilled in them.

A movable jaw and a screw to move the jaw are to be included in your drawing. Before attempting the drawing, make freehand sketches on scrap paper of a suitable movable jaw and a screw for moving the jaw. Note the following:

1. The jaw should move along the rib running down the centre of the base.

2. The diameter 12 mm hole in the back of the base must be threaded to take the thread of the screw which is to move the jaw.

3. Your design should include a device for closing the jaws together and also to move the jaw back as the screw is wound back.

Construct the following First angle orthographic projection of the complete vice – base, screw and movable jaw:

a) An End view as seen from the right hand end of the pictorial view of Figure 9.43.

b) A sectional Front view, taking dimensions from the given Front view. The section plane to run through the centre of the End view.

c) A Plan.

Include a title block and a Parts list. The Parts list should include the names of each part of your design, together with the materials from which you think they should be made.

11 Figure 9.44 is an incomplete three-view First angle orthographic projection of a *rod stand*. The rod is held in the 50 mm diameter hole. The

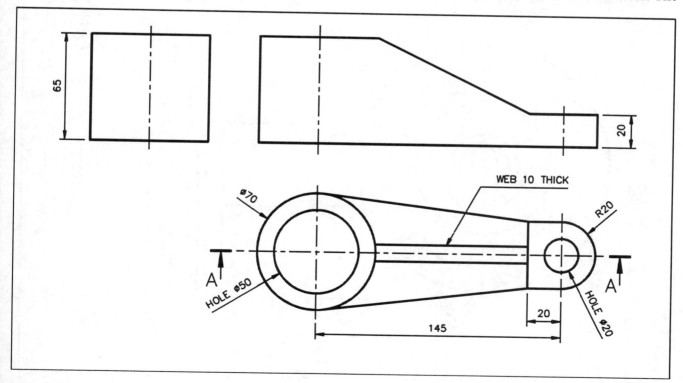

Figure 9.44 Exercise 11

stand is held in position by a bolt through the 20 mm diameter hole.

Copy the given drawing, Figure 9.44 and complete the Section A-A and the End view. Include the following:

a) All necessary dimensions.

b) A full title block.

c) Statement of angle and units of dimensions.

d) An M20 hexagonal headed bolt and a washer in the diameter 20 mm hole, with the head resting on the washer, which in turn is resting on the top surface in which the hole is cut.

e) A 120 mm length of 50 mm diameter cylindrical rod, fitted in the 50 mm diameter hole of the stand.

12 Figure 9.45 shows a *V-pulley* on its spindle. The pulley is held in place by a key – in this example the key is a **Woodruff key**. An example of a Woodruff key is included in Figure 9.45 showing that the key is less than a semi-circle in shape and made from steel plate material. Two other types of keys are shown in Figure 9.46 – a **taper key** and a **gib-headed key**.

Keys are fitted into grooves known as **key-ways**. Their purpose is to hold two parts together so that one will not rotate in or on the other. They are commonly used for fitting pulleys and gears to spindles. Some keys will allow movement between the parts along the length

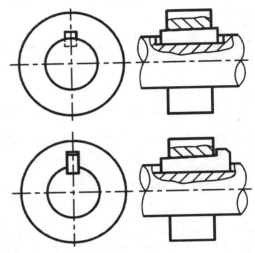

Figure 9.46 A taper key and a Gib-headed key

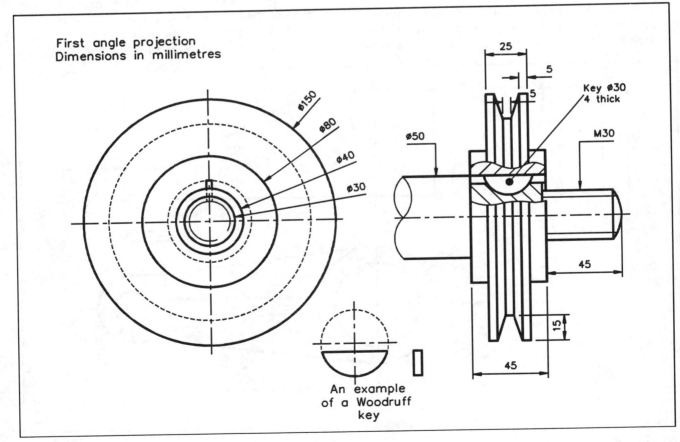

Figure 9.45 Exercise 12

of the key while restricting rotational movement between the parts.

Copy Figure 9.45 and include a hexagonal headed nut and a washer to secure the pulley from movement along the length of the spindle. Note the part section for showing the key and key-way.

Questions

1 What is meant by a sectional view?
2 What is a half section? Draw one.
3 What is the difference between a part drawing and an assembly drawing?
4 State the rule governing nuts, bolts, spindles and webs within sections.
5 What is the angle between the Vs of an ISO metric thread?
6 What would you use a square threaded screw for?
7 What do you think the difference is between a bolt and a screw?
8 Sketch two types of lock-nut.
9 What is a stud? Draw one.
10 Sketch two grub screws and explain where they would be used.

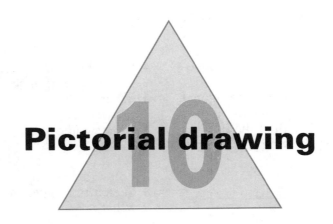

Pictorial drawing

Introduction

Pictorial drawings show a 'picture' of an article in three dimensions, as if one were looking at the article itself. Pictorial drawings are an important part of technical drawing. There are two main reasons for this:

1. Complex working drawings are sometimes very difficult to understand. Pictorial drawings of details in a complex drawing can help people to understand the drawing.
2. Pictorial drawings are an important part of showing people who cannot 'read' working drawings, what an article actually looks like.

Isometric drawing

Isometric drawing is a form of pictorial drawing based on lines at 30 degrees from the horizontal. Figure 10.1 shows the basic idea when making an isometric drawing of a rectangular prism. Vertical lines are drawn with the aid of the right angle of a set square, lines at 30 degrees are drawn with the aid of a 30,60 set square.

When constructing an isometric drawing, all measurements must be made along the **isometric axes** – either the vertical lines or along the 30 degree lines. This applies even when constructing arcs or curved lines in isometric drawings. Figure 10.2 shows the method of finding the sizes along the isometric axes for the construction of Figure 10.3. Figure 10.4 shows how lines which are not along the isometric axes must be constructed from measurements taken along the axes.

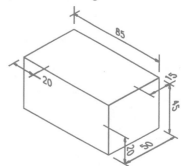

Figure 10.2 Sizes must be taken along isometric axes

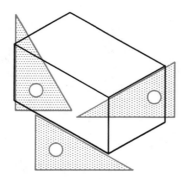

Figure 10.1 An isometric drawing of a rectangular prism

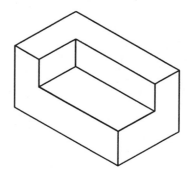

Figure 10.3 The finished isometric drawing to the sizes in Figure 10.2

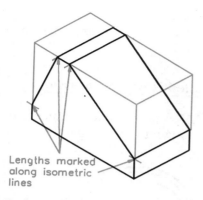

Figure 10.4 Sloping lines – sizes must be measured along axes

Constructing isometric curves

Figure 10.5 shows how an **isometric circle** is constructed:

1. Draw a circle of the required diameter – the lower drawing of Figure 10.5. Draw vertical lines – a, b and c – at any spacings across the circle.
2. Draw the two centre lines for the circle at 30 degrees each way – the upper drawing of Figure 10.5.
3. Mark off the lengths Oa, Ob and Oc, taken from the circle, along one of the isometric centre

lines, each side of the centre O. Draw 30 degree lines through the points a, b and c.
4. Each side of the centre line from a, b and c mark off the lengths a1, b2 and c3 along the 30 degree lines from a, b and c.
5. Mark the lengths Od each side along the centre line in the isometric drawing.
6. All necessary points for drawing the isometric circle have now been found. Draw a fair curve through the points to complete the required isometric circle – which is an ellipse.

Figure 10.6 shows a similar construction for circles in other isometric positions.

Figure 10.7 is an example of a simple isometric drawing and Figure 10.8 (page 154) another example which includes isometric 'circles'.

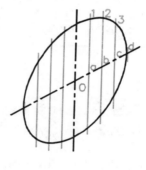

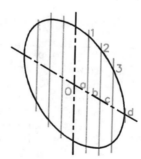

Figure 10.6 Other positions for isometric circles

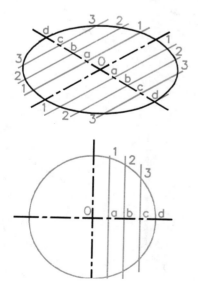

Figure 10.5 Method of constructing an isometric circle

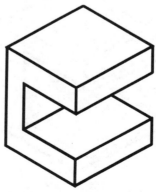

Figure 10.7 A simple isometric drawing

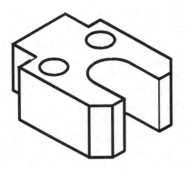

Figure 10.8 A simple isometric drawing involving circles

> **Note**: The reader is advised not to use isometric ellipse templates until he or she has had sufficient practise in constructing isometric ellipses as shown above.

Exploded isometric drawing

A simple exploded isometric drawing

Figure 10.9 is a simple 'exploded' isometric draw-

ing; its parts have been 'exploded' along the isometric axes.

An exploded isometric drawing

Figure 10.10 is an exploded isometric drawing of a *fork end*, showing the two parts – its *end piece* and

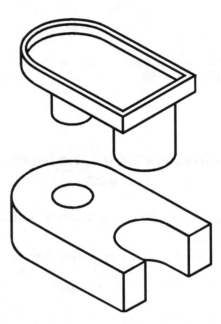

Figure 10.9 A simple exploded isometric drawing

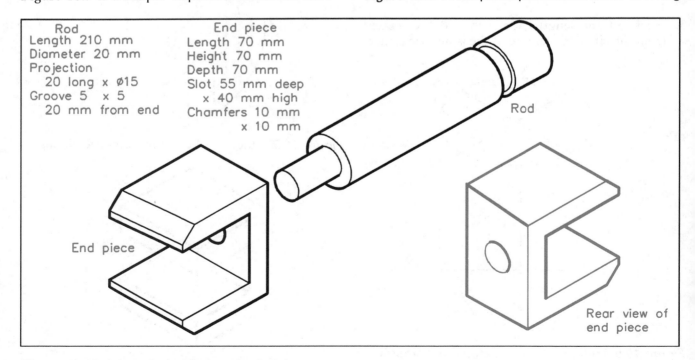

Rod	End piece
Length 210 mm	Length 70 mm
Diameter 20 mm	Height 70 mm
Projection	Depth 70 mm
20 long x ⌀15	Slot 55 mm deep
Groove 5 x 5	x 40 mm high
20 mm from end	Chamfers 10 mm
	x 10 mm

Rod

End piece

Rear view of end piece

Figure 10.10 An exploded isometric drawing

its *rod* in an exploded position. The *rod* is shown pulled out from the END along an isometric 30 degree axis. A rear view of the *end piece* is included to show that the *rod* fits into a hole in its back face. To construct the drawing:

1. Working to the sizes given with Figure 10.10, draw the *end piece*, remembering that the chamfer sizes must be taken along the isometric lines.
2. Construct the *rod* using the method shown in Figure 10.5 to draw the curves of the isometric circles.
3. Line in the required drawing outline and erase any unwanted lines.
4. Add a title block which includes your name and the title EXPLODED ISOMETRIC DRAWING in 8 mm high capital letters.

Freehand drawing

For preparing the layouts for orthographic drawings and for the necessary preparation work when designing, **freehand drawing** (or sketching) is a skill which should be gained by practice. HB or B grade pencils are more suitable for freehand work than the 2H or 3H pencils which are used for technical drawings made with the aid of instruments. If isometric and square grid papers are available, a good tip is to start learning how to draw freehand sketches on grid papers. Such grid papers can be purchased in A4 or A3 sheets with the grid lines printed in green or blue – either square grids or isometric grids are available. The spacing of the grid lines is either at 10 mm intervals or at 5 mm intervals. However, when you have gained sufficient skill in freehand drawing with the aid of grid papers, it is best to then sketch on plain paper without the grid lines. The examples given in this book are for freehand sketching on either the lines of orthographic projection or isometric drawing.

An example of a freehand drawing of a pedestal mounting as preparation for the layout of the drawing before constructing the views of an orthographic projection are shown in three examples – Figure 10.11 on an A3 sheet of 10 mm square grid paper, Figure 10.12 on a smaller sheet of grid

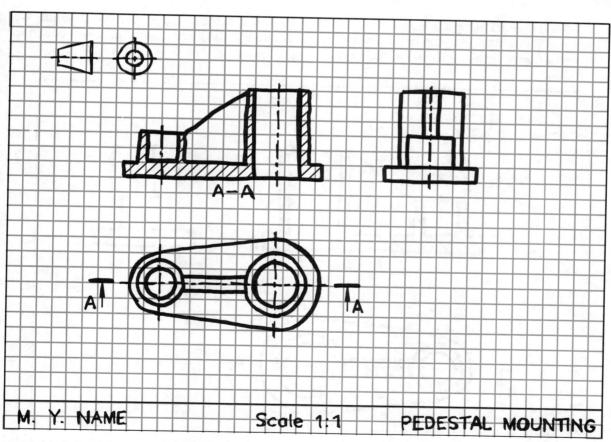

Figure 10.11 A freehand drawing on an A3 sheet of 10 mm square grid paper

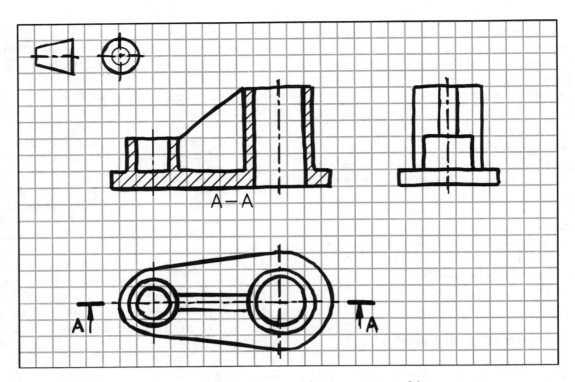

Figure 10.12 An example of a freehand drawing on 10 mm square grid paper

paper and Figure 10.13 on plain paper without a grid. Figure 10.14 shows a freehand isometric drawing on isometric grid paper with the grid at 10 mm spacing. Figure 10.15 is a similar freehand drawing on isometric lines on plain paper without grid lines.

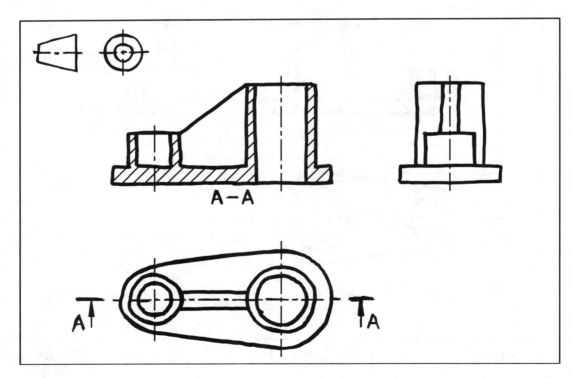

Figure 10.13 A freehand drawing of an orthographic projection on plain paper without grid lines

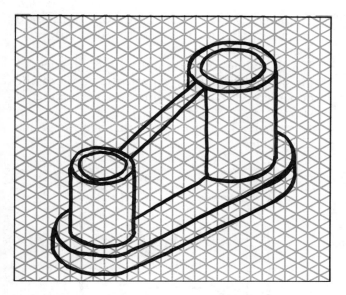

Figure 10.14 A freehand isometric drawing on isometric grid paper with line spacing at 10 mm

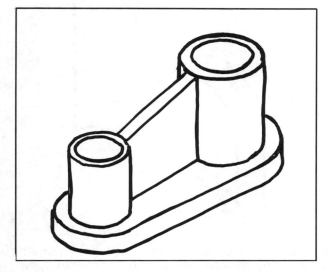

Figure 10.15 A freehand drawing on isometric lines on plain paper without grid lines

The 4-arcs method of drawing isometric circles

Figure 10.16 shows the method of drawing an isometric circle with the aid of instruments. This method has already been described on page 57 and is given here as a revision.

1. Draw the 30 degree lines which represent the square circumscribing the circle. Thus lines AB, BC, CD and DA are all at 30 degrees and are all the same length.
2. Draw the diagonal AC.
3. Draw BF and DE in which E is the centre point of AB and F is the centre point of CD.
4. With G, the intersection of AC and BF, as a centre, draw an arc of radius GF.
5. Draw an arc of centre H and radius HE.
6. With centre B and radius BF draw an arc.
7. With centre D and radius DE draw an arc.
8. You have now drawn the 4 arcs to complete the construction.

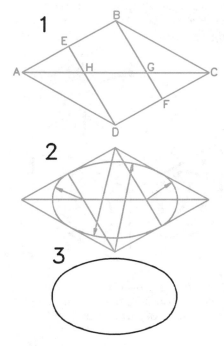

Figure 10.16 The 4-arcs method of constructing an isometric ellipse

Figure 10.17 shows similar methods for isometric 4-arcs in different isometric positions.

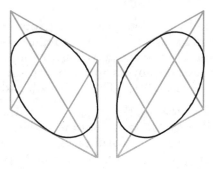

Figure 10.17 The 4-arcs method used in other isometric positions

Note: This method does not produce accurate isometric circles (ellipses), but is sufficiently accurate for the construction of isometric ellipses up to about 50 mm in diameter. For larger isometric ellipses, it is advisable to use the more correct method, involving the plotting of points along the ellipse curve and then drawing a fair curve through the points so obtained. If the 4-arcs method is used with larger ellipses, the resulting drawing will have a distorted appearance.

Figure 10.18 is an example of an isometric drawing which involved the construction of ellipses on three faces using the 4-arcs method of construction.

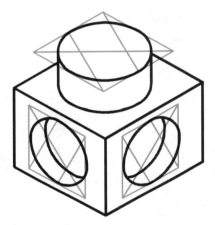

Figure 10.18 An example of an isometric drawing involving isometric ellipses on three faces using the 4-arcs method of construction

Drawing isometric curves

The method of drawing ellipses (from circles) in isometric drawings as shown in Figure 10.5 (page 153) is suitable for the drawing of more complicated shapes and curves in isometric drawings as shown in Figure 10.19. This illustration shows:

1. A Front view of the object to be drawn with vertical lines along its outline – these lines are often referred to as **ordinates**.
2. The vertical lines have been transferred to the isometric drawing with the same spacings between the verticals along the 30 degree axis.

3. The lengths of the lines have been transferred from the Front view onto the isometric drawing.
4. 30 degree lines of the length of the thickness of the shaped object have been drawn from the upper ends of each ordinate in the isometric view.
5. A fair curve has been drawn through the points so obtained.

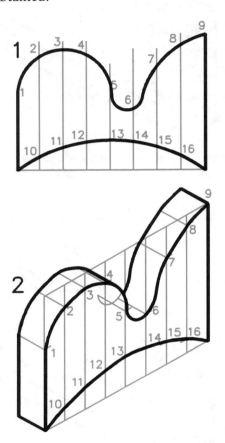

Figure 10.19 An example of drawing an isometric curve using the ordinate method of construction

Estimated one and two-point perspective drawing

If you look carefully at any object, lines along its sides appear as if they are inclined to vanish towards what is known as a **Vanishing Point** or **V.P.** This illusion can be readily seen by looking along a pair of straight railway lines. The idea of V.Ps is the basis of the two geometrical methods –

one-point (or single-point) and two-point **perspective drawing**.

> **Note**: True **perspective drawing** involves a third V.P., but 3-point perspective drawing is beyond the scope of a book of this nature. However it must be remembered that one-point and two-point perspective drawing do not give true perspective and so may at times appear inaccurate. The two methods do, however, provide an excellent and easy method of drawing very well suited to the preparation of drawings for designs.

Estimated one-point perspective drawing

Figure 10.20 is an example of a one-point perspective of a stepped platform. Note the following:

1. The position of the single V.P. can be in any position above, to the right, to the left or below a Front view of the object being drawn. If the V.P. is below, then a view from below the object will be drawn.
2. From the Front view draw lines to the V.P.
3. Complete the rear of the object with lines between the lines to the V.P. Lengths along the lines are estimated.

A second example is given in Figure 10.21, involving a semi-circular part. In this example a line from the centre of the semi-circle has been drawn to the V.P. in order to find the centre of the arc at the rear of the object.

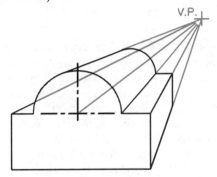

Figure 10.21 A one-point perspective drawing which includes an arc

Estimated two-point perspective drawing

In two-point perspective two V.Ps are positioned. They must be in line with each other horizontally, but can be above or below the object being drawn. The two-point perspective drawing Figure 10.22 was drawn as follows:

1. Position the two V.Ps in appropriate positions.

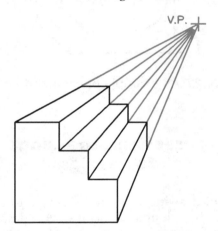

Figure 10.20 An example of a one-point perspective drawing

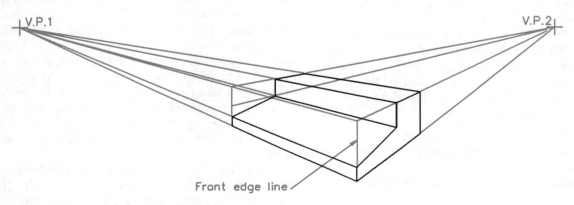

Figure 10.22 An example of two-point perspective

2. Draw a line representing the front edge of the object – this line to be of the same length as the total height of the object.
3. Draw lines from top and bottom of the line to the two V.Ps.
4. Estimate the depth of the object on the right-hand side, draw a vertical line between the two lines to V.P.2.
5. From the intersection of this line with the line to the V.P.2 draw another line to the V.P.1.
6. Continue in this manner to complete the perspective drawing.

> **Note:**
> • The positions of the V.Ps are critical to the appearance of the final drawing, so must be chosen with care to avoid distortion. Some experimenting is advisable. It is only necessary to draw the outline for the perspective to determine whether or not your drawing is going to look as if it is distorted.
> • The methods of one and two-point perspective are very suitable for freehand drawing, particularly when preparing work for designing.

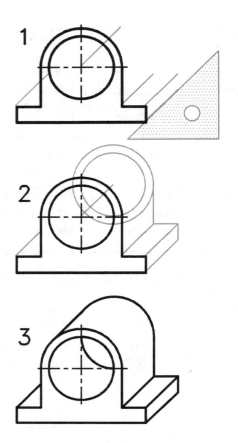

Figure 10.23 An example of cabinet drawing

Cabinet drawing

Another form of pictorial drawing is **oblique drawing**. In oblique drawing, a Front view of the object to be drawn is drawn. From the Front view, lines at any angle are drawn. This angle is usually at 45 degrees, although other angles are used. The depth of the object is marked off along the sloping lines and the rear of the drawing at the points so found.

Cabinet drawing is the most common form of oblique drawing. In this form of oblique drawing, the sloping lines are at 45 degrees and the lengths along the sloping lines are drawn to half scale. An example is given in Figure 10.23. The drawing was constructed as follows:

1. Draw the Front view of the object.
2. From points on the Front view, draw lines at 45 degrees.
3. Measure half the depth of the object along the 45 degree lines.
4. Complete the rear of the drawing as shown.

Freehand drawing for design

Freehand drawing is an important part of the preparation for design drawings. As described in Chapter 8, when a design brief has been determined, the next stage is to make notes and sketches for ideas of solutions to the design brief. Figure 10.24 is an example of a type of design solutions sheet suitable for technical drawing. The brief in this example was to design a clamp for holding small pieces of mild steel together while they were brazed. The shape of the grip has already been determined and Figure 10.24 is a sheet of freehand drawings of suggestions for the screw part of the required *Clamp grip*. Further sheets of such drawings will be required before the final design is determined.

The design sheet of Figure 10.24 includes a number of freehand drawings on isometric lines, together with a small sectional drawing through the washer at the end of the screw thread.

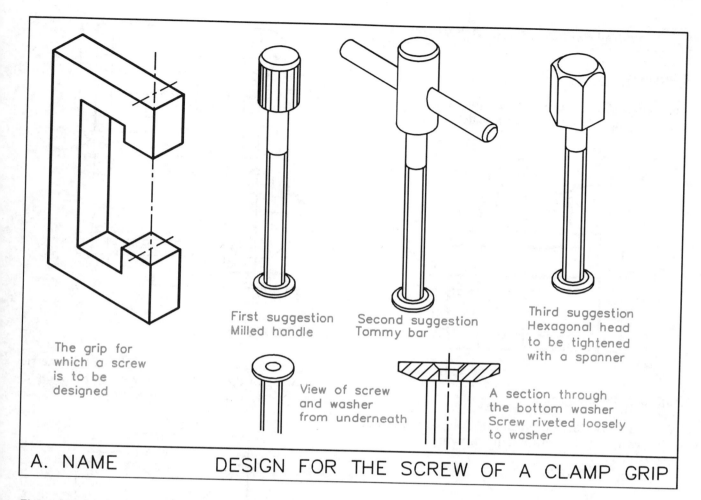

The grip for which a screw is to be designed

First suggestion Milled handle

Second suggestion Tommy bar

Third suggestion Hexagonal head to be tightened with a spanner

View of screw and washer from underneath

A section through the bottom washer Screw riveted loosely to washer

A. NAME   DESIGN FOR THE SCREW OF A CLAMP GRIP

Figure 10.24 An example of a design sheet involving freehand drawings

CHECK YOUR UNDERSTANDING

● **Isometric drawings** are constructed with the aid of a 30,60 set square. The sloping axes are at 30 degrees each side of the vertical axis.

● When constructing **isometric ellipses** (from circles), the **ordinate** method is the best for circles originally greater than about 50 mm in diameter.

● The **4-arcs**, geometrical method of constructing isometric ellipses is quite suitable for small ellipses for circles originally less than about 50 mm in diameter.

● **Exploded isometric drawings** should be drawn with their parts as if pulled apart along the isometric axes.

● Exploded drawings can be constructed in the oblique (or **cabinet**) **method** of pictorial drawing.

● **Freehand drawing** is an important part of the design process, particularly in the preparation of sheets of suggestions for solutions to a design brief.

● Freehand drawing in orthographic, isometric or cabinet drawing styles are suitable for design drawings involving technical drawings.

● Freehand drawings can be constructed on isometric or square grid papers. When satisfied that you have gained a sufficient degree of skill in using such grid papers, it is advisable to then sketch freehand on plain papers.

● Isometric drawings involving complicated curves or shapes can be constructed with the aid of the ordinate method of construction

● Cabinet drawing is an oblique method of drawing which involves sloping lines at 45 degrees and half-scale measurements taken along the sloping lines.

REVISION EXERCISES AND QUESTIONS

Exercises

1 Figure 10.25. Construct a cabinet drawing of the component shown to a scale of full size.

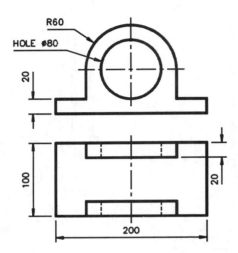

Figure 10.25 Exercise 1

2 Figure 10.26. Construct a full size cabinet drawing of the component shown.

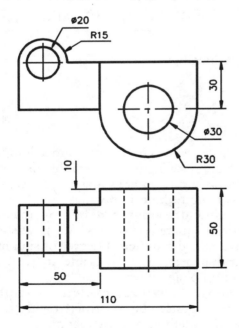

Figure 10.26 Exercise 2

3 Figure 10.27. Construct a full size isometric drawing of the component shown in the given two-view First angle orthographic projection.

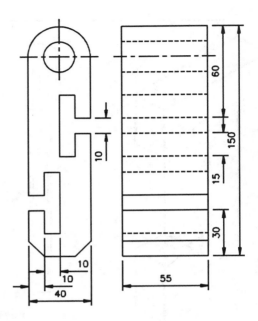

Figure 10.27 Exercise 3

4 Figure 10.28. Construct a full size isometric drawing of the *V-block* in the given First angle, two-view orthographic projection.

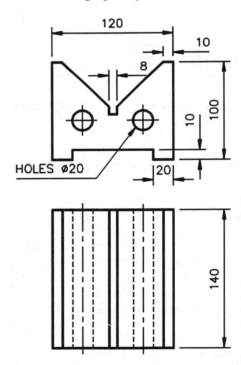

Figure 10.28 Exercise 4

5 Figure 10.29. Construct a full size isometric drawing of the *swivel block* in the given First angle, two-view orthographic projection.

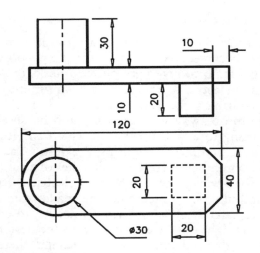

Figure 10.29 Exercise 5

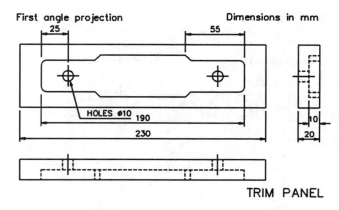

TRIM PANEL

Figure 10.31 Exercise 7

6 Figure 10.30 is a two-view First angle ortho-graphic projection of a *carrying case*. Construct a full-size isometric drawing of the case.
7 Figure 10.31 is a three-view First angle ortho-graphic projection of a *trim panel*. Construct a full-size isometric drawing of the component.
8 Figure 10.32. A three-view First angle ortho-graphic projection of a *filter plug box* is given. Construct a scale 2:1 (twice full size) isometric drawing of the component.

The *filter plug box* takes a 13 Amp electrical plug. Draw, freehand, a suitable plug for fitting into the three sockets of the *plug box*.
9 Figure 10.33 (page 164). A *vacuum control unit box* from a modern saloon car is given in a three-view First angle orthographic projection.

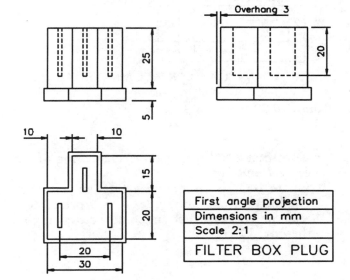

First angle projection
Dimensions in mm
Scale 2:1
FILTER BOX PLUG

Figure 10.32 Exercise 8

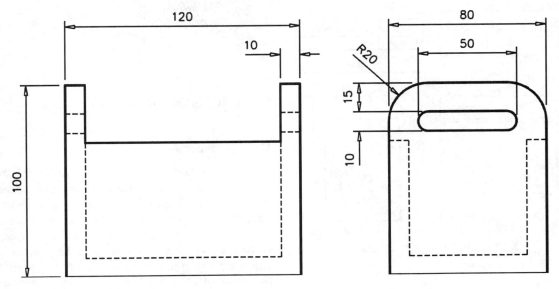

Figure 10.30 Exercise 6

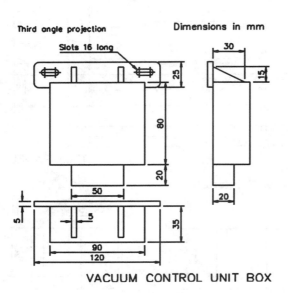

Figure 10.33 Exercise 9

Construct a full-scale isometric drawing of the *control unit box*.

10 Figure 10.34 is a three view First angle orthographic projection of a *filter box*. Working to a scale of 1:1 construct an isometric drawing of the *box*.

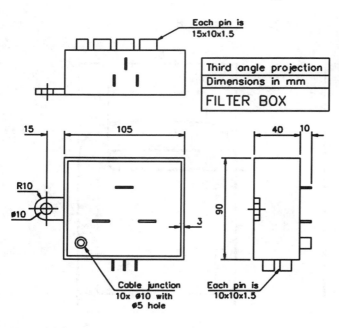

Figure 10.34 Exercise 10

Design Exercise 1

Figure 10.35 shows a corner of a room in which a shelf has been secured to a wall for the purpose of holding a lamp to give light above a desk top.

Because electricity has recently been run into the house of which the room is a part, it has been decided to do away with the lamp and fix an electrical fitting to a wall bracket in which an electric bulb could be fixed for lighting the desk area.

Make a number of freehand sketches of a suitable design for a wall bracket to hold an electrical fitting and the bulb. The bracket can be made from any suitable material. A lamp shade is needed to allow maximum light to be cast down on to the desk top.

Having decided one of your freehand sketches will provide a suitable solution for the design:

1. Make an accurate and fully-dimensioned orthographic projection of your design.
2. Construct a full-size surface development for your design for a suitable shade for the lamp.

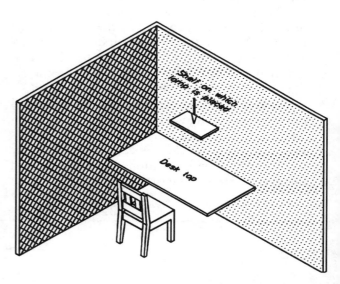

Figure 10.35 Design Exercise 1

Design Exercise 2

A pulley stand (made from cast iron) and two pulleys (made from aluminium) are shown in a First angle orthographic projection in Figure 10.36. The small pulley is to be connected by a drive belt to a motor. The large pulley is to be connected by a second drive belt to a machine. The purpose of the stand and its pulleys is to transfer the rotation of the motor to the machine at a slower rate of revolutions per minute (RPM).

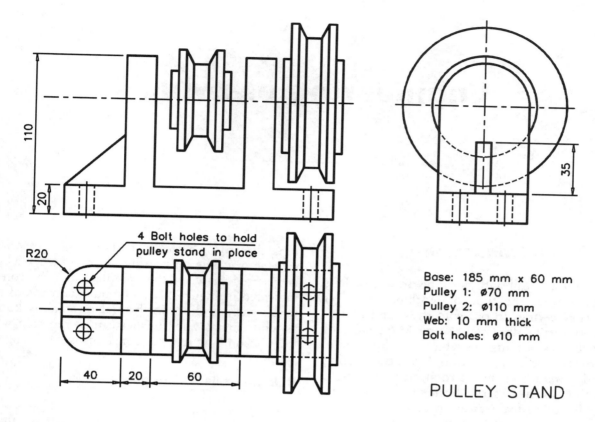

Base: 185 mm x 60 mm
Pulley 1: ⌀70 mm
Pulley 2: ⌀110 mm
Web: 10 mm thick
Bolt holes: ⌀10 mm

PULLEY STAND

Figure 10.36 Design Exercise 2

The pulleys spindle is missing from Figure 10.36. Make freehand sketches on scrap paper to show suitable designs for a spindle to allow the pulleys to rotate freely in the stand. Your design must:

a) Allow free rotation of the spindle in the stand. Being made from cast iron, holes in the stand will allow a spindle to rotate freely without the need for a purpose-made bearing system, although lubrication holes will be required.
b) Include some method of securing the pulleys firmly on the spindle.
c) Include a method which will prevent the pulleys from moving from side to side.
d) Include some method to prevent the spindle from slipping out from the stand.

When satisfied that you have a good design for the spindle and its fittings:

1. Draw a full size Plan.
2. Add a sectional Front view and End view in either First or in Third angle projection.
3. Your views should show clearly the design features for holding the pulleys to the spindle, preventing sideways movement of the pulleys and for preventing the spindle from slipping from the stand.
4. Fully dimension your drawing.
5. Include a suitable title block.

Questions

1 Why is it important that you learn how to produce pictorial drawings?
2 Name three methods of pictorial drawing used in technical drawing.
3 Make freehand sketches of small component parts of machines such as a motor car, a machine used in a workshop in your school or college. Make sure you carefully measure the components, so that you can make good pictorial drawings from them working with instruments.
4 What is meant by an 'exploded' drawing?
5 What are the advantages of using square or isometric grid papers when drawing freehand?
6 What is meant by the '4-arcs' method of drawing isometric circles?
7 What is a Vanishing Point? When will you need Vanishing Points?
8 Why is pictorial drawing so important when you are designing?

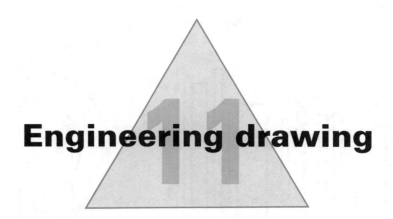

Engineering drawing

Introduction

In Chapter 9 we dealt with working drawings. This chapter describes the type of working drawings used in engineering. In order to draw and understand engineering drawings, some knowledge of features such as **bearings** in which spindles rotate, **gears** for transmitting motion between rotating parts and **cams** for changing rotation into straight line motion, is necessary. Basic principles concerned with these features are described, together with examples of and exercises in engineering drawing.

Bearings

Spindles and shafts in machines run in **bearings**, of which there are many different types. A few of the more common are shown here. A steel spindle can run in a hole in cast iron without any special type of bearing and this simple bearing requires lubricating from time to time with a lubricating oil. The steel spindle is usually **case hardened** – a thin skin of the spindle has extra carbon added by heat treatment and is then hardened. Although spindles run-

ning directly in holes in cast iron are reasonably satisfactory, a better bearing is formed when a **bush** is inserted between the spindle and cast iron, as indicated in Figure 11.1. The bush is made of materials such as phosphor bronze or an alloy known as white metal. Such bushes can be replaced when they become worn after constant use.

Ball and roller bearings

One of the more common forms of bearings are those incorporating steel balls or rollers. Figure 11.2 shows the general symbol for drawing any form of ball or roller bearing. Figure 11.3 is a two-view orthographic projection of a roller bear-

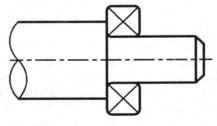

Figure 11.2 The standard drawing symbol for a ball or roller bearing

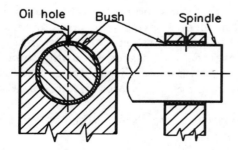

Figure 11.1 A bush and its lubricating hole

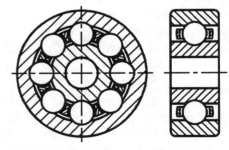

Figure 11.3 Sectional views through a roller bearing – a journal

166

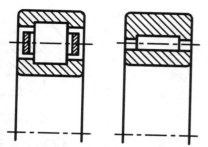

Figure 11.4 Sections through a roller bearing and a needle bearing – journals

ing, both views being in section. Figure 11.4 shows two sectional views, the first through a roller bearing. The second section is a view through a needle bearing – needles being rollers of very small diameter.

All ball and roller bearings consist of:

1. The roller element – balls, parallel rollers, taper rollers, spherical rollers.
2. Race rings holding the rollers.
3. A cage – separating the rollers.

There are three groups of ball and roller bearings:

1. **Journal bearings** – in which spindles run.
2. **Thrust bearings** – designed to take a load.
3. **Angular bearings**.

Figure 11.5 is a sectional view through a thrust bearing in which the roller elements are tapered rollers. Thrust bearings will take much heavier loads than journal bearings.

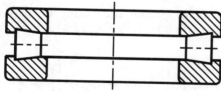

Figure 11.5 A thrust bearing with taper rollers

Spur gears

For transferring rotation from one spindle (or shaft) to another, **spur gears** are commonly used. A spur gear is a circular disc with a central hole, usually with a keyway cut in it for fixing to a spindle via a key. The gear has a number of gear teeth cut around its circumference. The profile of gear teeth in the majority of spur gears are based on the involute to a circle (see page 59). Some gears

(often those used in watches and clocks) are based on the cycloid to a circle.

The standard symbol for drawing spur gears in technical drawings is shown in Figure 11.6.

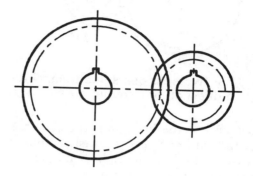

Figure 11.6 The standard symbol for two meshing spur gears

> **Note**: that the base circle centre lines for each gear (on which the involute is based) meet tangentially.

Figure 11.7 shows a number of gear teeth taken from two meshing spur gears. It is most unlikely that you will be required to draw such gear teeth. Figure 11.7 shows the appearance of **meshing involute gear teeth**. In technical drawings use the symbols for spur gears, not the actual outlines of the gear teeth.

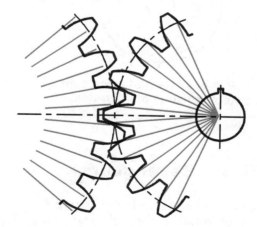

Figure 11.7 Enlarged view of involute gear teeth from two meshing gears

Figure 11.8 (page 168) is a Front view of a two-gear **gear train**. The rotation of either gear brings about a rotation in an opposite direction in the gear

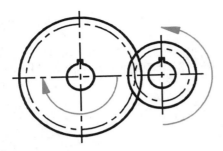

Figure 11.8 Two spur gears in a train. Note the change in direction of rotation

with which it is meshed. Thus the clockwise rotation of the left hand gear is translated into an anticlockwise rotation in the right hand gear.

Figure 11.9 is another gear train, in which the rotation of the uppermost gear is repeated in the bottom gear via what is known as an **idler gear**.

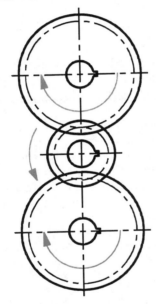

Figure 11.9 A gear train of three spur gears, the middle one of which is an idler gear

Bevel gears

Bevel gears are suitable for changing the angular direction of rotation through gear trains. Figure 11.10 is a two view orthographic projection showing the standard technical drawing method of drawing a bevel gear. The gears shown in Figure 11.10 are for changing the angle of rotation through 90 degrees, but bevel gears are made for changing the angular rotation through any angle.

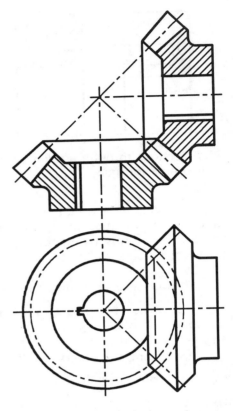

Figure 11.10 A pair of bevel gears drawn using standard technical drawing methods

Radial cams

Radial cams, diagrammatic examples of which are given in Figures 11.11 to Figure 11.14 are for con-

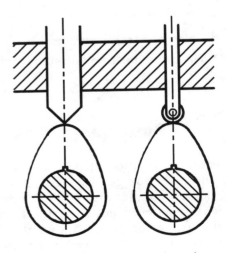

Figure 11.11 Rotary cams – wedge shaped and roller followers

verting radial motion into straight line motion. As a radial cam rotates, the **follower** running on its surface moves up and down according to the outline of the radial profile of the cam.

All cams are designed for the purpose of converting one form of motion into another.

Radial cams can have different types of follower. In Figure 11.11 wedge-shaped and roller followers are shown. In Figure 11.12 flat and off-line followers are shown.

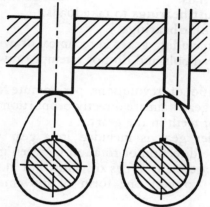

Figure 11.12 Rotary cams – Flat and off-line followers

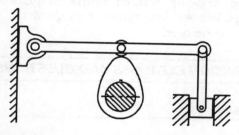

Figure 11.13 An arm and roller follower with a rotary cam

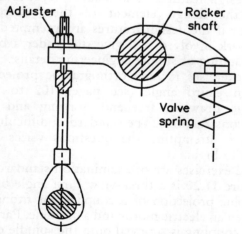

Figure 11.14 A cam system from an overhead valve system in a car engine

Figure 11.13 shows a cam associated with a rocker arm for transferring the rotation of the cam into an up and down vertical movement. Figure 11.14 shows one of the most commonly used cams in modern machinery – the cam system designed to operate the valves in an internal combustion engine driven by petrol.

Welding symbols

If you are required to show a welded joint in technical drawings which include welded plates, a number of standard ISO symbols for a large number of different forms of weld are in use. The symbols for the most common of the welded joints for plate work are shown in Figures 11.15 to 11.19.

- Figure 11.15 – Welding symbol for a **fillet weld**.
- Figure 11.16 – Welding symbol for a **V butt weld**.
- Figure 11.17 – Welding symbol for a butt weld between plates.
- Figure 11.18 – Welding symbol for a **spot weld**.
- Figure 11.19 – Welding symbols for a V butt weld and a fillet weld.

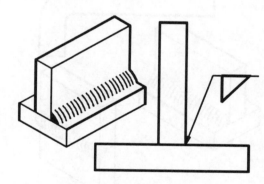

Figure 11.15 A fillet weld and its symbol

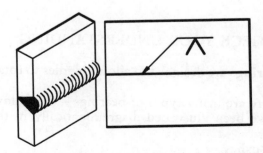

Figure 11.16 A V butt weld and its symbol

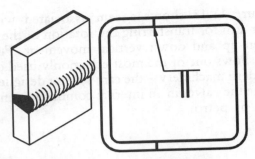

Figure 11.17 A butt weld and its symbol

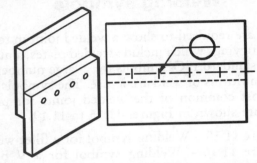

Figure 11.18 Spot welds and the spot weld symbol

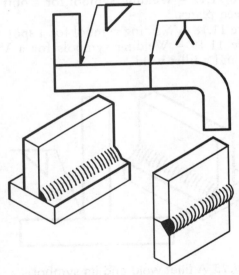

Figure 11.19 A fillet weld and a V butt weld and their symbols

■ CHECK YOUR UNDERSTANDING

● **Bearings** are designed to allow spindles to rotate freely.
● There are many types of bearings – the following have been illustrated diagrammatically in this chapter:
  a) **Bushes**.
  b) **Ball and roller bearings**.

● Ball and roller bearings consist of:
  a) The ball or roller – spheres, parallel rollers, taper rollers, needle rollers.
  b) Race rings to hold the balls or rollers.
  c) A cage to separate the balls or rollers.
● In technical drawings use the ISO symbol and not precise drawings for bearings.
● There are three main types of ball and roller bearings:
  a) **Journals**.
  b) **Thrust bearings** to take loads.
  c) **Angular bearings**.
● When including **gears** in technical drawings use the ISO symbols and do not attempt drawing the gear teeth.
● The ratio of revolutions per minute between gears in a gear train are directly proportional to the number of teeth in the gears.
● An **idler gear** is included in a gear train to change the direction of rotation between gears.
● There are many types of **cams**, but all are designed to convert one form of movement into another.
● **Radial cams** convert rotary movement into straight line movement.
● When drawing **welded joints** in plate work drawings, use welding symbols to show the types of welds to be used.

REVISION EXERCISES AND QUESTIONS

Exercises

This section is devoted to exercises which involve engineering drawings. Some of these exercises include design features. The reader may choose to ignore the design element of these exercises. However if the design features are attempted, the extra work involved will give the reader a better understanding of simple engineering details.

The exercises include orthographic projection, some in Third angle (see pages 102 to 103), isometric drawing, freehand drawing and geometric constructions. The standard of difficulty involved in attempting the questions varies from average to high.

These exercises are of examination standard.

1 Figure 11.20 is a three-view First angle orthographic projection of a coupling for fitting between an electric motor and a machine. Part 1 of the coupling is screwed onto the spindle of the motor and Part 2 onto the spindle of the machine. As the motor rotates, so the rotation

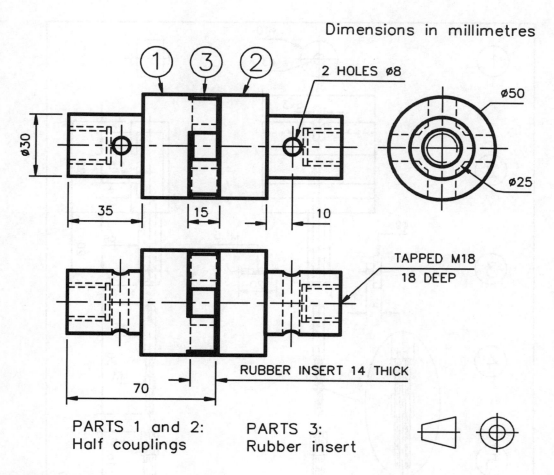

Dimensions in millimetres

2 HOLES ⌀8

⌀50

⌀30

⌀25

35   15   10

TAPPED M18
18 DEEP

RUBBER INSERT 14 THICK

70

PARTS 1 and 2:   PARTS 3:
Half couplings   Rubber insert

Figure 11.20 Exercise 1

is transferred to the machine. The rubber insert (Part 3) between Parts 1 and 2 of the coupling absorbs much of the strain involved when the motor is started and when the machine is running. It also allows slight misalignments between the line of the motor and the machine spindles.

Make a full size (scale 1:1) **freehand and exploded drawing** of the three parts of the coupling. Do not attempt to dimension your drawing or to include hidden detail.

Explain in note form why both Part 1 and Part 2 have holes of diameter 8 mm bored in them.

2 Figure 11.21 (page 172) is an exploded Third angle orthographic projection of the 5 parts of one of the two heads from a **beam compass**. A beam compass is a technical drawing instrument designed for drawing very large circles. A beam compass has two heads, one of which holds a pencil lead, the other holds a needle point. The heads are fitted on an aluminium girder, along

which they can be moved by rotating a roller (Part 1 of Figure 11.20). The girder (the beam) can be of any length, thus allowing very large circles to be drawn.

Working to a scale of 5:1 (five times full size) and in First angle orthographic projection, draw the following views of the assembled head.

a) A Front view taking the left hand views of Figure 11.20 as the Front view of the exploded drawing.
b) A sectional End view, the section plane to run vertically through the centre of the Front view.
c) A Plan.

Dimension your drawing and include a title block.

3 A three-view Third angle orthographic projection of a clip from an electric reading lamp is given in Figure 11.22 (page 172). The clip is made from plastic material. The hole in the clip is designed to fit onto the upright rod of the

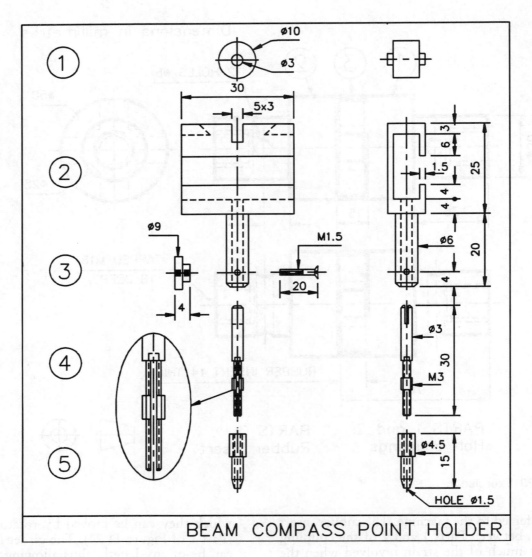

BEAM COMPASS POINT HOLDER

Figure 11.21 Exercise 2

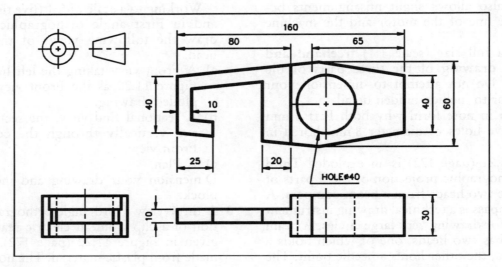

Figure 11.22 Exercise 3

stand. The open part of the clip is designed to hold the electric cable near to the rod of the stand.

Construct an accurate twice full size (scale 2:1) isometric drawing of the clip.

4 Figure 11.23 is the dimensioned outline of a handle for a handsaw. The handle was designed for saw blades which could cut either wood or metal. The holes for the bolt holding the blade to the handle are not included in the given outline.

Make a full size (scale 1:1), accurately constructed drawing of the handle. Your drawing should include all the constructions needed to obtain accurate tangents between the various points of the outline.

5 Figure 11.24 includes a Third angle orthographic projection of a *spindle support*. The drawing consists of a Front view, a part Plan and an isometric drawing of the component. The support is made from cast iron and is intended to be bolted on to a bed, also made from cast iron with the aid of four M15 studs with

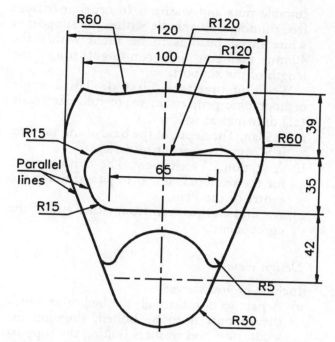

Figure 11.23 Exercise 4

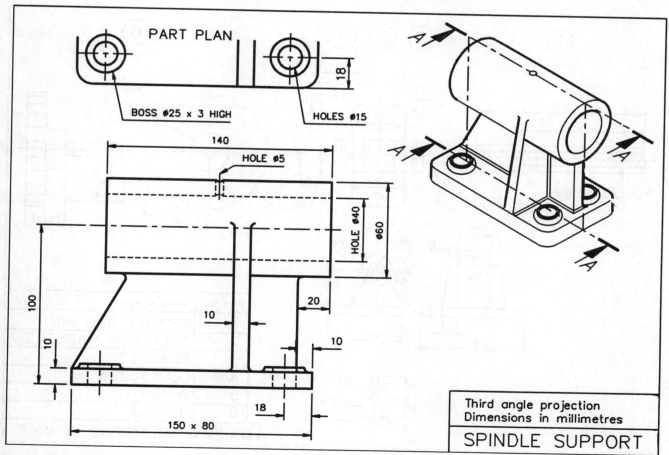

Figure 11.24 Exercise 5

suitable nuts and washers. In order to ensure free running of a spindle within the support, a white metal bush is to be fitted within the 40 mm diameter hole running through the length of the support.

Working in either First or Third angle orthographic projection, make full size (scale 1:1) drawings as follows:

a) A Plan. The depth of the base of the support is 90 mm from front to back.

b) A sectional Front view. The cutting plane for the sectional view is to pass through the centre of the Plan.

c) An End view as seen from either end of the component.

Design element

Include in you views:

a) A part section through the bed onto which the support is to be bolted, showing the studs, nuts and washers bolting the support to the bed.

b) A suitable bush in which the spindle would rotate.

c) Part of a spindle to which a V pulley of 150 mm diameter is fixed, the pulley being on the right hand end of the support.

Dimension your views and add a suitable title block, which includes a parts list, naming all the parts in the drawing and naming the materials for the parts.

6 Figure 11.25 is an exploded Third angle orthographic projection of the 6 parts of a *machine adjusting spindle* from a wood planer machine. Figure 11.26 (page 175) is a photograph of the assembled machine spindle. The adjusting spindle allows for the positioning of the bed of the planer to determine the thickness of wood being planed from a plank passing through the machine.

Working in either First or Third angle projection, make a full size (scale 1:1) accurate drawing of the assembled machine adjusting spindle as follows:

a) The sectional Front view A-A.

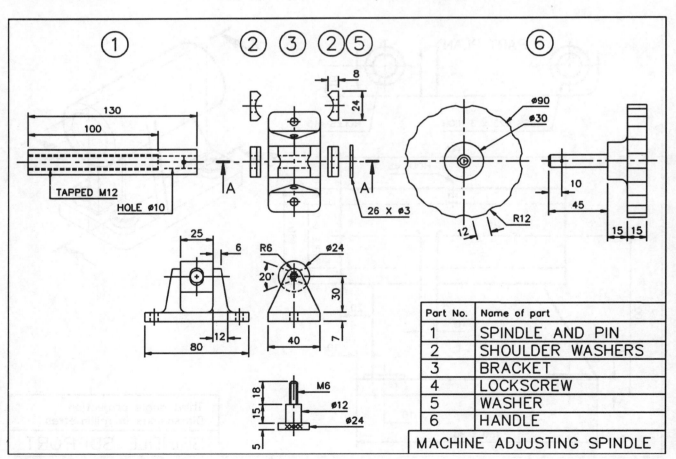

Figure 11.25 Exercise 6

Figure 11.26 Photograph for Exercise 6

b) An End view as seen from the right hand end in the photograph.
c) A Plan.

Add to your drawing:
  i) Six important dimensions.
  ii) A title block including your name, the scale and the title of the assembly.
  iii) The given Parts list.

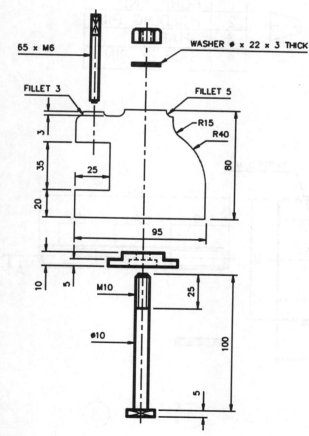

Figure 11.27 Exercise 7

7 Figure 11.27 shows the outline only of a Front view of the *tool holder* from a screw cutting lathe. Figure 11.28 is a photograph of the casting for the *tool holder*. The casting is held in the slide rest of the lathe by a purpose-made screw, washer and nut, the square head of which fits into a slot in another purpose-made Tee piece. Tools are held in the *tool holder* by two M6 screws, with square heads. They are included in Figure 11.27. Details of these holding screws, nuts and washer and of the Tee piece are included in Figure 11.27.

Figure 11.28 Photograph for Exercise 7

Construct a twice full size (scale 2:1) sectional view through the assembled *tool holder* showing all three screws and the nut, washer and Tee piece of the main holding screw in their positions in the casting.

Fully dimension your drawing.

8 Using standard symbols for the gears, draw the following spur gear trains:
  ● Gear 1 – 72 teeth – diameter 144 mm.
  ● Gear 2 – idler gear – 24 teeth – diameter 48 mm.
  ● Gear 3 – 96 teeth – diameter 192 mm.

The ratio of rotation between one spur gear and that with which it meshes is in a direct proportion to the number of gear teeth around the circumference of a spur gear. Thus if the 72 tooth gear is revolving at 100 R.P.M, the 24 tooth gear will be revolving at

$$72/24 \times 100 = 300 \text{ R.P.M.}$$

and the 96 tooth gear will be revolving at:

$$72/96 \times 100 = 75 \text{ R.P.M.}$$

Note that the idler gear does not alter the ratio between the driving gear (the 72 tooth gear) and the driven gear (the 96 tooth gear).

9 Draw the following in-line gear train:
- Gear 1 – 100 teeth.
- Gear 2 – 25 teeth.
- Gear 3 – 125 teeth.
- Gear 4 – 75 teeth.

    At what R.P.M. does gear 4 rotate and in which direction in relation to gear 1?

10 Draw a Front view and Plan of a pair of 90 degree bevel gears, one with 48 teeth, the second with 36 teeth. Assume the diameters of the two parts of the gear are in direct ratio to the number of teeth in each part of the gear.

11 Figure 11.29 is an exploded Third angle orthographic projection of a *fork*, its shaft and holding pin. A safety pin (Part 4), fits tightly into the 5 mm diameter hole in the holding pin (Part 2).

In either First or Third angle projection and working to a scale of 1:1 (full size), accurately construct the following views of the 4 Parts properly assembled:

a) A sectional Plan on A-A.
b) A Front view.
c) An End view as seen looking into the mouth of the fork end.

Add 4 major dimensions to your drawing and a title block containing your name, the scale and a title for the drawing.

Design element

Design another fork assembly which includes a shaft and which will fit inside the fork end (Part 1) of the assembly you have drawn in such a manner that it can swing around the holding pin (Part 2) within the limits of the shape of the fork end.

Include this second fork assembly in the three views already drawn.

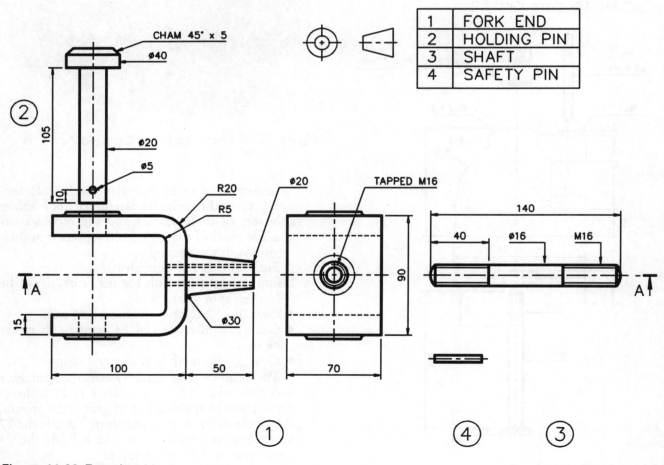

1	FORK END
2	HOLDING PIN
3	SHAFT
4	SAFETY PIN

Figure 11.29 Exercise 11

Note: As with other designs, before attempting the final drawing for the design element of this exercise, make several freehand sketches of solutions to the design problem and only when satisfied you have a suitable and sensible design should you include the designed parts in your final drawing.

12 This is a more difficult exercise than the earlier exercises in this chapter.

Figure 11.30 is a First angle Front view and a sectional End view of a *lathe tailstock*. Note the broken lines indicating the lathe bed on which the tailstock can slide and to which it can be locked when in a chosen position.

Do not copy the given views but construct the following views of the tailstock. Work in either First or Third angle projection and to a scale of 1:1 (full size):

a) The given Front view.

b) An End view – not in section, but a full End view as seen when looking from the left hand end of the Front view.

c) A Plan in section, the section cutting plane to be as is indicated by B-B.

Include 6 major dimensions in your views and add a title block to your drawing which includes your name, the scale, the date and a suitable title.

Design element

Taking ideas from any lathe at hand add the following to all three views in your drawing:

● A handwheel and screw, which will move the lathe centre in its spindle in and out of the tailstock casting.

Remember to make several freehand sketches of suitable handles and screws before attempting to include details of the handle and screw to your drawing.

You will need to look at the design of such handles from either any lathe which you may be

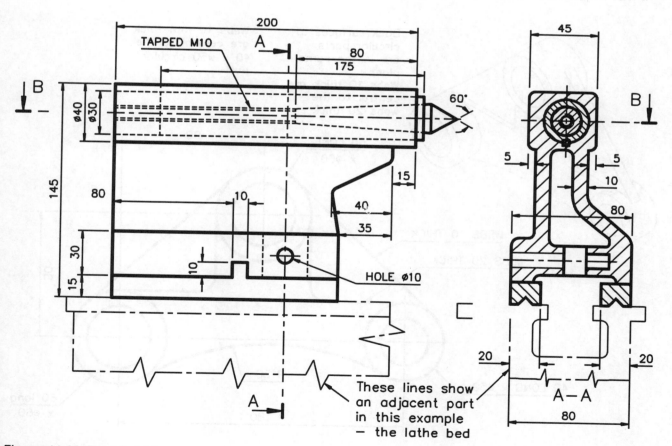

Figure 11.30 Exercise 12

able to study, or from technical drawings in machine manuals showing details of lathes and their tailstocks.

13 Figure 11.31 shows a Front view of a casting for a gear train support from a screw cutting lathe, together with an isometric drawing of the support. Details of sizes are included with the drawings.

Three spur gears on spindles are fitted into the three holes in the support, each with a suitable bush. The three gears form a gear train and together are part of a more complicated gear train.

Working in either First or Third angle projection construct the following three views of the support:
a) The given Front view.
b) A sectional End view, the cutting Plane to be taken vertically through the upper holes in the Front view.
c) A Full Plan.
Dimension your drawing and add a title block which includes your name, the date, a scale and a title for the drawing.

Design element

The three spur gears to be fitted into the support are to be mounted on spindles in such a manner that they are held firmly in bushes within the support and yet can rotate freely in their bushes. Details of the gears are:
● Gear 1 – left hand hole in the support: 24 teeth; 26 mm diameter hole.
● Gear 2 – upper hole in the support: 48 teeth; 36 mm diameter hole.
● Gear 3 – right hand hole in the support: 48 teeth; 36 mm diameter hole.
Add details of all three gears to your drawing showing:
a) Correct symbols for the gears.
b) The spindles and how they are prevented from moving out of the holes in the supports.
c) The method of attaching the gears to the spindles.
d) The bearing bushes and suitable lubricating holes.

14 Figure 11.32 is a Front view, together with an

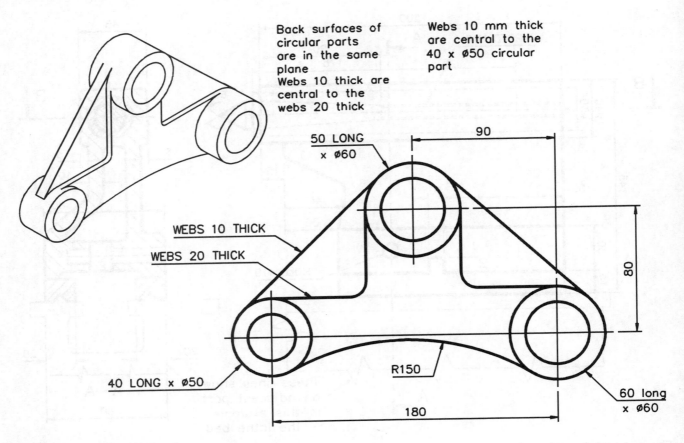

Figure 11.31 Exercise 13

isometric drawing of a spindle support. The support is to be bolted against the side of a metal framework via the 20 mm diameter hole in the support. A spindle of 20 mm diameter is to revolve within a ball bearing set within the 40 mm diameter hole.

Working in either First or Third angle projection construct the following views of the support:

a) A sectional view with details taken from the given Front view and with the cutting plane taken centrally through the shaped hole in the web.

b) A Plan showing the horizontal edge of the cutting plane.

c) An End view looking from the left hand end of the Front view.

Design element

After making a series of freehand sketches to determine a sensible solution for the design, add the following to your drawings:

a) A method by which the support can be bolted to its metal framework without any possibility of it slipping under the weight of the support and its spindle.

b) A length of spindle (show both ends as if broken) showing a bush and a suitable lubri-

cating hole for the spindle within its bush.

15 The four drawings of Figure 11.33 (see page 180) show a method of designing the profile of a rotary cam with either wedge or a roller follower. This method is only suited to these two types of follower. Designing profiles when other types of follower are used is beyond the scope of this book.

The details for this exercise, which is worked for you in the four drawings, is based upon the following dimensions:

• Rotation of cam is clockwise.
• Basic radius of cam = 25 mm.
• Follower stays stationary for first 90 degrees of rotation of the cam.
• Follower rises at a regular velocity through 40 mm for the next 90 degrees of rotation – from 90 to 180 degrees.
• Follower rises 60 degrees with regular velocity for the next 90 degrees of rotation – from 180 to 270 degrees.
• Follower falls back to commencing point in the next 90 degrees – 270 to 360 degrees of rotation.

Drawing 1 – the basic circle of the cam, together with its follower.
Drawing 2
1. Draw a line of any length – e.g. 120 mm.
2. Divide the line into 12 equal parts.

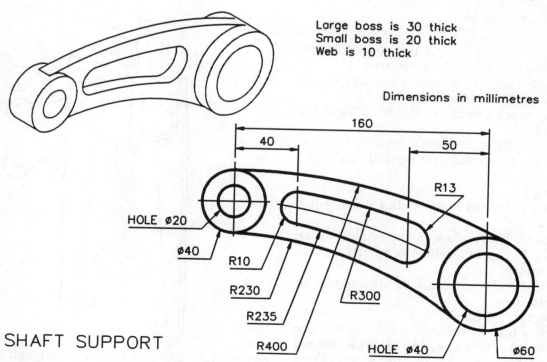

Large boss is 30 thick
Small boss is 20 thick
Web is 10 thick

Dimensions in millimetres

HOLE ⌀20
⌀40
R10
R230
R235
R400
R13
R300
HOLE ⌀40
⌀60
160
40
50

SHAFT SUPPORT

Figure 11.32 Exercise 14

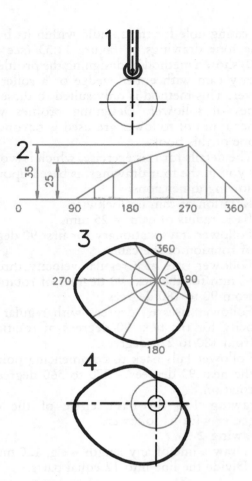

Figure 11.33 Exercise 15

3. Number 30 degree spacing – only 90, 180, 270 and 360 are really necessary.
4. At 180 mark off 25 mm vertically; at 270 mark off 35 mm vertically.
5. Draw lines between the 90, 180, 270 and 360 marks.
6. At the 30 degree marks draw verticals to meet the lines joining the verticals at 180 and 270.

Drawing 3

1. Divide a circle of 30 mm radius into 12 equal parts.
2. At each division transfer the height of each of the 30 degree heights from Drawing 2 to Drawing 3.
3. Draw a fair curve through the points so obtained.

Drawing 4

1. Draw a fillet at the points 360 and 90. The follower, whether wedge or roller shaped would tend to stick or jam at any sharp corners in the profile.

16 Construct the profile of a rotary cam to the following details:
● Cam basic radius – 40 mm.
● Rotation clockwise.
● Follower rises 10 mm for first 60 degrees of revolution.
● Rises 15 mm for next 60 degrees.
● Falls 5 mm for next 60 degrees.
● Remains stationary for the next 90 degrees.
● Falls back to starting point with regular velocity for remaining part of the revolution.

17 Figures 11.34 to 11.36 on pages 180 to 181 show a pictorial drawing and orthographic projections of a *bearing removal tool* which removes bushes of diameter 30 mm from bearings.
    Working in either First or Third angle projection and to a scale of 1:1 (full size) draw:
a) A front view of the assembled tool.
b) An End view in section, the section plane taken along the centre line of the screw.
c) A Plan.
Add 6 main dimensions to your drawing and a title block containing:
    i) Your name.
    ii) The scale.
    iii) The date.
    iv) A title.

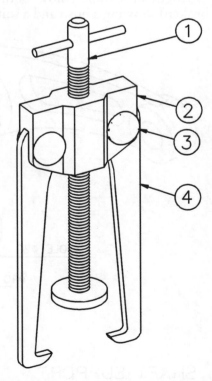

Figure 11.34 Exercise 17. The assembled *bearing removal tool*

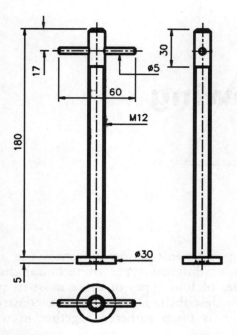

Figure 11.35 Part 1 of the *bearing removal tool*

Questions

1 What would an engineer mean by the term journal?
2 What is the difference between a ball bearing and a roller bearing?
3 Why is it necessary to fit bushes into some bearings? Name materials you think suitable for bushes.
4 When is it necessary to use an 'idler' gear?
5 What is the difference between a spur gear and a bevel gear?
6 Which geometric curve is used to design the faces of a gear tooth?
7 What is the purpose of using radial cams?
8 Sketch some of the welding symbols you have learned.
9 Examine a motor car engine. Can you name some of the bearings in the engine?
10 What are the differences between a three-view orthographic projection in First angle and one in Third angle?

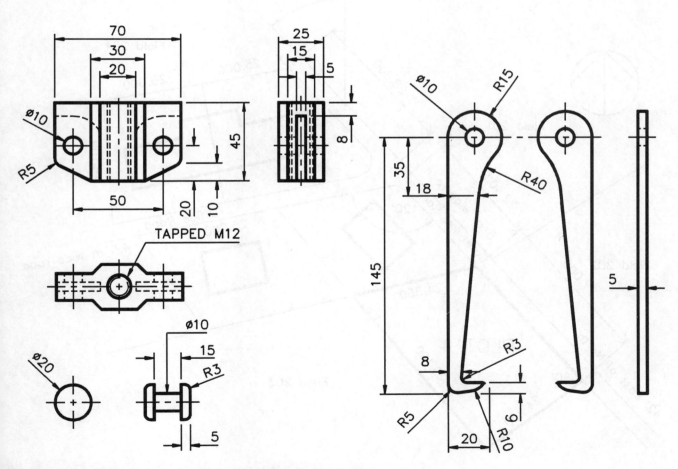

Figure 11.36 Parts 2, 3 and 4 of the *bearing removal tool*

Building drawing

Introduction

This chapter deals with basic technical drawing for the building and construction industries. The building and construction industries use a large number of different types of technical drawing. Examples of four types of those most frequently used are described. Drawing in the construction industries is often gathered together in what is

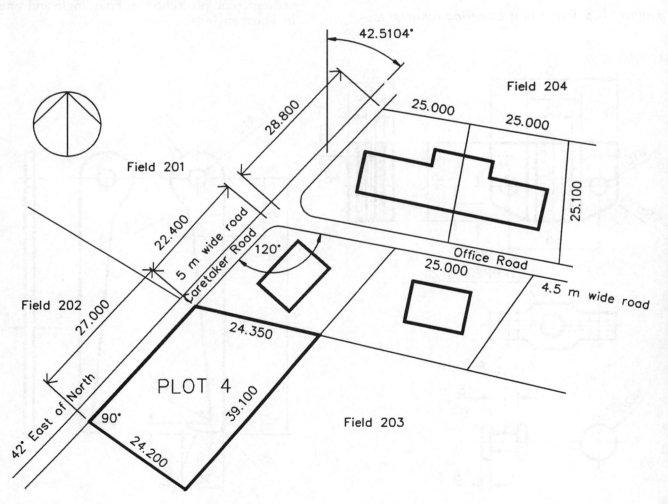

Figure 12.1 A freehand drawing for a site location plan

182

Types of building drawing

Four types of drawings used in building are shown in this chapter. These four types are:

1. **Site location plans.**
2. **Site plans.**
3. **Building plans.**
4. **Sectional views** through features in buildings.

Other types of drawings are more the concern of the architects who plan and supervise the construction of buildings, for example:

- Installation plans to show the positioning of features such as electrical circuits in building, water supply, sewage systems.
- Block plans describing large areas to be built on.
- Schedule drawings showing the schedule of operations for constructing buildings.

Site location plan

Figure 12.1 and Figure 12.2.

A site location plan shows the position and dimensions of a site on which a building is to be constructed. In order to draw an accurate site location plan, it is often necessary for someone to visit the site and make a freehand sketch drawing of the location of the site in relation to its immediate surrounding areas.

Figure 12.1 is a freehand drawing of the site location plan for a building site on which a small single storey house (bungalow) is to be built on PLOT 4. The freehand drawing contains enough information for an accurately scaled 1:200 site location plan to be drawn – Figure 12.2. In the freehand drawing note the following:

1. Dimensions are in metres to three decimal places. Three decimal places allows millimetre

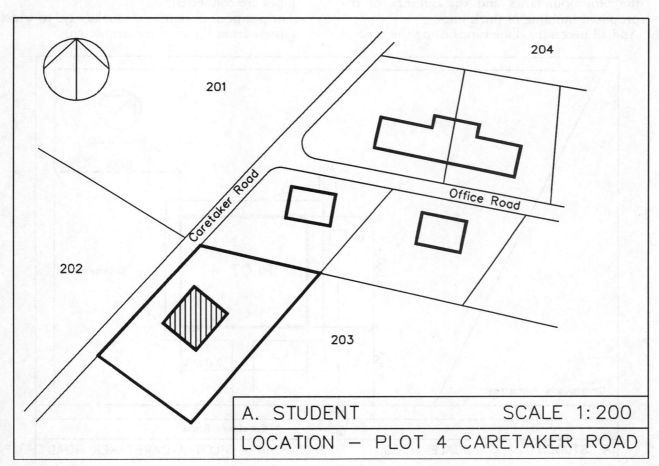

Figure 12.2 A site location plan

sizes to be read – because there are 1000 millimetres in a metre and 1 millimetre = 0.001 metre.

2. The arrows are different to those in drawings in previous pages. The type of arrows shown are often used in building drawings in place of the filled type of arrow.
3. Field and building plot boundaries are thin lines.
4. Existing building outlines and the outline of the plot to be developed are in thick lines.
5. The inclusion of a true North symbol.
6. Field numbers.

Figure 12.2 is the site location plan drawn with instruments to a scale of 1:200 on an A3 sheet of paper.

Exercise

a) Copy this drawing as an example of a simple site plan. Try to show existing buildings on the site, the plot boundaries and the outlines of the proposed building in thick lines.
b) Add all necessary dimensions using the type of arrow given in Figure 12.1. The dimensions for the position of the single storey building within Plot 4 can be taken from Figure 12.3.
c) Add a suitable title block.

Site plan

Figure 12.3 is a scale 1:100 site plan for the building to be constructed on PLOT 4. The drawing shows:

1. The position of the building within its plot.
2. Dimensions in metres to three decimal places.
3. The 'building' type arrows to the dimensions.
4. The building outline in thick lines.
5. All other lines are thin lines.
6. The inclusion of a true North symbol.
7. A title block with the title of the drawing, its scale and the name of the person who made the drawing.
8. The positions of manholes to which sewage pipes are connected.
9. The positions of rain water soakaways to which gutters from the roof are connected.

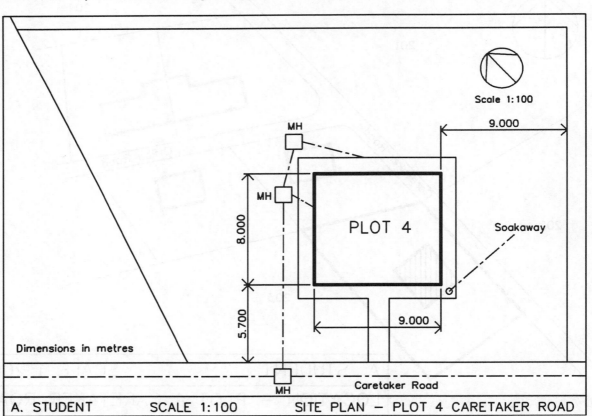

Figure 12.3 A site plan

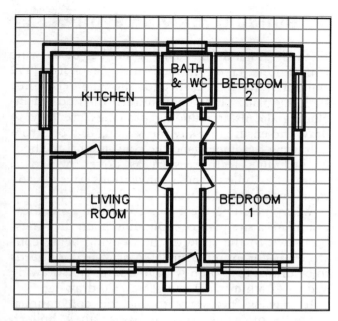

Figure 12.4 A freehand drawing of a building plan drawn on square grid paper

Exercise

a) Copy the given drawing working to a scale of 1:100.
b) Add all necessary dimensions.
c) Try to draw the outline of the building position in thick lines and all other lines thin.
d) Include a true North symbol.

Building plan

Figure 12.4 is a freehand drawing of a building plan, on 10 mm square grid paper, of a design for the single storey house to be built on PLOT 4. Figure 12.5 is an accurately drawn building plan with details taken from the freehand drawing.

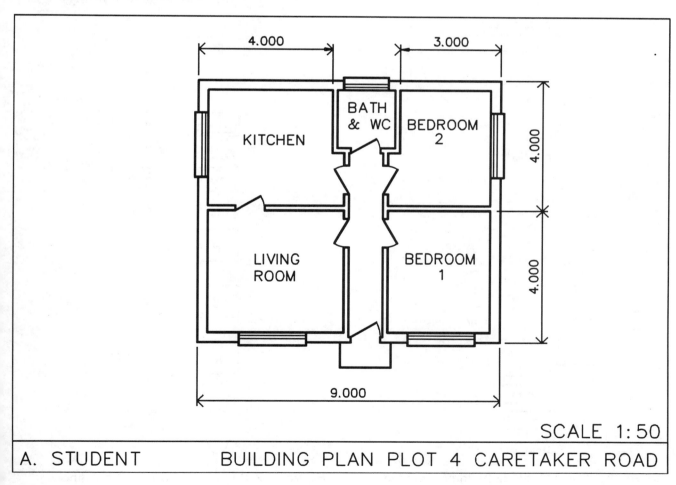

Figure 12.5 A building plan

Exercise

a) Copy the given building plan to a scale of 1:50. Figure 12.6 shows the building drawing symbols to be used when making this drawing.
b) Include all necessary dimensions.
c) Add a suitable title block.

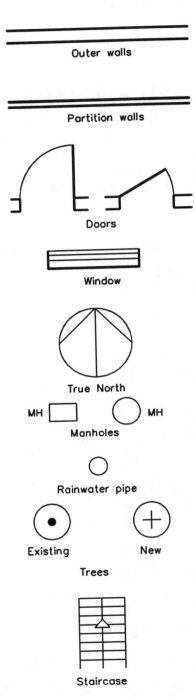

Figure 12.6 Some BS:1192 building drawing symbols

Building drawing symbols

Figures 12.6 and 12.7 show a number of drawing conventions taken from British Standard 1192 Building Drawing Practice for showing details in a building plan. These conventional methods of including details in building drawings are easy to draw and ensure that anyone wishing to work from a drawing can understand the conventional methods of including features such as doors, windows, stairs, etc. Some of these conventions have already been included in Figures 12.2, 12.3 and 12.5.

When including these conventions in a site location plan, a site plan or a building plan, they must be drawn to the scale of the drawing being constructed. For example an 850 mm wide door needs to be drawn to 17 mm wide in a scale 1:50 drawing and to 42.5 mm wide in a scale 1:20 drawing.

It may be necessary to include conventional drawings of fittings such as baths, sinks, boilers, etc. in building plans. Figure 12.7 includes standard methods of showing some of such fittings.

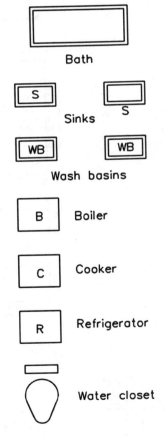

Figure 12.7 Some more BS:1192 building drawing symbols

Sectional drawing through features in buildings

Example 1

Figure 12.8 is a sectional view through a single brick wall, the foundations on which it is resting, together with a concrete roof and floor. This is a typical example of a sectional view showing the method of construction of part of a building.

Exercise

1. Calculate a scale required to enable you to copy the given drawing, Figure 12.8, working on an A3 sheet of drawing paper.

2. When you are satisfied the chosen scale is all right, copy the given drawing. The sizes for a standard brick are included with the drawing. From the dimensioned brick, you should be able to estimate other sizes suitable for your drawing. The height of the building is not required because the sectional view is broken into upper and lower parts.

3. Note the different types of section hatching to show different materials. Your drawing should include these differences.

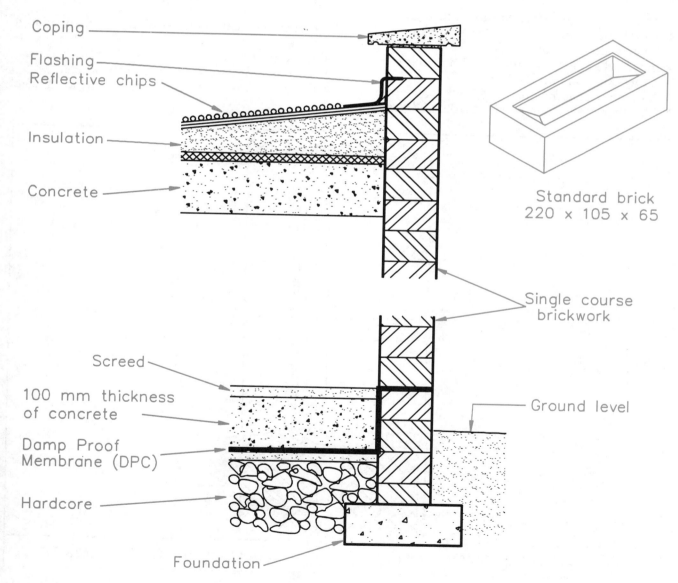

Figure 12.8 A sectional view through a single brick wall

Example 2

Sectional view through a glazed window

Figure 12.9 is another example of a sectional view through part of a building. This particular section is through a glazed, fixed window set into a double wall with a cavity between the inner and outer walls. Note again, the different types of section hatching for different materials.

Exercise

Copy the given drawing, Figure 12.9, working to a suitable scale to fit the drawing onto an A3 sheet of drawing paper. Use the following dimensions:

- Bricks – standard sizes as shown in Figure 12.8.
- Mortar between bricks – 10 mm thickness.
- Inner wall – 110 mm thick.
- Inner sill – 160 mm wide by 25 mm thick.
- Outer sill – 90 mm by 30 mm.
- Window frame members – 65 mm by 45 mm.
- All other dimensions – left to your judgement.

Example 3

Sectional view through a glazed door

Figure 12.10 shows details of a glazed door such as could be fitted as an outer door to a building. The drawing shows a sectional view through the door, an enlarged view of the sectional shape of the upper door frame and details of the tenons on the upper and central rails of the door. Note that the tenons are **long** and **short shoulder** in order that they may fit into the rebates in the vertical parts of the door – which are known as **styles**.

Exercise

Take dimensions as follows:

- Upper and central rails – 90 mm wide by 35 mm thick.
- Bottom rail – 65 mm wide by 35 mm thick.
- Tenons – one-third of the rail thickness.
- Other sizes – in relation to those already given.

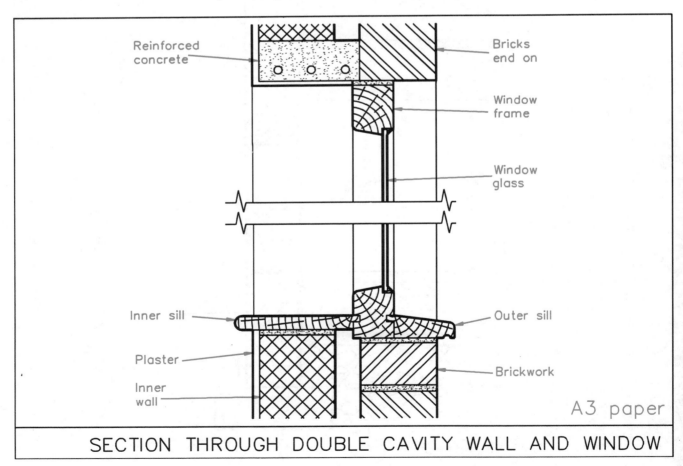

SECTION THROUGH DOUBLE CAVITY WALL AND WINDOW

Figure 12.9 A sectional view through a double cavity wall and a window

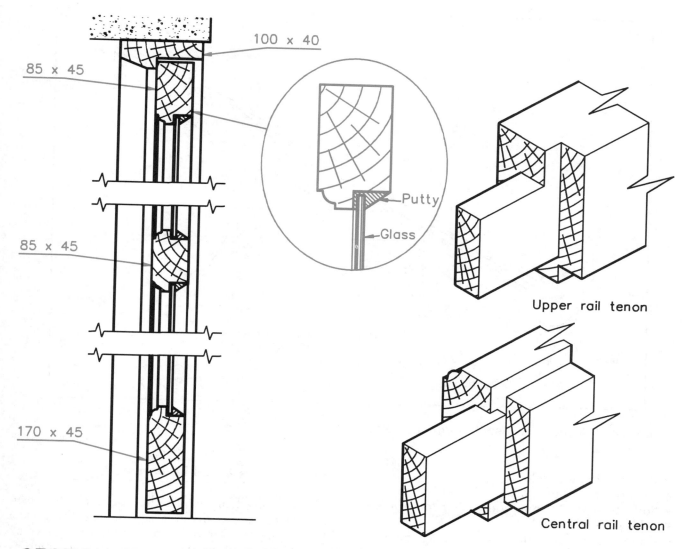

100 × 40

85 × 45

85 × 45

170 × 45

Putty

Glass

Upper rail tenon

Central rail tenon

SECTION THROUGH A GLAZED HOUSE DOOR

Figure 12.10 A sectional view through a glazed door with pictorial views of its jointing details

Note: Because the door is in a broken sectional view, the height of the door space does not affect this exercise.

Make the following drawings to a scale suitable for placing the views on an A3 sheet of drawing paper:

a) The given sectional view.
b) The given isometric drawings.
c) A further isometric drawing showing the bottom rail tenon. This rail should contain a double tenon.

Example 4

A sectional view through a sloping tiled roof

Figure 12.11 (see page 190) is a sectional view through a tiled roof mounted on a single brick wall. Note the terms used in the construction involved in the roofing method shown.

Exercise

Working to dimensions:

● Bricks – standard brick sizes given in Figure 12.9.

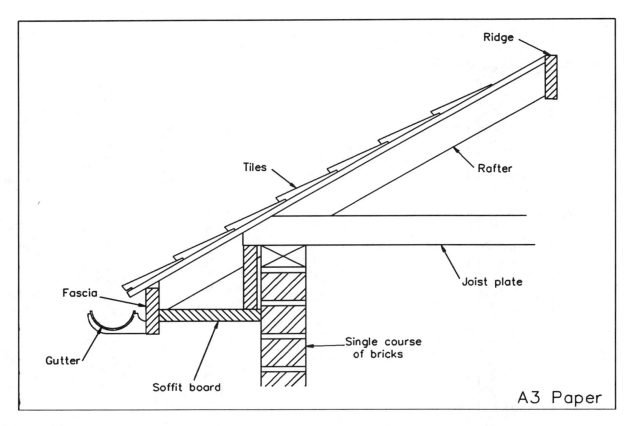

Figure 12.11 A sectional view through a sloping roof

- Rafter – 75 mm wide.
- Joist plate – 70 mm wide.
- Soffit board – 200 mm wide by 25 mm thick.
- Tiles – 150 mm wide.
- Other dimensions – left to your judgement.

a) Copy the given drawing to a scale suitable for an A3 sheet of drawing paper.
b) Include a method by which you think the soffit board should be jointed to the fascia board.
c) Much more difficult – make an isometric drawing showing a pictorial view of the soffit board, the fascia board and the board behind the soffit board.

Drawings for furniture making

The technical drawing methods for engineering are well suited to drawings for woodworking and furniture making in general as is shown in the next four pages.

Example 1 – A wall bookrack

The drawing from which the bookrack shown in Figure 12.12 was made is a scale 1:5, three-view First angle orthographic projection. The bookrack was designed to be made in a hardwood, such as Niangon (an African mahogany style hardwood).

Exercise

Working in either First or Third angle projection on an A3 sheet of drawing paper:

a) Draw the three views in correct projection.
b) Include all necessary dimensions.
c) Add a suitable title block and the two statements – First angle projection and dimensions in millimetres.

Example 2 – An exploded isometric drawing

Figure 12.13 is an exploded isometric drawing showing the construction for the bookrack shown in Figure 12.12 on page 191. The drawing shows the top shelf, back rail and plywood back explode

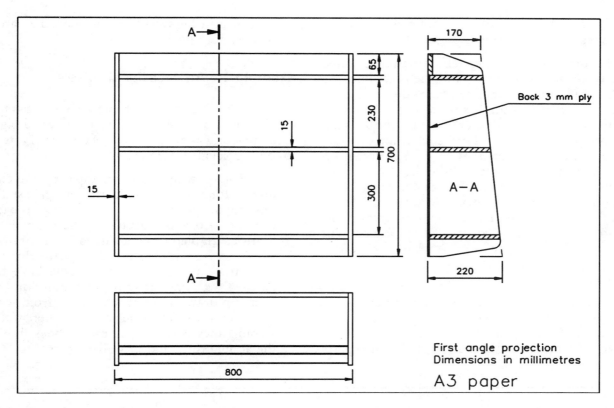

Figure 12.12 A working drawing of a wall bookrack

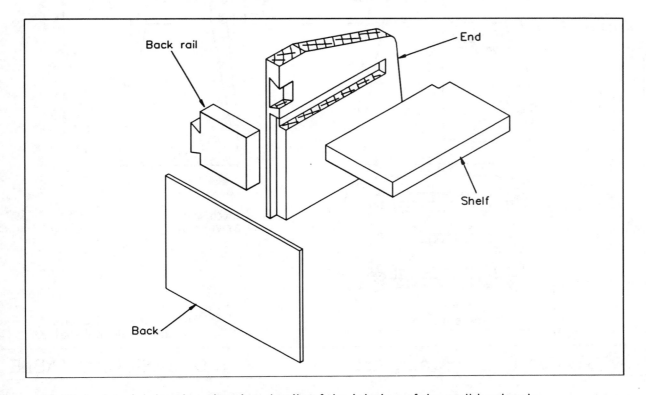

Figure 12.13 A pictorial drawing showing details of the jointing of the wall bookrack

from one of the ends of the bookrack. Note the following drawing details in Figure 12.13:

1. The outer lines of all parts of the exploded drawing are thick lines, while the inner lines are thin. This method of emphasising the outlines of an isometric drawing has been shown before in this book. The thick outer lines give the drawing more of a 3-D (three-dimensional) look.
2. Curved and straight lines have been drawn on the part of the drawing where the end grain of the wood would show. This is a practice commonly used when showing wooden articles in technical drawings. The curved lines (arcs) indicate the annual rings of the wood. The straight lines indicate the medullary rays of the wood.

Exercise

a) Working to a scale of 1:5 draw the given exploded isometric drawing Figure 12.13 on an A3 sheet of drawing paper.
b) On the same sheet of paper, draw the same parts

as shown in Figure 12.13, but with the parts in their jointed positions.

Example 3 – An occasional table

Figure 12.14 is a scale 1:5 three-view orthographic projection of a small table. The table was designed to be made in the hardwood Mansonia. Note the following details in Figure 12.14:

1. The Plan drawing shows the top drawn in **chain lines** – long dash, short dash lines. These lines indicate the position and plan shape of the table top and also allow details of the leg rails and 'buttons' in plan to be included in the drawing.
2. The End view is a sectional view. In this view the parts cut by the section plane have been hatched with lines at 45 degrees and 3 or 4 mm apart. In drawings of articles made from wood, the hatch lines in sections can be either straight, sloping lines as shown, or can be lines showing the annual rings and medullary rays.

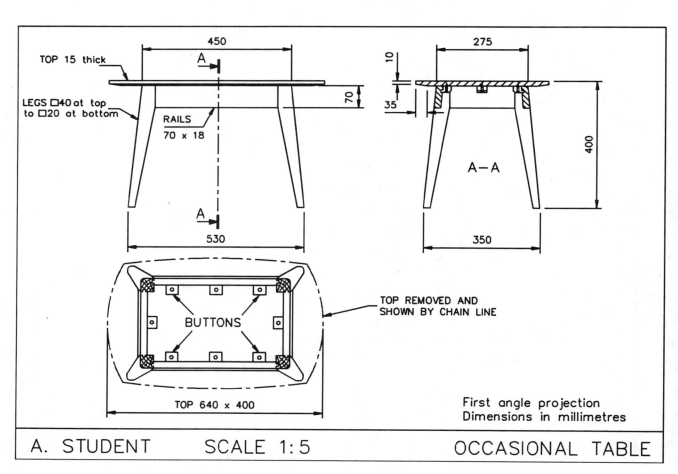

Figure 12.14 A three-view orthographic projection in First angle of a small table

Exercise

Working to a scale of 1:5 and in either First or Third angle projection, draw the following views of the table:

a) A Front view.
b) A sectional End view.
c) A Plan as shown in Figure 12.14 with the top in chain lines.

Include a title block and the statements First (or Third) angle projection and Dimensions in millimetres.

Example 4 – An exploded isometric drawing

Figure 12.15 is another example of an illustration of furniture constructions in the form of exploded isometric projections. This method of showing how the parts of furniture are jointed is commonly used in technical drawings of articles made from wood. Figure 12.15 includes:

1. An exploded isometric drawing of one corner of the table showing the **mortices** (in the legs) and **tenons** (in the rails) by which the framework of

the table is jointed. Note the two views of one of the tenons. The second (upper) view shows the shape of the tenons more clearly than the lower view.
2. An isometric drawing of one of the 'buttons' which are made for joining the top to the framework. The tongues of the buttons are held in grooves cut in the insides of the rails of the table and screws through the hole in the buttons allow the top to be screwed to the rails via the buttons.
3. An enlarged Front view of one end of the top to show the chamfer of the underside of the top more clearly.

Exercise

Working on an A3 sheet of drawing paper and full size, copy the given isometric drawings.

■ CHECK YOUR UNDERSTANDING

● Of the many types of building plans used in the building industry, four are shown in this chapter:
a) **Site location plans.**

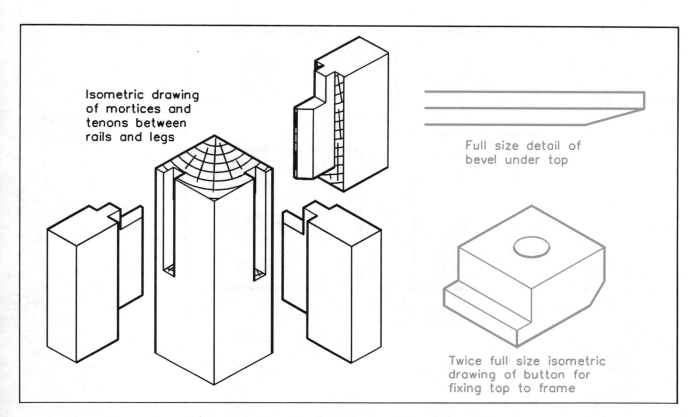

Figure 12.15 Pictorial drawings showing the jointing details for the small table

b) **Site plans.**
c) **Building plans.**
d) **Sectional views** through features.

● A site location plan shows the positions and dimensions of a site onto which a building is to be constructed.

● A site plan describes the plot onto which a building is to be constructed. Details of the outline and dimensions for the plan are taken from the site location plan.

● A building plan shows details of the layouts of rooms etc. in the building to be constructed on a plot.

● Use building conventional drawings for details within building drawing where possible.

● Sectional drawings through features show the construction and the materials used for the construction of parts of a building.

Technical drawing methods for engineering and/or building drawing are suitable for technical draw-ings involved in the design and construction of furniture.

● **Annual rings** and **medullary rays** can show end grain in drawings of woodwork features.

● Exploded isometric drawings are a useful method by which the methods of jointing parts of a design can be clearly shown.

● Use grid papers for the freehand sketching of designs when working on building designs.

REVISION EXERCISES AND QUESTIONS

Design Exercises

Design Exercise 1

Figure 12.16 shows, in outline only, on a 10 mm square grid, details for the layout of the rooms of a

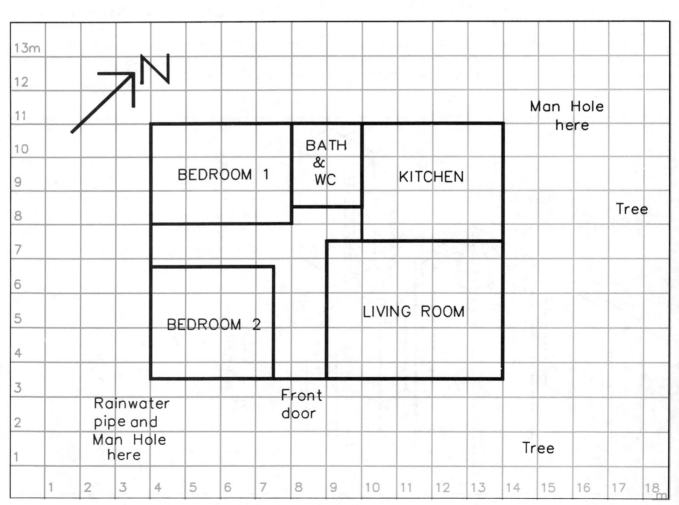

Figure 12.16 Design Exercise 1

small single-storey house. Working to a scale of 1:50 and using correct building drawing conventions (as given on page 186):

1. Draw an accurate building plan of the house which includes doors and windows in suitable positions.
2. Include the North symbol and the conventional methods of showing the manholes, rainwater pipes and trees with your drawing.
3. Include a title block.

Design Exercise 2

Figure 12.17 is a freehand drawing on 10 mm grid paper of a design for a single-storey house. A model for the house has been made in cardboard and a photograph of the model is given in Figure 12.18. A start has been made to a building drawing for the house on 10 mm grid paper in Figure 12.19 (page 196).

Working to a scale of 1:50 and including correct conventional methods of building drawing

1. Make an accurate building plan of the house on an A3 sheet of drawing paper.
2. Include a suitable title block with your drawing.

Design Exercise 3

Figure 12.9 on page 188 is a sectional view through a glazed window. The exercise connected with the drawing gave details of the sizes of the various parts shown by the section. The window frame for

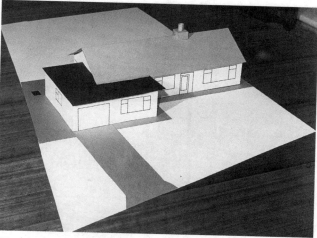

Figure 12.18 Photograph of a cardboard model of the bungalow in Design Exercise 2

which this section has been drawn is 1.200 metres square.

It has been decided to fit double glazing panels to the window frame by making two sliding glazed frames fitted by grooves in the rails of the frames sliding on wooden runners and placed so as to slide one behind the other. The frames are to be fitted between the window sill and the reinforced concrete beam above the window opening (see Figure 12.9).

A sectional view through the two frames is given in Figure 12.20 (page 197), together with some details of the methods of making the frames into which glass is to be fitted.

Working on an A3 sheet of paper draw to a suitable scale the following view:

1. A sectional End view through one of the frames placed in position within the sectional view you will have drawn in answer to the exercise on page 188.

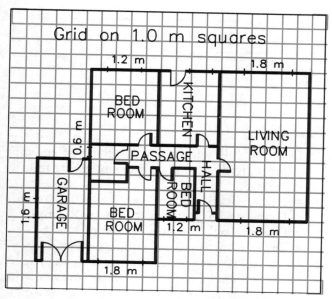

Figure 12.17 Freehand drawing for Design Exercise 2

Note the method by which the frames can be lifted up and out from their runners — the depth of the grooves in the top rails is twice that of the depth of the grooves in the bottom rails.

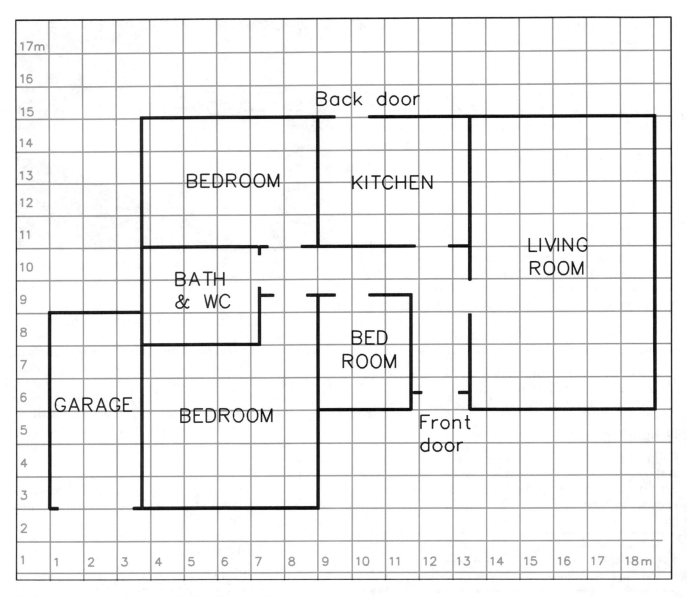

Figure 12.19 Outline details for Design Exercise 2

Design Exercise 4 – Drawer making

Figures 12.21 to 12.24 show the classic method of making drawers for furniture and Figures 12.25 and 12.26 show a simplified method of making drawers. There are many other methods of constructing such drawers, but the two methods shown here are in common use for either first-class furniture making (Figures 12.21 to 12.24) or for cheaper furniture (Figures 12.25 and 12.26).

Exercise

1. Drawing full size on an A3 sheet of drawing paper, copy Figure 12.21 working to the following sizes:
   - Drawer **front** 150 mm × 75 mm × 15 mm.
   - Drawer **sides** 160 mm × 75 mm × 8 mm.
   - Drawer **back** 150 mm × 60 mm × 8 mm.
   - Drawer **bottom** 3 mm thick plywood.
2. Draw full size on an A3 sheet of drawing paper:
   a) A sectional Front view of the drawer with details taken from your isometric drawing.
   b) An End view of the drawer.
   c) A plan of the drawer.

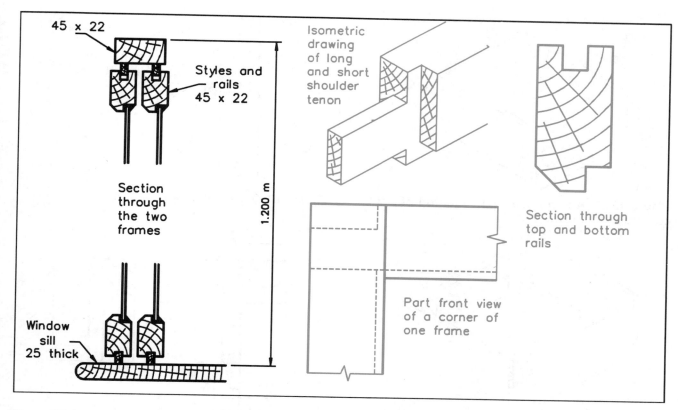

Figure 12.20 Details for Design Exercise 3

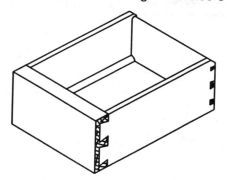

Figure 12.21 Pictorial drawing of a well-made drawer

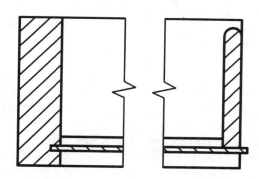

Figure 12.23 Sectional view through the drawer Figure 12.21

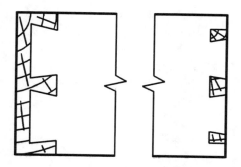

Figure 12.22 End view of the drawer shown in Figure 12.21

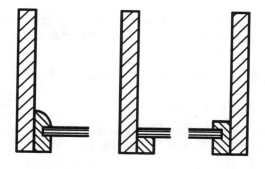

Figure 12.24 Sectional views showing methods of fixing a bottom to the drawer Figure 12.21

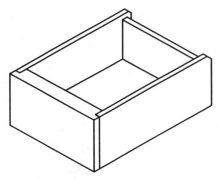

Figure 12.25 Another (cheaper) method of constructing a drawer

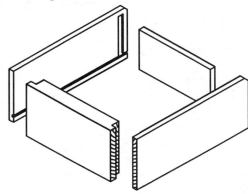

Figure 12.26 An exploded pictorial drawing of the drawer in Figure 12.25

Design Exercise 5

Figure 12.27 is an incomplete section through a lean-to roof and the wall to which the roof is fixed. The drawing shows the rafter onto which the roofing tiles are to be fixed, a single brick wall and a beam already fixed to the wall to which the roof rafters are jointed. Make a full size drawing of a complete sectional view of the part of the roof and wall shown by adding:

a) The 'flashing' which prevents water from running off the roof behind the wall to roof join.
b) Tiles for the roof.

Sizes not shown are left to your judgement.

Design Exercise 6

Part of the frame into which a door is to be fitted into a brick wall is shown in a three-view First angle orthographic projection in Figure 12.28. An incomplete isometric drawing of the part of the frame is also included in Figure 12.28.

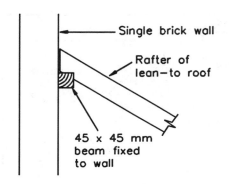

Figure 12.27 Design Exercise 5

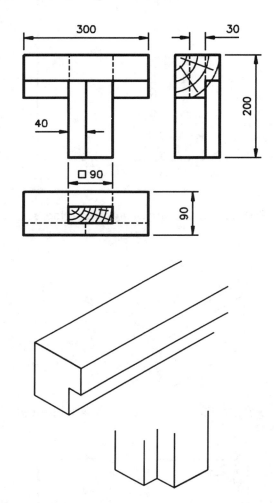

Figure 12.28 Design Exercise 6

Working to a scale of 1:1, make an accurate and complete isometric drawing of the part.

Design Exercise 7

Figure 12.29 is a site plan for a 2-bedroom bungalow and an out-house to be built within the plot shown by the boundary lines.

1. Freehand sketches showing designs for paths and a play area for children to be added in the site plan, the play area to include a slide and a sand pit.
2. A second set of freehand sketches for designs for the layout of rooms within the proposed building.
3. An accurately drawn, scale 1:100 site plan to include the best of your design ideas for the paths and play area.
4. Working to a scale of 1:50, on a separate sheet of paper and working to the best of the designs you have sketched, draw a building plan showing the layouts of rooms within the bungalow.
5. Fully dimension your two drawings and add suitable title blocks and necessary labels identifying parts of the drawings.

Questions

1 Four types of building drawings are described in this chapter. Can you name them all?
2 One of the types of drawing is a site plan. Make a freehand drawing of an area of ground which you think might be suitable for building a house. Then design a site plan for the piece of land showing where you think a house could be built.
3 Make a sketch of the room in which you learn technical drawing. Then make an accurate drawing with instruments showing the positions of all chairs and desks in the room.
4 Make sketches of sectional views through the door of a room.
5 Make sketches of a sectional view through the window of the room you sleep in.
6 Take any piece of furniture in your home or in your school and make sketches showing the types of joints you think are used in making the piece of furniture.
7 Make a sketch of a section through a flat roof showing the methods of making sure the roof will not leak.

Figure 12.29 Design Exercise 7

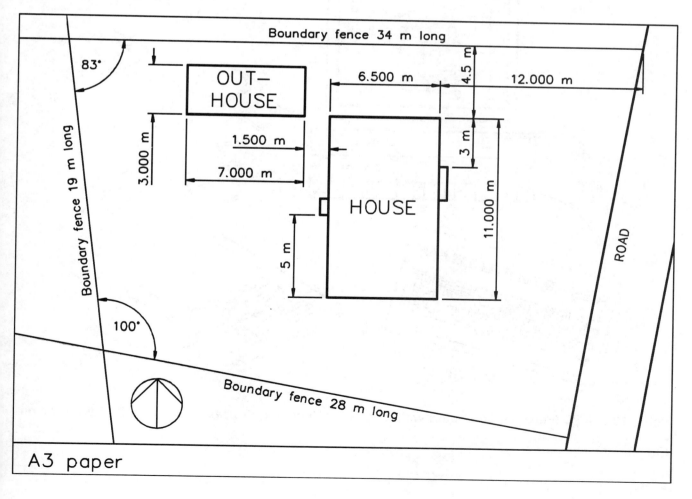

Computer aided drawing and design (CAD)

Introduction

Technical drawing is the major design method by which ideas about the shape, form, dimensions, materials, machining methods and finishes of articles being made or constructed are passed between those working in the manufacturing and building industries. These industries are increasingly using computers for the production of their technical drawings. It is possible at the present time for a skilled computer operator to be able to design and draw very advanced drawings on a PC (Personal Computer) with the aid of those computer software packages known as **CAD (Computer Aided De-**

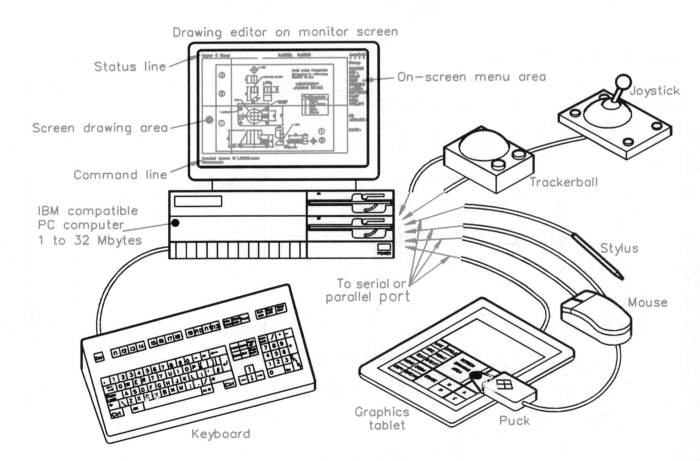

Figure 13.1 A PC (Personal Computer) with a variety of 'pointing devices' set up as a CAD workstation

sign). There are many CAD software packages available at the present day for use on a computer which will stand on the desk of a draughtsman. For the purpose of describing CAD, we will only be dealing with two of these packages. The first – *AutoCAD* – is expensive but is capable of producing any technical drawing, no matter how complicated in the hands of a skilled operator. AutoCAD is by far the most popular of all. There are more CAD workstations equipped with AutoCAD throughout the world than any other package. The second – *AutoSketch* – is an inexpensive CAD package for constructing 2-D (two-dimensional) drawings. Both packages are produced and sold by the same firm Autodesk.

When working with the aid of CAD, in place of a drawing board, Tee square, other instruments and pencils, drawings are constructed on a computer monitor screen with the aid of the computer keyboard and a hand controlled 'pointing device'. The computer, its monitor, keyboard and pointing device are known as a *workstation*. See Figure 13.1.

A typical workstation comprises:

1. The computer, its monitor and keyboard. The monitor screen displays the drawing being constructed. The keyboard allows the typing of features such as commands which determine the type of feature being drawn – e.g. LINE, CIRCLE, ARC, or lettering or dimensions.
2. A pointing device, which controls the movement of a cursor on the screen. The cursor may be a pair of crossing lines or an arrow. The pointing device may be any one of:
   a) A **mouse** – as the mouse is moved over the desk surface, its movements are followed by the cursor.
   b) A **graphics tablet** with a **puck**. As the puck is moved over the graphic tablet, its movements are followed by the cursor on the screen. The puck can also be used to pick command names, such as LINE or CIRCLE from the graphic tablet.
   c) A **trackerball**. Rotation of a ball in its holder

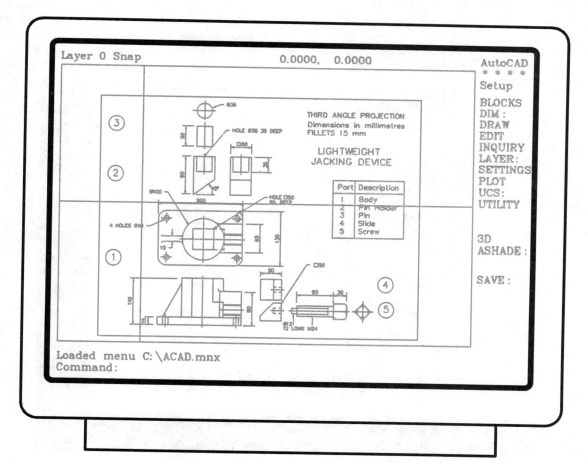

Figure 13.2 A computer monitor screen showing a drawing constructed in AutoCAD

causes the screen cursor to move to any required position.

d) A **joystick** with which the cursor is controlled.

Only one of these pointing devices is usually fitted to the computer, although some operators prefer to have two fitted so as to be able to use either at any one time. The monitor screen in Figure 13.1 shows a drawing in an AutoCAD drawing editor on the monitor screen and Figure 13.2 (see page 201) shows more clearly details of the drawing in the drawing editor on the screen.

Figure 13.3 is what is known as a **screen dump** of the monitor screen shown in Figure 13.2. It shows what the drawing editor with its drawing actually looks like. Note the following:

1. The **menu** of commands in the right hand column of the screen.
2. The **pull-down** menu showing drawing commands.
3. The **command line** into which commands can be typed from the computer keyboard.
4. The menu names along the top edge of the screen.

Why use CAD?

There are many reasons why CAD is now being increasingly used in industry:

1. Speed of production of drawings. Accurate drawings can be produced by a skilled operator in a tenth (or even less) of the time it takes for a draughtsman to produce the same drawing.
2. Drawings or parts of drawings can be placed in other drawings very easily, which saves having to draw the same detail twice. This is one of the major reasons why CAD drawing is so much quicker than drawing by hand. A rule that CAD operators quickly learn is:
   Never draw the same thing twice
3. Drawings can be printed or plotted from a drawing on screen with great accuracy. The drawings can be saved to a computer disk to be printed or plotted at any time. Space required to store disks is a fraction of the space required to store drawings on paper.
4. Drawings can be printed or plotted from disk to any scale, saving the necessity of having to make up several drawings to different scales for different purposes.

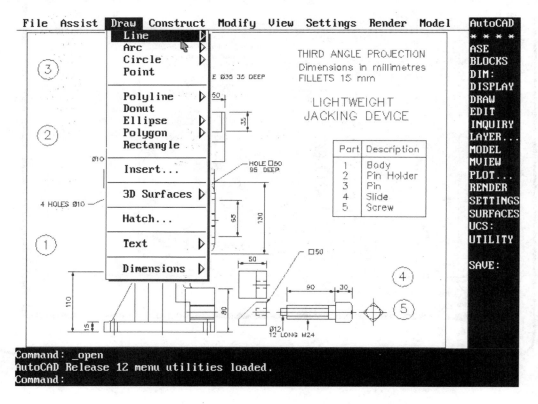

Figure 13.3 A drawing constructed in the drawing editor of AutoCAD

5. Parts of drawings can be printed or plotted to any scale, saving the need to re-draw parts of drawings to different scales.

6. Parts of drawings can be re-drawn in the case of design changes. Both old and revised drawings can then be saved to disk for recall. When drawing by hand, design changes usually require the whole drawing to be re-drawn.

7. Features such as dimensions can automatically be added, ensuring complete accuracy. A good CAD system measures the part which is being dimensioned and then automatically applies that dimension. This avoids dimensioning errors creeping in.

Why then learn technical drawing?

Even the most skilled computer expert working as a draughtsman with a CAD system must have a good technical drawing background. Without a good knowledge of the practice of technical drawing methods learned 'at the drawing board', a CAD operator cannot produce technical drawings with his/her equipment. It is only by practising with the aid of drawing instruments that computer drawing skills can be gained. A good practical knowledge of plane and solid geometry, an understanding of the theory of orthographic projection, the use of good standard drawing conventions can only be learned by constant practice 'at the drawing board'. So – first learn how to produce good quality technical drawings 'by hand', then learn how to produce them with CAD.

Zoom

One major feature of all CAD software packages is the use of the command ZOOM. A computer monitor screen is smaller than the sheet of paper which a draughtsman would be using. Because of this when a drawing of say A2 size, is on screen, some small parts of the drawing may not be easily drawn. With the aid of ZOOM, even the smallest area of the drawing can be examined and drawn on. Figure 13.4 shows details from the drawing in Figure 13.3 after part of the drawing has been placed in a ZOOM **window**. Note the command

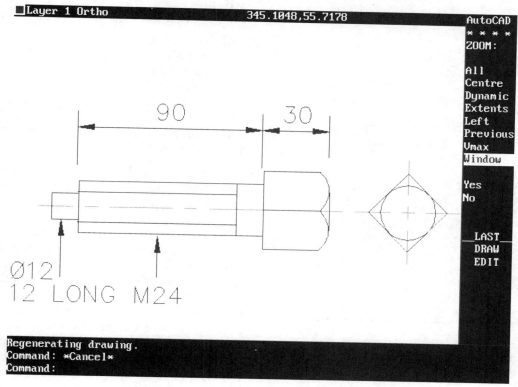

Figure 13.4 Part of the drawing of Figure 13.3 in a 'Zoom' window

and prompt names in the menu on the right of the screen. The prompt **Window** is **highlighted** in the zoom menu. A window in CAD terms is a small area from part of the screen.

Cartesian coordinates

Another feature common to CAD packages is two-dimensional (2-D) coordinates. These allow any point on a screen to be determined in terms of x and y. Units horizontally are in x units, units vertically are in y units. Any one point on screen is then determined in terms of x,y. If one is working on a screen configured to allow a drawing to be constructed as if on an A3 sheet of drawing paper, the screen would be set so that the drawing editor on screen is 420 units wide and 297 units high (A3 paper is 420 mm by 297 mm). In this case any point on the screen can be determined in units taken from the bottom left hand corner of the screen. Thus the bottom left hand corner is x,y = 0,0; the top right hand corner is x,y = 420,297. Figure 13. 5 shows the x,y positions of four points on a computer screen.

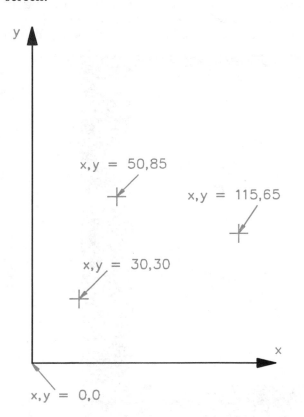

Figure 13.5 The theory of x,y 2-D coordinate geometry

An example of a drawing with CAD

Figure 13.6 shows a simple line outline within which a circle and a square have been drawn. In a CAD system, a typical method of working to construct this outline could be by typing commands and coordinate numbers at the keyboard. In Auto-CAD as the details are typed, they would appear at the command line at the bottom of the drawing editor. In AutoCAD such a sequence would be:

> **Command:** line
> **From point:** 100,200
> **To point:** 250,200
> **To point:** 250,150
> **To point:** 350,150
> **To point:** 350,80
> **To point:** 170,80
> **To point:** 170,150
> **To point:** 100,150
> **To point:** close
> **Command:**

Outline drawn

> **Command:** circle
> **Circle centre:** 130,175
> **Radius:** 25

Circle drawn

> **Command:** line
> **From point:** 300,130
> **To point:** 330,130
> **To point:** 330,100
> **To point:** 300,100
> **To point:** close
> **Command:**

Square drawn

At first glance this sequence may appear to take more time than if the drawing was constructed by hand at a drawing board, but the pointing devices have buttons which allow rapid changes between the different commands. Also many of the commands are keyed in with a single letter abbreviation – thus LINE is keyed in as l, CIRCLE is entered as c. The commands can be picked from the menus on the screen – an arrow, moved by movement of the pointing device is placed over a menu name and a pointing device button pressed, which causes the command name to appear in the command line. It is the combined use of a pointing device – mouse, puck, etc. – and entering letters and figures at the keyboard that allows a skilled operator to work very speedily in producing drawings on screen.

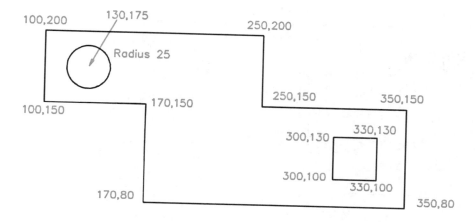

Figure 13.6 A drawing constructed in CAD by typing coordinate positions of points

Three-dimensional CAD

It is 3-D (three-dimensional) drawing that CAD excels at in industrial work. In very advanced CAD systems such as AutoCAD (among others), drawings can be produced in 3-D. The 2-D coordinate system is replaced with a 3-D coordinate system with an extra z coordinate – its positive direction is as if it were coming out of the screen towards the operator. It is not so much the value of the actual 3-D drawing that is so important, it is that such 3-D drawings can be shaded and coloured (**rendered**) to appear as if they were photographs of the component the drawing is portraying. In addition, in engineering industries, the mathematical data for a 3-D drawing held in the computer file for the drawing, can be passed on computer aided machinery and the component actually made in such machines from the data in the file. This method of production is known as **Computer Aided Machining (CAM)**. It must be noted that it is only advanced CAD packages which can be used for passing data to CAM machinery in this manner.

> **Note** how important the learning of technical drawing skills is. When one has acquired good basic technical drawing skills at the drawing board, this leads onto CAD and CAM in modern engineering industry. In building and architecture similar systems are used. In building the CAD systems are known as **Architectural Engineering Computing (AEC)** packages.

Further examples of CAD software packages

Figure 13.7 (see page 206) shows a drawing constructed in the 2-D CAD package **AutoSketch**. AutoSketch is a typical 2-D CAD system. Many such packages are available at present and all are relatively inexpensive. They only allow 2-D drawings to be constructed and most work in a similar manner to that already described for drawing in AutoCAD – by selecting or typing commands, followed by selecting points on screen with a pointing device or typing coordinates from the keyboard.

One of the more interesting features in CAD software in recent years has been their development for use in the major software system known as **Windows**.

Figure 13.8 (page 206) is the AutoSketch for Windows drawing editor on screen with a drawing constructed. Figure 13.9 (see page 207) is an example of a drawing constructed in the AutoCAD for Windows package.

There are many advantages of drawing with CAD packages developed for working in Windows. Among these are that an operator can work in several computer packages during one session of work. For example:

1. Notes can be written in a word processing package.
2. Switch to AutoCAD for Windows. Add the note to a drawing.
3. Switch to a spreadsheet package. Enter details of a component in the spreadsheet.
4. Switch back to AutoCAD for Windows. Add the details from the spreadsheet to the drawing.

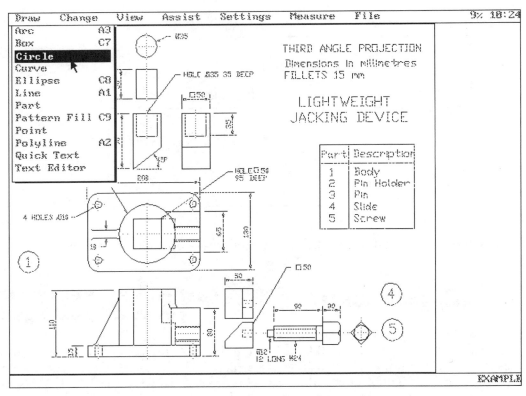

Figure 13.7 A drawing constructed in AutoSketch

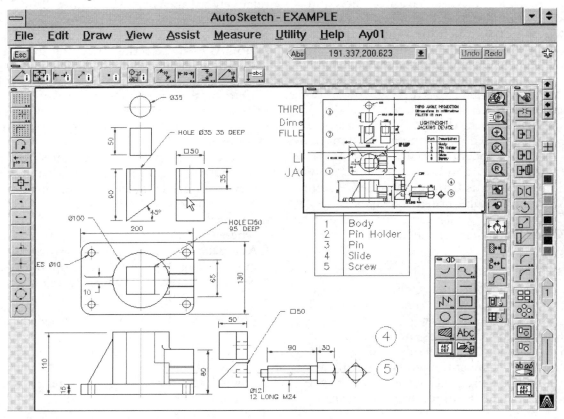

Figure 13.8 A drawing constructed in AutoSketch for Windows

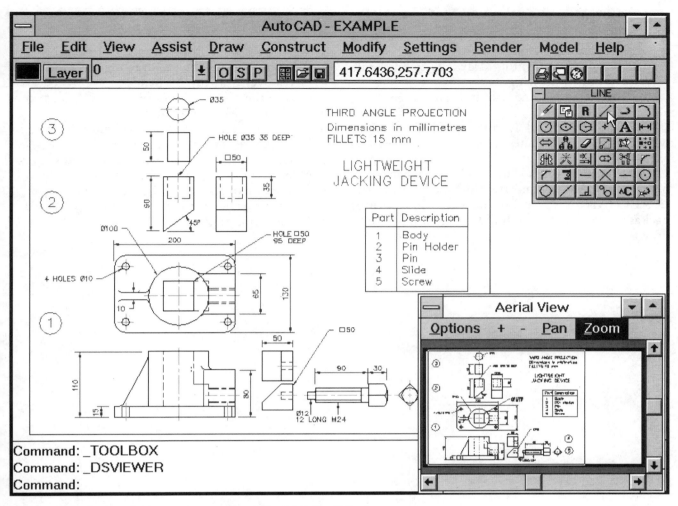

Figure 13.9 A drawing constructed in AutoCAD for Windows

5. Construct a drawing – say a map showing a friend how to find one's home.
6. Switch to a word processing package and write a letter inviting the friend to your home.
7. Switch back to the CAD package and save the map into a Windows style drawing.
8. Switch back to the word processor and add the map to your letter.

■ CHECK YOUR UNDERSTANDING

● Before you can expect to be able to use CAD software you must become skilled at drawing 'by hand'.
● CAD stands for **Computer Aided Design**. CAD is often taken as being an abbreviation for Computer Aided Drawing, but it is really an abbreviation for Computer Aided Design.

● Drawings in CAD are always constructed with the aid of a **pointing device**, in conjunction with the entering of details and data from the computer keyboard.
● What is being drawn in CAD shows up on the computer monitor screen.
● A CAD workstation consists of the computer, a monitor, a pointing device and a keyboard.
● All CAD packages rely on 2-D or 3-D coordinate systems in x,y (2-D) or x,y,z (3-D) units. Units horizontally are in x units. Units vertically are in y units. Units outwards from the screen are in z units.
● CAD is now becoming increasingly popular in industry because of:
  a) The speed by which drawings can be constructed.
  b) The ease by which drawings or parts of drawings can be inserted into other drawings.

c) The saving of space by storing drawings on file on disks compared with saving drawings on paper.

d) The speed of printing drawings to any scale without re-drawing.

e) Automatic adding of dimensions ensuring accuracy.

● A major command feature of CAD is **zoom** which enables the smallest area of a drawing to be examined.

● Data on file from advanced CAD packages can be used in **CAM (Computer Aided Machining)**.

● **AEC (Architecture Engineering Computing)** packages are available for building and architectural drawing.

QUESTIONS

1 What does the abbreviation CAD mean?
2 What are the advantages drawing with the aid of CAD over drawing by hand?
3 State some disadvantages of using CAD as compared to working by hand.
4 Why is it necessary to learn technical drawing by hand before starting to use CAD?
5 What is meant by the term 'coordinates' as applied to working on a CAD system?
6 Can you name any CAD software packages?
7 What is meant by the term 'pointing device'?
8 Name a pointing device.

Answers to exercises and questions, and answering hints

Introduction

This chapter provides you with all the answers to the variety of questions and most of the exercises given in the book. Always try a question or exercise yourself before you look at the answer. This will increase your understanding of the topic and give you practice in answering questions. If you are not sure of a particular answer, re-read the relevant section or chapter in the book to revise the work. You need to understand why a question has a particular answer, so that you can apply your understanding to similar types of question or exercise in your examinations and course assignments.

The book contains a variety of types of question and exercise. Find out the types of question that you will be expected to answer and their pattern. If possible, obtain past papers to support your work and revision. Some of the questions in the book require longer answers. We have provided hints on how to tackle these questions, and on the range of topics that you should include. Practise giving full answers to these questions and then check the answering hints to see that you have included all the relevant topics.

To revise a topic quickly you can also refer to the 'Check your understanding' sections given at the end of each chapter, and the list of key words with definitions given at the end of the book.

Hints to answering questions in examinations and course work

- Read all the questions carefully before you try anything. Make sure that you understand what each question is asking you to do.
- Plan the time that you will spend on each question. Use the marks as a guide: the more marks a question is worth, the more time it is worth spending on it.
- If you have a choice of questions, try to make your choice and stick to it. Don't change your mind halfway through the examination.
- Make sure that you earn all the 'easy' marks. Do not spend too long on a question you find difficult. Leave it; if you have time, you can try it again later when you have finished all the other questions.
- Keep an eye on the time. Make sure that you try all the questions you are required to answer.
- Always present your work as clearly as you can, whether you are writing or drawing. Make your work easy to follow for the examiner or assessor.
- Try and allow some time at the end to check your answers and improve them.
- In practical work, make sure that you understand what you are being asked to do by re-reading the question before you start. Follow all instructions carefully.

Answers to exercises

This chapter contains a number of drawing answers to many of the exercises given throughout the book. Not all the exercises have been answered, but a sufficient number have been included to show the reader how to work the exercises in each chapter. Most of the design element of the exercises has not been included with the answers, because hints for answering the design elements have already been given with many of the exercises. In any case, the answers to the design exercises will depend upon the reader – there are many different answers to all design questions. However, the design exercises throughout this book are based on technical drawing methods.

Introduction

1. Read 'Why learn technical drawing' on page x.

Chapter 1

1. International Standards Organisation; British Standards.
2. 1 square metre.
3. Read 'A size drawing sheets' on page 1.
4. Drawing board, sticky tape, Tee square, set squares (45, 45 and 60, 30), protractor, compasses, dividers, eraser, pencils, curve aid.
5. Read 'Storing equipment and drawings' on page 6.
6. 17–9 H grades, 6 B grades, F and HB.
7. See Figure 1.9 on page 4.
8. See Figure 1.11 on page 4.

9. In industry, articles are made from details read from technical drawings. The sizes of these manufactured articles can only be obtained from the dimensions included in the drawings.

Chapter 2

Answers to Exercises 1, 2, 3, 4, 6, 7, 8 and 9 are given in Figure 14.1.
5. Bisections are shown in Figure 14.1 for Exercise 4.
Answers to Exercises 10, 13, 14, 15 and 16 are given in Figure 14.2.
11. The answer will be the same as Figure 2.19.
12. The answer will be the same as Figure 2.20.
17. The answer will be the same as Figure 2.21.
18. The answer will be the same as Figure 2.22.

Chapter 3

Answers to Exercises 1, 5, 7, 8 and 13 are given in Figure 14.3.
2. Similar to Exercise 1 – construct the triangle with the aid of a compass, set to the required lengths. The triangle is an isosceles triangle.
3. Construct in a similar manner to answers to

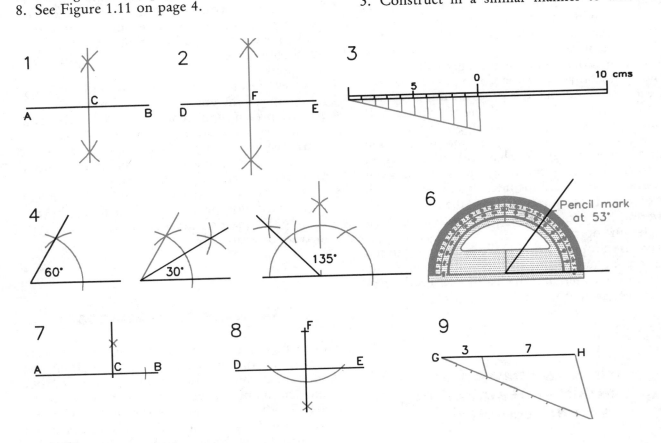

Figure 14.1 Answers to Exercises in Chapter 2

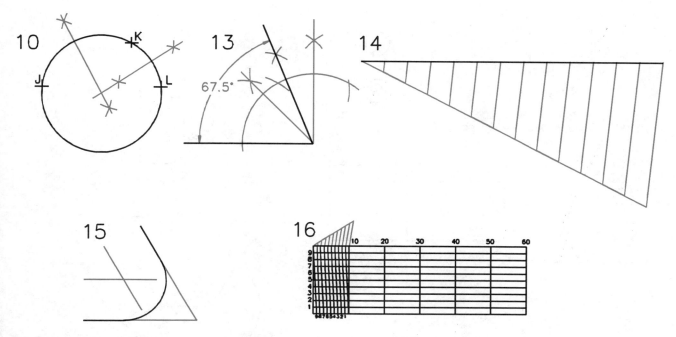

Figure 14.2 Answers to Exercises in Chapter 2

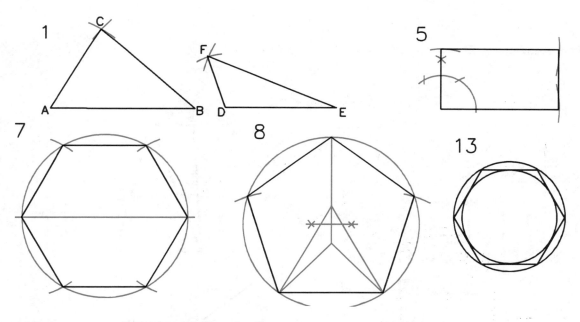

Figure 14.3 Answers to Exercises in Chapter 3

Exercises 1 and 2. The triangle is an equilateral triangle.

4. The triangle is a right-angle triangle, because its sides are in the ratio 3:4:5.

Exercises 9, 10, 11 and 12: The answers are given in Figures 3.22 to 3.25.

Exercises 14 to 20: The answers are the same as the given Figures 3.27 to 3.33.

Chapter 4

Answers to Exercises 1, 3, 4, 9 and 17 are given in Figure 14.4 (page 212).

2. Use methods similar to those given for Exercise 1 in Figure 14.4.

5. Methods of drawing tangents to an ellipse are given in this chapter.

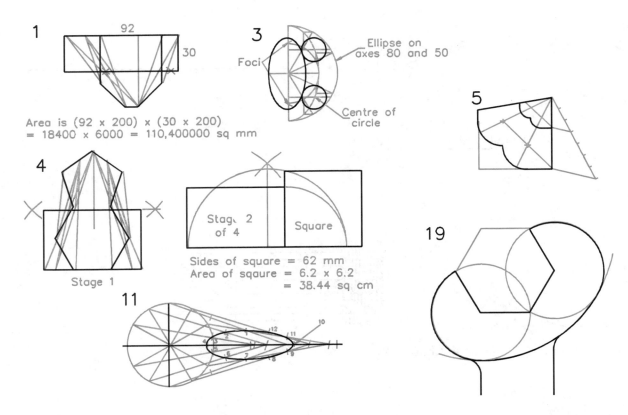

1 92 / 30

Area is (92 x 200) x (30 x 200)
= 18400 x 6000 = 110,400000 sq mm

3 Ellipse on axes 80 and 50 / Foci / Centre of circle

5

4 Stage 1

Stage 2 of 4 / Square

Sides of square = 62 mm
Area of sqaure = 6.2 x 6.2
= 38.44 sq cm

11

19

Figure 14.4 Answers to Exercises in Chapter 4

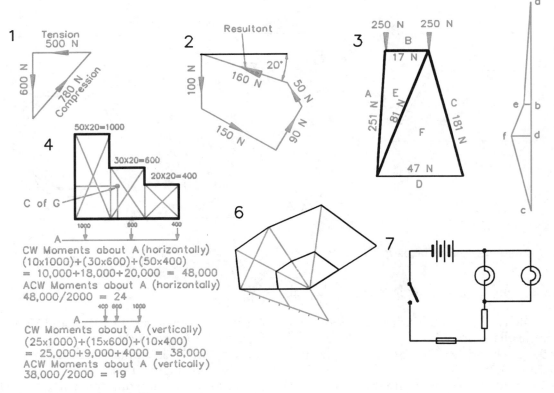

1 Tension 500 N / 600 N / 780 N Compression

2 Resultant / 20° / 100 N / 160 N / 50 N / 150 N / 90 N

3 250 N / 250 N / B / 17 N / A / E / C / 251 N / 81 N / 181 N / F / 47 N / D / a / e / b / f / d / c

4 50X20=1000 / 30X20=600 / 20X20=400 / C of G / 1000 / 600 / 400

CW Moments about A (horizontally)
(10x1000)+(30x600)+(50x400)
= 10,000+18,000+20,000 = 48,000
ACW Moments about A (horizontally)
48,000/2000 = 24

A / 400 600 1000
CW Moments about A (vertically)
(25x1000)+(15x600)+(10x400)
= 25,000+9,000+4000 = 38,000
ACW Moments about A (vertically)
38,000/2000 = 19

6

7

Figure 14.5 Answers to Exercises in Chapter 5

6. Follow the instructions given with the Exercise.
7. Use a construction similar to that shown in Figure 14.4 for Exercise 9.
8. Use a construction similar to that shown in Figure 14.4 for Exercise 9.
10. Use a similar construction to that shown in Figure 14.4 for Exercise 9.
11. See page 59.
12. See page 60.
13. See page 61.
14. Either divide the hexagon into a number of triangles, or reduce the hexagon to a triangle of equal area.
15. See page 54.
16. The eccentricity of a parabola is 1. The eccentricity of a hyperbola is greater than 1.
18. Use a similar method to that shown for Exercise 9 in Figure 14.4.

Chapter 5

Answers to Exercises 1, 2, 3, 4, 6, 7 and 11 are given in Figure 14.5.
5. Use the same method as for Exercise 4 in Figure 14.5 for finding moments about end of beam.
8. Follows a similar method to that shown for Exercise 7 in Figure 14.5.

Chapter 6

Answers to Exercises 1, 2, 7 and 11 are given in Figure 14.6.
4. Answer to Exercise 4 is given in Figure 14.7 (page 214).
Exercises 3, 5 and 6: Follow the same methods of construction as for Exercise 1 and 2 in Figure 14.6.
8. Follow the same methods of construction as for Exercise 7 in Figure 14.6.
Exercises 9, 10 and 12: Follow the same method of construction as for Exercise 11 in Figure 14.6.
An answer to Exercise 13 is given in Figure 14.8 (page 214).

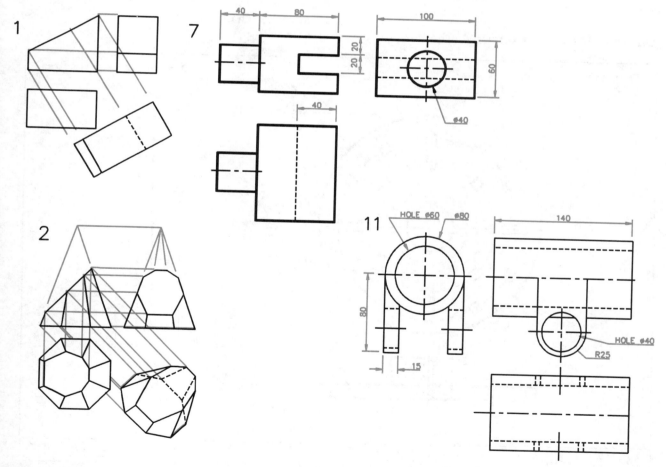

Figure 14.6 Answers to Exercises in Chapter 6

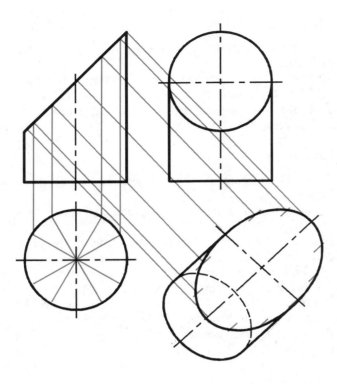

Figure 14.7 Answer to Exercise 4, Chapter 6

14. Follow the same methods of construction as for Exercise 13 in Figure 14.8.

Chapter 7

Answers to Exercises 1, 2, 3 and 7 are given in Figure 14.9.
Answers to Exercises 4 and 10 are given in Figure 14.10.
5. Use a construction similar to that shown for Exercise 2 in Figure 14.9.
6. A method of construction for this exercise is given on page 114 of this chapter.
8. Use a construction similar to that as shown for Exercise 7 in Figure 14.9.
9. Use a method of triangulation for this surface development – see the example for Exercise 4 in Figure 14.10.

Chapter 8

The exercises in Chapter 8 are included to give you some idea of the type of design question you may see in an examination paper. When you have revised earlier chapters, attempt to answer the design questions.

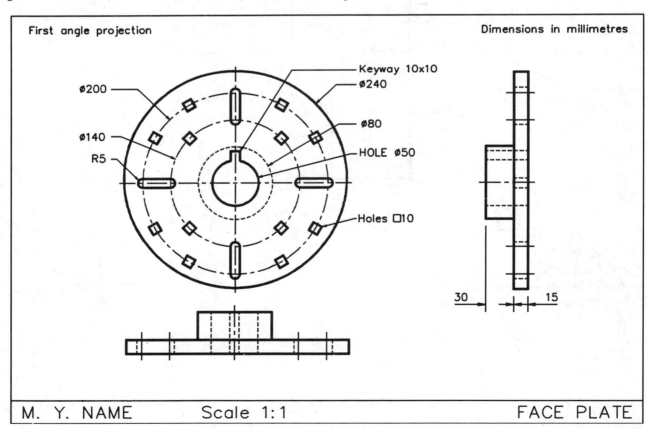

First angle projection   Dimensions in millimetres

Keyway 10x10
Ø200
Ø240
Ø140
Ø80
R5
HOLE Ø50
Holes □10

30   15

M. Y. NAME   Scale 1:1   FACE PLATE

Figure 14.8 Answer Exercise 13, Chapter 6

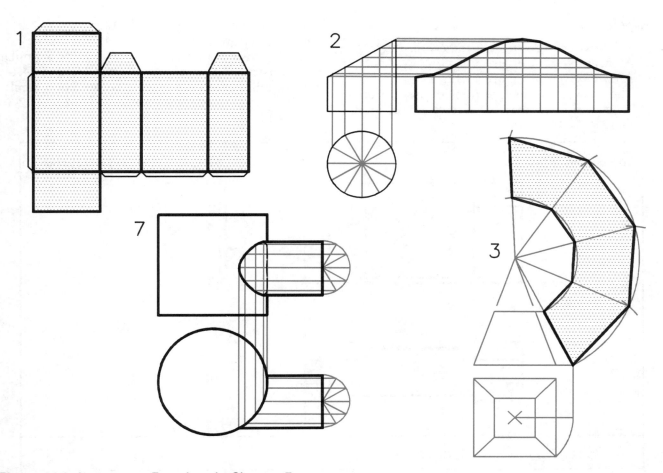

Figure 14.9 Answers to Exercises in Chapter 7

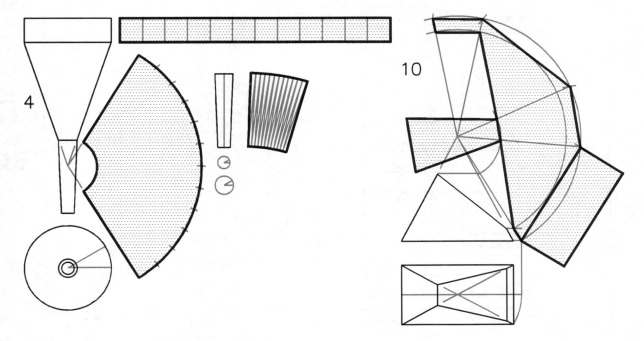

Figure 14.10 Answers to Exercises in Chapter 7

Chapter 9

1. The answer is given with the exercise.
2. Answer given in Figure 14.11.
3. Answer given in Figure 14.12.
4. The answer to this question follows a similar construction to that for Exercise 3 in Figure 14.12.
5. Answer given in Figure 14.13.
6. Answer given in Figure 14.14.
7. The answer to this exercise follows a similar construction to those in Figures 14.12 to 14.14.
8. Another exercise requiring construction similar to those in answers given in Figures 14.12 to 14.14.

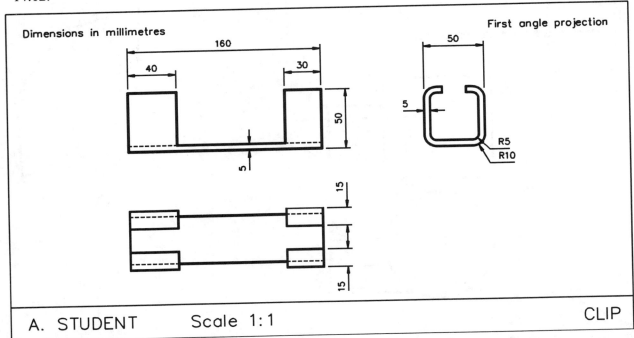

Figure 14.11 Answer to Exercise 2, Chapter 9

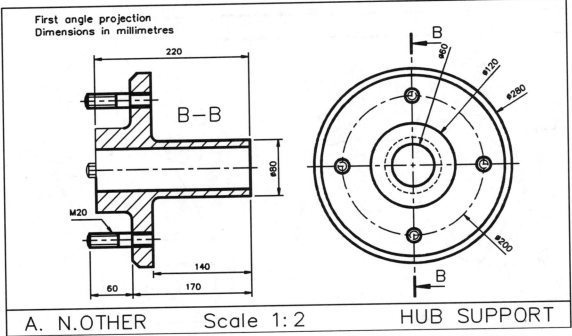

Figure 14.12 Answer to Exercise 3, Chapter 9

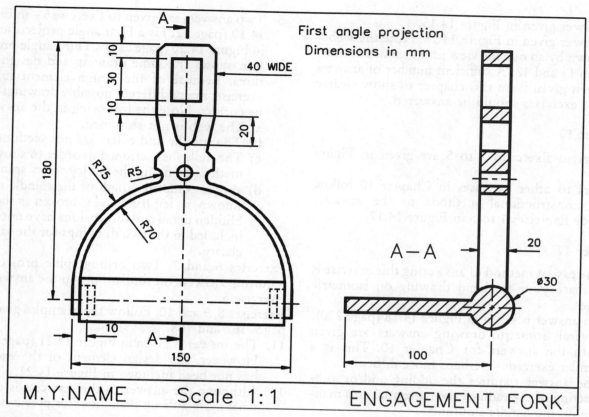

Figure 14.13 Answer to Exercise 5, Chapter 9

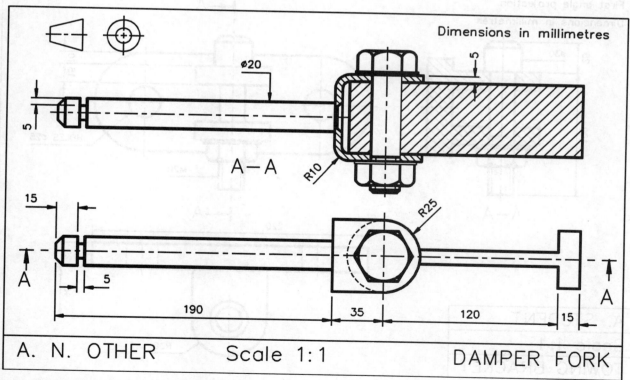

Figure 14.14 Answer to Exercise 6, Chapter 9

9. Answer given in Figure 14.15.
10. Answer given in Figure 14.16. Note the web – shown by an outside view in the sectional view.

Exercises 11 and 12: A sufficient number of answers have been given from this chapter to show clearly how the exercises should be answered.

Chapter 10

Answers to Exercises 1 to 5 are given in Figure 14.17.

Answers to other exercises in Chapter 10 follow similar constructional methods to the answers given for Exercises 1 to 5 in Figure 14.17.

Chapter 11

1. The easiest method of answering this exercise is to base your freehand drawing on isometric lines.
2. An answer is given in Figure 14.18 (page 220).
3. Several isometric drawing answers are given with the answers for Chapter 10. This is a similar exercise – perhaps more difficult.
4. The answer requires the adding and/or subtracting of the radii of the tangential arcs making up the handle's outline.

5. Two answers are given to Exercise 5 – in Figure 14.19 (page 220) is a First angle projection and in Figure 14.20 (page 221) a Third angle projection shows the same drawing and design features. Because of the design element in this exercise, many different possible drawings may be correct. Note the following in the answers:
   a) The web is not sectioned.
   b) The spindle and collar are not sectioned.
   c) The pulley is sectioned in order to show the method of fixing the pulley to its spindle.
   d) As the complete length of the spindle is not known, its left hand end is broken as shown.
   e) Hidden detail and dimensions have not been included in the two drawings for the sake of clarity.

Exercises 6 and 7. Two orthographic projections requiring answers on similar lines to the answer for Exercise 5.

Exercises 8, 9 and 10. Follow the examples given on pages 167 and 168.

11. The answer is given in Figure 14.21 (page 221). However, the design element of the exercise has not been included in Figure 14.21.
12. Although the answer to this exercise is somewhat more difficult than those for previous exer-

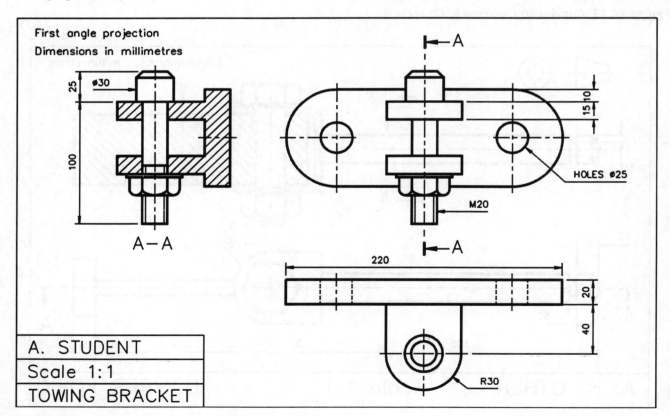

Figure 14.15 Answer to Exercise 9, Chapter 9

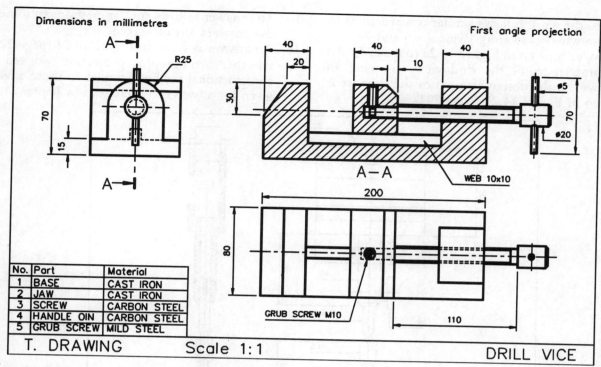

Figure 14.16 Answer to Exercise 10, Chapter 9

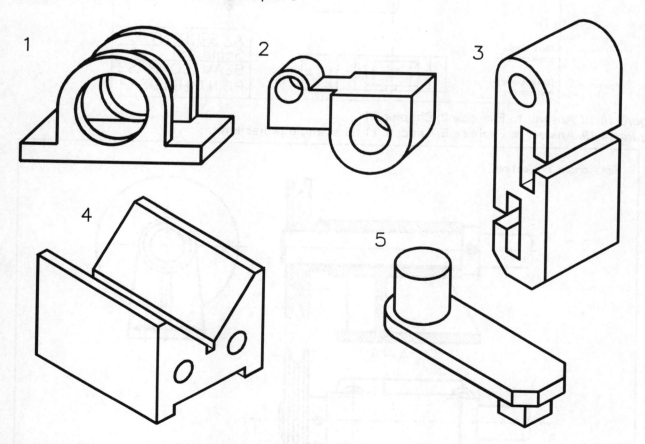

Figure 14.17 Answers to Exercises in Chapter 10

cises, the work follows similar constructions to those when answering Exercises 5 and 7.

13. Answer is given in Figure 14.22 (page 222). An enlarged part of the End view, showing an answer to the design element of the exercise is given in Figure 14.23 (page 222).

14. The answer follows similar methods to some of the answers already given.

16. An answer is given in Figure 14.24 (page 222).

17. Another orthographic projection worked on constructional methods similar to those already given for answers to exercises in Chapter 11.

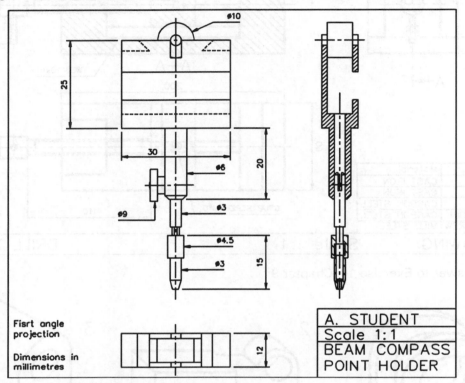

Figure 14.18 Answer to Exercise 2, Chapter 11

Figure 14.19 Answer to Exercise 5, Chapter 11 (First angle projection)

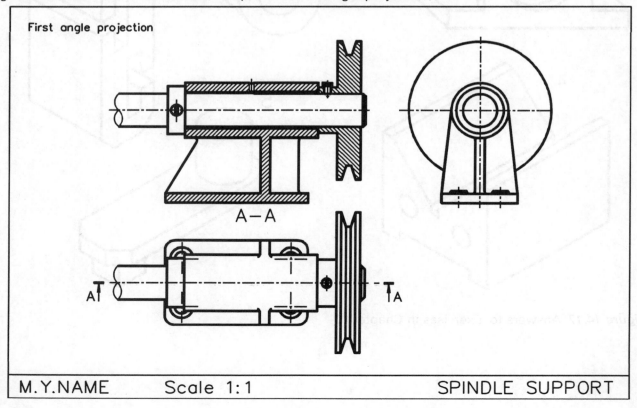

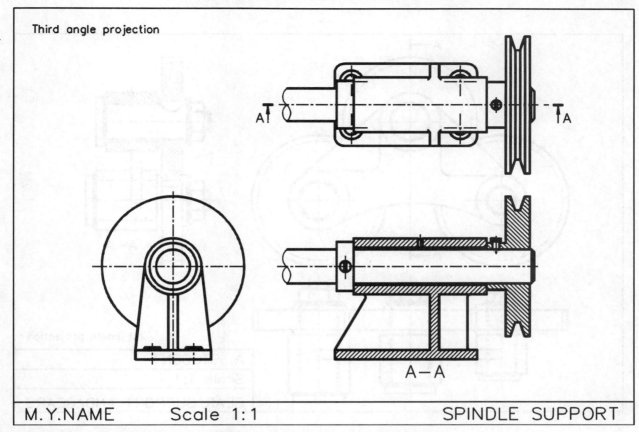

M.Y.NAME   Scale 1:1   SPINDLE SUPPORT

Figure 14.20 Answer to Exercise 5, Chapter 11 (Third angle projection)

Figure 14.21 Answer to Exercise 11, Chapter 11

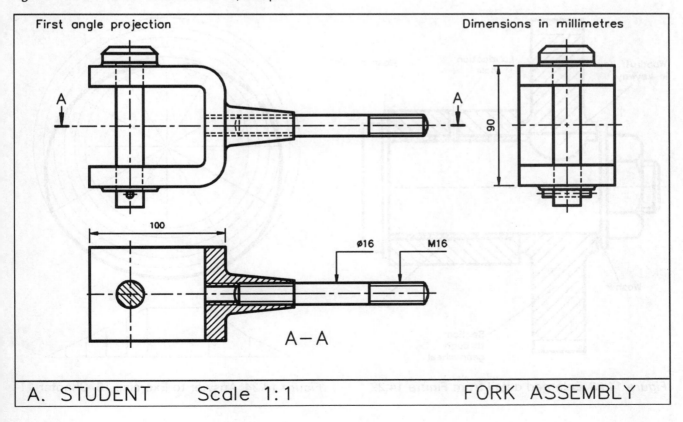

A. STUDENT   Scale 1:1   FORK ASSEMBLY

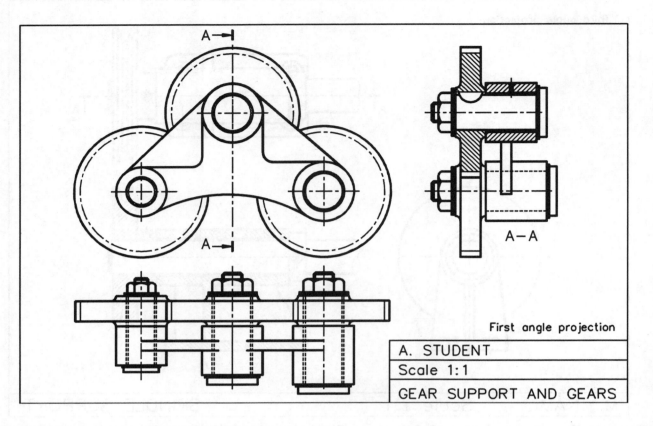

First angle projection

A. STUDENT

Scale 1:1

GEAR SUPPORT AND GEARS

Figure 14.22 Answer to Exercise 13, Chapter 11

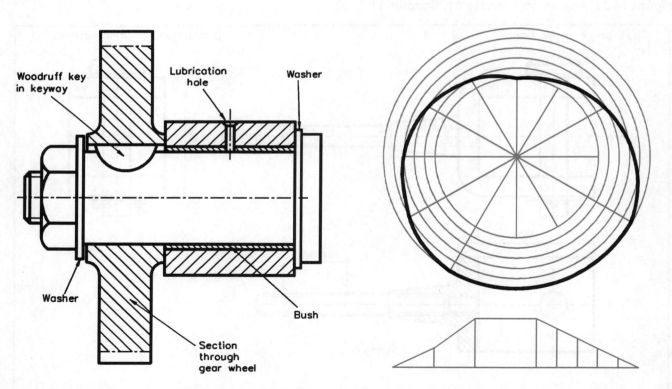

Woodruff key in keyway

Lubrication hole

Washer

Washer

Bush

Section through gear wheel

Figure 14.23 Enlarged detail from Figure 14.22

Figure 14.24 Answer to Exercise 16, Chapter 11

Chapter 12

1. An answer to Design Exercise 1 is given in Figure 14.25.
2. The method of answering this exercise is similar to that for Exercise 1.
3. An answer to Design Exercise 3 is given in Figure 14.26.
4. An answer to Design Exercise 4 is not given.
5. An answer to Design Exercise 5 is given in Figure 14.27.

Exercises 6, 7 and 8: The answers to these three exercises are obtained when doing the exercise.

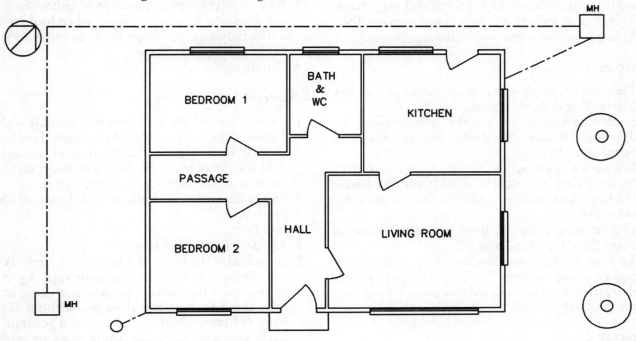

Figure 14.25 Answer to Design Exercise 1, Chapter 12

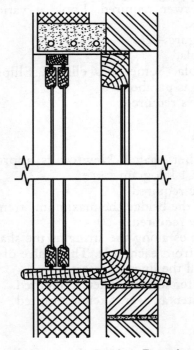

Figure 14.26 Answer to Design Exercise 3, Chapter 12

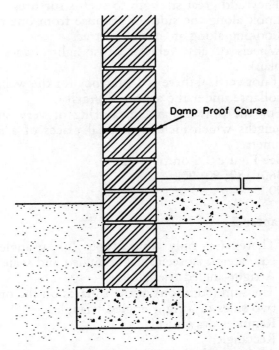

Figure 14.27 An answer to Design Exercise 5, Chapter 12

Answers to questions

Introduction

1 In industry – engineering, building. Maps are a form of technical drawing. Technical drawings are often included in newspapers and magazines. Technical drawings are sometimes seen on TV.
2 You must have some personal suggestions.

Chapter 1

1 There are several – the most common are the Metric B and the Imperial.
2 So that anyone in the world can understand the drawings. British Standards and International Standards Organisation.
3 Requires a drawing.
4 Examples are other curve aids; larger compasses for large arcs and/or circles; technical pens for ink work.
5 The set square can be used for drawing angles other than 30, 45, 60 and 90.
6 To keep the instruments clean. To prevent pencil points being broken. To keep compass points sharp. The instruments are in a place where they can be easily found.

Chapter 2

1 They add great strength to such structures.
2 Look along the sides of a house from one end. Looking along an evenue of trees.
3 Wheels of any vehicle. Most light shades (in plan).
4 If not vertical there is a tendency for the walls to collapse under the action of gravity.
5 For the drawing and measuring of very small lengths which include decimal places of a millimetre.
6 See Figure 3.8 on page 32.
7 360; 180; 90; 90.
8 90.

Chapter 3

1 There are only four types of triangle – equilateral, isosceles, right-angled and scalene.
2 A right-angled triangle.
3 The sum (addition) of the squares on the other two sides of a right-angled-triangle.
4 Requires drawings.
5 Rectangle.
6 All four sides are of equal length.
7 Hexagon.

8 Pentagon.
9 The heads of nuts or bolts.
10 Inscribed.
11 Many shapes require drawing of lines tangential to circles so as to achieve a smooth outline.
12 Requires drawings.
13 Any circular shape becomes an ellipse when it is titled around a diameter. Thus when looking at a naturally circular shape from an angle to the circle you see an ellipse.
14 Duodecagon.

Chapter 4

1 Draw a plan of the play area to a suitable scale. Divide it into a number of triangles. Find the area of each triangle. Scale up your answers. Add the areas together. Multiply the result by the cost of tarmacing per square metre.
2 Parabolic with the bulb at the focus of the parabola.
3 Involute.
4 An electric cooking ring.
5 A cycloid is the locus of a point on a circle as it rolls along a straight line without slipping. An epicycloid is the locus of a point on a circle as it rolls along the outside of an arc without slipping. A hypocycloid is the locus of a point on a circle as it rolls along the inside of an arc without slipping.
6 No answer required. Look at various screw threads.
7 See Figure 4.26.
8 Parabola.
9 Parabola. Sometimes ellipse. Ellipse not as strong as parabola.
10 Sketches required.

Chapter 5

1 Remember that 1 Newton is approximately equal to 1 kilogram force.
2 Estimate required.
3 To give the bridge the maximum strength.
4 Estimate required.
5 Draw lines along the string as the shape is suspended from each hole. The centre of gravity is where all the lines intersect.
6 No written answer. Sketch required.
7 No written answer. Sketch required.

Chapter 6

1 No written answer. Sketch required.
2 No written answer. Sketch required.

3 No written answer. Sketch required.

4 To hold together two pipes of different diameters, the end of one fitting inside the end of the other.

5 To bolt a vertical part of a machine to a horizontal part.

6 A faceplate on an engineering lathe.

Chapter 7

1 Requires a drawing and a model.
2 Requires a drawing and a model.
3 Requires the use of a cardboard tube.
4 Requires a model.

Chapter 8

1 Requires a drawing or sketch.
2 Explain the purpose for which the design is being made.
4 A description of the design which is to be made.
5 Make the design.
6 As an aid in producing sketches and accurate drawings of ideas to solve a design problem.
7 Finding essential dimensions. Testing ideas in models. In some designs finding answers to mathematical problems relating to strength. Making the design from drawings.
8 Unless considerations of safety problems are properly looked at, a design might cause an accident to those who are intending using the design.
9 Shape usually refers to a two-dimensional outline in a design. Form usually refers to a three-dimensional part of a design.
10 A rectangle with sides in the approximate proportion of 8:5.

Chapter 9

1 A view looking at the cut surface of an object which has been cut by a plane.
2 A view looking at half of a cut surface, with the other half showing the outer surfaces of the object.
3 An assembly drawing with the parts separated and in positions showing how parts of the assembly should be put together.
4 They should be shown by outside views within the section.
5 120 degrees.
6 When great pressure is being applied along the length of the screw.
7 No written answer. Sketch required.
8 No written answer. Sketch required.

9 A stud is a length of rod, without a head and with screw threads at both ends.
10 Sketch required. Grub screws are for holding parts on to spindles or shafts.

Chapter 10

1 Pictorial drawings can be used to explain parts of working drawings. They are also of good value for drawing ideas for solutions for ideas when designing.
2 Isometric, cabinet, planometric.
3 No written answer. Sketches required.
4 A drawing which shows parts of an assembly in positions as if they were being placed together in their final assembled form.
5 As an aid in drawing lines along reasonably correct angles – 30 degrees each way with isometric grid papers and vertically and horizontally with square grid papers.
6 An approximate method of drawing isometric ellipses.
7 In perspective drawing where lines are drawn as if meeting at a distant point. The distant point is the vanishing point of the drawing.
8 To allow quick and reasonably accurate drawing (sketches) to be constructed when producing ideas for solving design problems.

Chapter 11

1 A bearing in which a spindle or shaft rotates.
2 In a ball bearing, the bearing surfaces are steel balls. In roller bearings the bearing surfaces are pieces of cylindrical steel (the rollers).
3 To allow replacement of the bearing surfaces after prolonged use or wear.
4 To ensure that the rotation of a driver gear is in the same direction as the gear being driven.
5 A spur gear can only be used to cause rotation in one plane. A bevel gear can change the plane of rotation.
6 Involute.
7 To change the direction of motion from circular to linear.
8 No written answer. Sketches required.
9 There will be journals with bushes, roller bearings and ball bearings, among others.
10 In first angle projection end views and plans face outwards. In Third angle projection end views and plans face inwards.

Chapter 12

1 Site location plan, site plan, building plan, sectional views through features.
2 No written answer. Sketches and drawing are required.
3 No written answer. Sketches and drawing are required.
4 No written answer. Sketches required.
5 No written answer. Sketches required.
6 No written answer. Sketches required.
7 No written answer. Sketches required.

Chapter 13

1 Computer Aided Design.
2 Speed of drawing. Ease of inserting drawings within drawings. No need to draw any part twice. Saving of space. Ability to print drawings to any scale without having to re-draw. Dimensions can usually be added automatically.
3 Need for equipment – computer, monitor, printer or plotter. Need for skilled operators. Equipment costs originally higher than for hand drawing, although savings in productivity eventually more than make up for these original costs.
4 Without a good knowledge of technical drawing, you will not be able to produce drawings either by hand or with the aid of CAD on a computer.
5 All units of length on a monitor screen (VDU) are measured horizontally in terms of X and vertically in terms of Y. Any point on a computer screen can be determined in terms of X and Y (x,y).
6 AutoCad, AutoSketch, Generic CADD. Many others.
7 The instrument – mouse, puck, stylus connected to the computer usually by cable, the movements of which on a surface are repeated on a computer screen.
8 Mouse, puck, stylus.

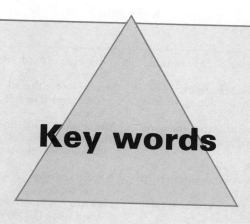

Key words

A size drawing sheets   A set of sheets based on a sheet size A0 of area 1 square metre

Acme thread   A screw with threads machined at angles of 29 degrees

AF (Across Flats)   Distance across the flats of a hexagonal nut or bolt head

Angle   Two lines which lie apart, but are joined to each other at one end (see also protractor)

Arc   Part of the circumference of a circle

Area of a circle   The area of a circle is π × radius squared

Area of triangle   The area of a triangle = 1/2 base × vertical height

Assembly drawing   An orthographic drawing (usually) of the parts of an assembly fitted together

Auxiliary Plane   The plane in orthographic projection which lies at an angle to the Horizontal Plane (H.P.) or to the Vertical Plane (V.P.), or to both

Auxiliary View   A view in orthographic as seen when looking at an object from an angle to the H.P. or V.P. (or both)

Ball bearing   A bearing incorporating steel balls

Bevel gear   A gear with gear teeth cut in such a manner as to allow a change in direction of angular rotation

Bisection   Dividing a line or angle (or any other shape) into two equal parts

British Standards   A set of documents setting standards for methods of working in industries. About 4,500 are available

BS:1192   A British Standard describing methods of constructing technical drawings for building

BS:308   A British Standard describing methods of constructing technical drawings for engineering

Building plan   A plan showing the layout of the floors in a building

Bush   A thin lining placed inside a cylindrical hole and within which a spindle can rotate

Cartesian coordinates   A mathematical method of determining in terms of x and y any position on a plane

Cartridge paper   A drawing paper suitable for pencil drawings

Centre line   A line drawn through the centres of arcs and circles, consisting of thin long and short dash lines

Chord   A straight line with each end touching the circumference of a circle

Circumference of a circle   The line of a circle, which is π × diameter

Circumscribing circle   A circle around a plane figure which touches all the vertices of the figure

Computer Aided Design   CAD for short. A method of constructing technical drawings with the aid of a computer

Computer Aided Machining   The methods for manufacturing objects under the control of a computer system

Conic sections   Four conic sections – circle, ellipse, parabola and hyperbola

Cycloid   Is the locus of a point on a circle as it rolls in a straight line along a flat plane

Degrees   The unit of measurement for an angle between two lines

Degrees in a circle   There are 360 degrees in a circle

Design office   An office where designers and draughtsmen produce technical drawings in an industrial firm

Detail paper   A light-weight, yet strong paper for pencil and colour work

Diagonal scale   Scales for drawing to great accuracy where measurements smaller than about 0.5 mm are required

Dimensioning figures   On A4 sheets – 3 mm high; on A3 sheets – 5 mm high; on A2 sheets – 6 mm high

Diameter of circle   A line touching the circumference of a circle and passing through its centre

Dividers   A piece of drawing equipment for measuring lengths on a drawing

Drawing boards   Usually made from wood, but may be made from plastic. Made to sizes suitable for A size papers

Drawing sheet layouts   Sheet set horizontally – 'landscape'. Set vertically – 'portrait'

Ellipse   The locus of a point which moves so as to be equidistant from two fixed points

End view   Or 'End elevation'. An orthographic view seen as though looking at the side of an object

Epicycloid   Is the locus of a point on a circle as it rolls around the outside of the circumference of an arc

Equilateral triangle   A triangle in which sides are of equal length and all angles are 60 degrees

Erasers   For removing mistakes in drawings. May be made from rubber or from vinyl

Exceptions in sections   Bolts, nuts, washers, screws, spindles, webs and the like are shown by outside views in a section

Exploded drawing   Technical drawing showing the parts of an assembly as if taken apart along orthogonal lines

First angle projection   Orthographic projections of objects in the first angle of two planes crossing at right angles

Front view   Or 'Front elevation'. A view in orthographic projection when looking at the front of an object

Grid papers   Papers with grids based on either lines in squares or at isometric angles of 30, 30 and 90 degrees

Half section   Sectional view in which only half the view is sectioned. Only for objects symmetrical about an axis

Hardware   The name applied to computer equipment

Hatching   Lines (usually) at 45 degrees and about 4 mm apart drawn over a sectioned surface

Helix   The locus of a point as it rotates round a cylinder and moves with regular velocity along its axis

Heptagon   A polygon with seven sides. Note 'septagon' is wrong

Hexagon   A polygon with six sides

Hidden detail line   A line showing details in a drawing which lie behind the outer surfaces of the object being drawn

Horizontal Plane   Or H.P. The plane in orthographic projection which lies horizontally

Hypocycloid   Is the locus of a point on a circle as it rolls around the inside of the circumference of an arc

Hypotenuse   The side of a right-angle triangle which is opposite the right angle

Hyperbola   The locus of a point which moves so as to be at a distance in a ratio from a line that it is from a point

Inscribing circle   A circle inside a plane figure which touches all the sides of the figure

Involute   The curve formed by the end of a line wrapped around the edge(s) of a plane figure as it is unwound

Irregular polygon   A polygon with sides of unequal length

Isometric drawing   Pictorial drawing with axes at 30 degrees each side of vertical lines

Isosceles triangle   A triangle with two of its sides of equal length and two of its angles of equal size

Journal bearing   A bearing designed to allow a spindle to revolve freely

Landscape drawing   A drawing laid out on a sheet of paper set horizontally

Line of intersection   The line seen in orthographic views showing the join line between two solids meeting at an angle

Lock nut   Nut which, when fitted onto screw threads will not work loose

Major axis   The longest axis of an ellipse

Masking tape   Sticky tape suitable for fixing drawings to a drawing board. Removable without damaging the drawing

Metric screw thread   A screw with threads machined at 60 degrees. The full name of a metric thread is ISOmetric thread

Minor axis   The smaller axis of an ellipse

Moment   The action of a force at a distance from the point about which the action is taking place

Needle bearing   A bearing incorporating thin cylindrical steel rollers

Newton   A unit of force approximately equal to 9.81 kilogram force (1 kgf)

Oblique drawing   Pictorial drawing based on horizontal and vertical lines plus lines at angles such as 30 or 45 degrees

Octagon   A polygon with eight sides

Orthographic projection   Parallel projections of solids placed between vertical and horizontal planes

PC   Personal Computer

Parabola   The locus of a point which moves so as to be always the same distance from a line as from a point

Parallel lines   Lines which are the same distance apart throughout their length

Parallelogram   A polygon with opposite sides parallel

Part drawing   An orthographic projection (usually) of one part only from an object made up from assembled parts

Part section   Sectional view in which only part of the view shows the section

Pencils   Many grades – 9 grades of H (hard); 6 grades of B (black) + HB and F

Pentagon   A plane figure with five sides

Perpendicular   A line at right angles to another line

Pictorial drawing   Technical drawing showing a 'picture' of an object. Isometric, oblique, perspective drawings

Plan   A view in orthographic projection as seen when looking at an object from above

Plane geometry   Methods for accurately constructing two-dimensional drawings

Polygon of forces   A polygon showing four or more vectors of forces in equilibrium

Portrait layout   A drawing on a sheet set vertically

Protractor   A piece of drawing equipment for setting or measuring angles in a drawing

Quadrilateral   A polygon with four sides

Radial cam   A mechanical device which converts radial motion into straight line motion

Regular polygon   A polygon in which all sides are of equal length and all angles are of equal size

Removed section   Sectional view taken through any position along an object and placed to one side

Revolved section   Sectional view drawn over another view, showing the section through an object at a given position

Rhombus   A polygon with all sides equal and opposite angles equal

Right-angle triangle   A triangle in which one angle is a right angle

Roller bearing A bearing incorporating cylindrical steel rollers

Scales All parts of a drawing to scale are reduced or enlarged by the scale factor

Scalene triangle A triangle in which all sides are of different lengths and all angles are of different sizes

Sectional view Or 'section'. A view of a surface of an object which has been cut by a plane

Sector Part of a circle enclosed by two radii

Segment Part of a circle enclosed by a chord

Semi-circle The angle within a semi-circle is always 90 degrees

Site location plan A building drawing showing the position of a building site in relation to the surrounding country

Site plan A building plan which shows details of the layout of the site on which building is contemplated

Software The name applied to the programmes which are used to run applications such as CAD on a computer

Spring bow compass A compass which can be accurately set by means of a screw, for drawing small circles or arcs

Spur gear A circular plate with gear teeth (usually of involute outline) cut into its outer circumference

Square thread A screw with thread sides machined at 90 degrees

Surface development A drawing showing the true shapes of the surfaces of a solid

Tangent A line, arc or circle touching an arc or circle

Technical drawing Drawings constructed for accurately describing the shape and form of a product for manufacturing purposes

Third angle projection Orthographic views of objects in the third angle of two planes crossing at right angles

Three-dimensional drawing Drawings which describe the width, height and depth of an object

Thrust bearing A bearing designed to allow loads to be taken along the length of a spindle revolving in the bearing

Tracing paper A transparent paper for laying over a master drawing and on which the drawing can be copied

Triangle of forces A triangle of vectors of force showing the vectors of three forces in equilibrium

Triangles The sum of angles in a triangle is 180 degrees

Triangulation A method of development by which the surfaces of a solid can be accurately drawn

True length The full length of a line when viewed at right angles to the line

Two-dimensional drawings Drawings which describe the width and height, but not the depth of objects

Truncated solid Part of a solid which has been cut by a plane

Two-dimensional drawings Drawings which describe the width and height, but not the depth of objects

Vectors A line which shows both magnitude and direction

Vertical Plane Or V.P. The plane in orthographic projection which lies vertically

Vertices The corners of any plane figure

Whitworth thread A screw with threads machined at angles of 55 degrees

Working drawing A drawing which is an orthographic projection (usually) of an object which is to be manufactured

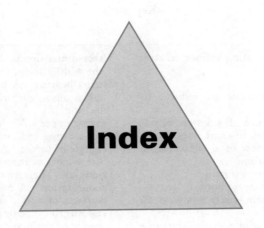

Index